AN AUTOBIOGRAPHICAL NOVEL

For my daughters
Mary and Katharine
and for Carol

AN
AUTOBIOGRAPHICAL
NOVEL

KENNETH
REXROTH

A NEW DIRECTIONS PAPERBOOK

Any writer, reading over the typescript of a book for the last time before sending it off to the publisher, must wonder what all the effort was for. An autobiography is specially in need of justification to its author. It is a work of self-justification which itself needs justifying. Why have I written this book? Why have I written it the way I have? What does it mean to me? What do I hope it will mean to others?

Each human being has at the final core of self a crystal from which the whole manifold of the personality develops, a secret molecular lattice which governs the unfolding of all the structures of the individuality, in time, in space, in memory, in action and contemplation. Asleep there were just these dreams and no others. Awake there were these actions only. Only these deeds came into being.

Every cell in the body is marked with the pattern of the genes that stripe the chromosomes of the original fertilized egg. This is the physiological fact, the minute, infinitely complicated pattern of organic individuality. So, too, there is a psychological secret determinant. Each of us is a specific individual, that one and no other, out of billions. I think each of us knows his own mystery with a knowing that precedes the origins of all knowledge. None of us ever gives it way. No one can. We envelop it with talk and hide it with deeds.

Yet we always hope that somehow the others will know it is there, that a mystery in the other we cannot know will respond to a mystery in the self we cannot understand. The only full satisfaction life offers us is this sense of communion. We seek it constantly. Sometimes we find it. As we grow older we learn that it is never complete and sometimes it is entirely illusory.

I suppose in the first impulse the telling of these twenty-one years of my own life was a gesture of communion with those I love, with my daughters especially. Secondly, of course, it was an attempt to understand myself. I am not so naïve as to believe that one reveals oneself by talking about oneself. But possibly out of the narrative a self can be deduced, as Pluto was discovered by an analysis of the perturbations in the orbit of Neptune.

The last and, as a published book, the only justification—I think it is an interesting story of a minor historical importance. To many people it may seem a most atypical childhood and youth. I do not think it is, or if it is, it is at least characteristic of one kind of American life.

Today we hear a great deal about Organizational Men, Mass Culture, Conformity, the Lonely Crowd, the Power Elite and its Conspiracy of Mediocrity. We forget that the very volume of this criticism is an indication that our society is still radically pluralistic. Not only are there plenty of exceptionalists who take exception to the stereotyping of the mass culture—but that very string of epithets comes from a series of books that have been recent best-sellers, symptoms of a popular, living tradition of dissent from things as they are.

Most American families that go back to the early nineteenth century, and certainly those whose traditions go back to the settlement of the country, have a sense of social and cultural rather than nationalistic responsibility. The sense that the country is really theirs, really belongs to them, produces radical critics, rebels, reformers, eccentrics.

The conviction they have the right to demand their society live up to their expectations does not necessarily mean traditional Americans are crackpots or cultists, or even odd at all. True, an obstreperously pluralistic society shades out through Brook Farm, the Oneida Community, the Fourierist phalanxes of the early nineteenth century into all sorts of cults both political and religious. On the other hand, people who insist on exercising their right to determine their social environment are eminently normal. This does not mean they are common. Most people in the world, anywhere, any time, just make up bulk. As we look back after history has passed by, hundreds of their contemporaries in American politics are forgotten and Senator Norris or the elder La Follette or Eugene Debs or Bryan or even a rascally character like Borah stand out. They were the actors in political history, even though lesser men finally obtained the goals for which they fought. Leaders of causes stand out unduly.

Through this story of my own life runs the thread of the Abolitionist heritage. It is one of the strongest factors in the shaping of my mind. Yet those of my ancestors who were Abolitionists were modest people indeed. They were inconspicuous while they lived and are lost to history. Yet they were no less convinced than John Brown, just as brave, perhaps a little saner. Similarly with those who were suffragists, Socialists, Mutualists, and were sexually, politically, and economically liberated people of the early years of the nation. It was they, most of them common, normal people, who built into our society those structures and relationships which have always redeemed it from the evils Aristotle said were characteristic of democracies. I think this is the actual framework of American life, and I doubt if it is really collapsing today under the onslaughts of mass man. Mass man has always been around. It is a measure of our concern and our responsibility that we take his doings so seriously.

I surely was taught by parents, grandparents, by all members of a widely extended family, that I was different from irresponsible people, that it was up to me to be better mannered, more courteous, more concerned, as the Quakers say, in all social relationships, direct in speech and unostentatious in behavior and clothing.

Although I was unaware of being taught anything I absorbed a clear and rigorous code. You were not only honest, but forthright in speech and never used polite evasions or euphemisms. On the other hand, you never volunteered unwanted advice. You never bargained. In Cairo or Paris or Cleveland you either paid the price asked or walked out—and so in the more subtle bargains of life. You never gambled. Although my father was a constant gambler he presented this aspect of himself to me as a very bad example, a vice not to be imitated. You never overindulged in food or drink. You never hunted or wore furs. You never dressed in fashion, like undignified people. You never went to court or got your name in the papers. Everything you did, but especially acts of charity, you did as inconspicuously as possible.

This kind of training produces a hauteur I know many people find offensive. It may be arrogance, but I prefer to think of it as an expression of the sense of responsibility and the desire to keep efficient for the exercise of that responsibility. It comes not only from the pietistic Germans in my ancestry, but, at least I like to think, it is the ethic of free men growing up in a free country.

Schwenkfelders, Mennonites, German revolutionaries of '48, Abolitionists, suffragists, squaws and Indian traders, octoroons and itinerant horse dealers, farmers in broad hats, full beards, and frogged coats, hard-drinking small-town speculators, all have gone to make a personality that has proved highly resistant to digestion by the mass culture and yet, I think, conservative of the characteristic values of American life rather than the reverse.

So much for the inheritance from the more distant past. Directly from my parents comes another heirloom—an unusually strong memory of and feeling for the world before the Other War.

While I was dictating the first chapters of this story in Vicenza I took Marthe and the girls to a performance of *La Traviata* by one of those traveling companies that play the small Italian cities all year round. Usually the stage-set for the opening scene is so grandiose that it looks like nothing but a stage-set. This was a simple drawing room of the turn of the century and the costumes were equally authentic and uninflated. The moment the show opened I was overcome by the feeling I was back home at a party in the Midwest about 1910. The old-fashioned tenor had the same damp, romantic, slightly babyfied look as my father—the acme of good looks of those days—and Violetta was in every way my mother. Played straight and realistically, this was my mother's world and her attitudes to life. True, in her case Edwardian sentiment was stiffened with American radicalism, high reading, and high living, but then Violetta and the Lady of the Camellias were not illiterate reactionaries, either. It was my world as a child, too. That first scene of *La Traviata* seemed a grown up make-believe revival of the New Year's party at dancing school in a small Middle Western town before the Other War.

That gracious Edwardian world was not only the last flowering of capitalist civilization—it was permeated with a foreboding of its own end. A few pessimists—H. G. Wells, for instance, when he spoke from the heart in his scientific romances—thought it was doomed. Most people thought it was going to turn into something much better.

As a boy I had on my wall a picture of a high-society revel at Delmonico's. Supporting the floor like half-prostrate caryatids were workers, men, women, and children, kneeling, bowed, crawling figures in a shallow cellar under the black and white tile floor. Above them, handsome men with ribbons across their shirt fronts and women with their breasts showing above their evening gowns were dancing. In the center of the picture a worker had thrust his clenched fist up through the floor and all the nearby revelers were staring at it aghast.

The truth is that upstairs in Delmonico's all sorts of people were aware of the rumblings under the floor. It was the world of Little Nemo or the Land of Oz, more grand than any the ruling classes have been able to manage since. Still, all through that autumnal society circulated men and women with a profound sense of their responsibility and an awareness of the need for social change.

People like my parents had a moral confidence in the future that is incomprehensible today. They and everybody like them believed that soon all life from clothing design to the game of chess was going to change for the better. It wasn't a political attitude as we understand that word today; in fact, nobody I knew until after my minority was over thought politically in the present meaning of the word—except the Russians who began showing up in American radical circles after the first war. This moral content of the old radical movement has vanished altogether. The classics of Socialist and Anarchist literature seem at mid-century to speak a foolish and naïve language to minds hardened by two generations of *realpolitik*.

It was not just the sophisticates and the reformers who had no belief in the validity or endurance of the system. Everybody in what they used to call the master class, from the Pope to William Howard Taft, believed in his bones that the days of his kind were strictly numbered and found wanting. What happened instead of apocalypse and judgment was a long-drawn-out apocalypse of counterrevolution against the promise and potential of a humane civilization. It began with the world economic crisis of 1912, and the First and Second World Wars and the Bolshevik Revolution have been episodes, always increasing in violence and plain immorality, in the struggle of our civilization to suppress its own potential.

Whether it was listening to the birth of jazz at the Clef Club or Schiller's Café, or wandering wide-eyed through the Armory Show behind my gesticulating parents, I watched, unawares, the laying of all the foundations of a century's culture. The positive achievements were set in train and largely consummated in my boyhood. After the First War would come Dadaism and Surrealism, organized movements of the broken heart, or Bolshevism, the "dialectical negation of the negation" of capitalism. Somewhere in his travels my father had met Soddy and Rutherford; he did not live to know Oppenheimer and Teller.

So much for general principles and motives. Far more important, I believe, in the formation of my character has been the memory and example of actual ancestors and immediate family. I may be mistaken. Genealogy certainly doesn't determine character. My genealogy is far from spectacular, but at least in my own mind all these living and dead people provided me with a kind of family epic in which I thought, and still think of myself, as called to play a role. So, as introduction to my own life, I will try first to give a picture of the web of lives, the cast of characters, out of which it came. I have started off by trying to describe my family from the outside—not from outside myself, which would be impossible, but from outside the narrative of my own life. In contemporary society many people are almost totally free of such background and antecedents. I feel that for myself they are as potent and determinative as they ever were in a social order which is gone. They are how I understand myself so that even if I am wrong they are essential in one way or another to understanding me. In an atomized mass culture a life motivated by inherited standards may well seem eccentric and revolutionary.

If this story has a plot or a theme it is the tale of a boy's effort to select and put in order the tools with which he would live his adulthood. It would be easy to say that my adolescence, like that of any boy in any other culture, moved steadily toward fulfillment in matrimony, or that my abstract painting was a reassertion of the canons of classic art, or that bohemianism was a search for the natural relations of any small community, or that political revolt was a quest for the largest organic community, or that my religious adventures were attempts to insure an abiding sense of transcendent meaning. I look on this as the story of the youth of a conservationist if not a conservative.

Unlike many contemporary writers I have never felt the need to be free. I have always had as much freedom as I needed for the task at hand, for the taking. I have never felt any inhibition on the development of my personality. In fact, that concept is so abstract that I have great difficulty understanding it. I have always been too busy being a poet or a painter or a husband or a father or a cook or a mountain climber to worry about my personality, and this book is my first attempt to consider it at all. Reading the typescript over I discover that it is largely straight factual narrative, a great deal of it about other people.

I did not actually write this book but talked it. Some years ago I decided to leave a record for my young daughters of what I thought my own youth had been like. I started to talk into a tape recorder. These tapes were eventually broadcast over the Pacifica stations KPFA, KPFK, and WBAI and attracted the interest of publishers. I have tried to preserve the spontaneous, oral character of the style and the direct simplicity of the narrative. I believe in this sort of thing on principle. I admire Defoe and the great Chinese novelists and I have spent my life striving to write the way I talk. So I have worked over these tapes not by rewriting the transcriptions but by redictating them. This has led to an immense amount of labor on the part of a succession of devoted secretaries. I am deeply indebted to their skill, patience, and advice. I hope they have made it possible for me to preserve in the printed book something of the character of speech.

In the years since I first told this story on tape, there have been many delays in moving the book toward publication. Meanwhile society has caught up with me in frightening fashion. It gives to ponder. Maybe history is just hallucination.

Everybody knows that the avant-garde in the arts in The Beautiful Epoch was a small circle of friends, who felt they knew one another however separated geographically. Machado, James Joyce, Mondrian, Stravinsky, and their anonymous tiny audience had in fact almost all met one another by the time the world economic crisis, Fascism, and war put an end to the avant-garde forever. It is startling to realize that what was once a way of life for a tiny international band of emancipated people has now become commonplace in Irkutsk, Krakow, Des Moines, and Kobe. Racial equality, folk songs, beards and sandals, red wine and marijuana, conscientious objection and direct action, poetry readings and jam sessions—it's all here in the lives of a couple thousand people in London, Paris, Chicago, New York, and San Francisco. Today it's only to be expected that the intellectual world would overtake its pioneers in the course of a half century of disorder and early sorrow. What is most amazing to me is that the Church has caught up with me. I who was once a troubled, irregular peg in a complicated hole now find myself in agreement with Jesuit theologians and Broad Church bishops.

Behind this story of picaresque adventure, I hope there is apparent the beginning of a spiritual awakening and growth which I have shared however clumsily with the best of my time. The free, creative, loving people who shine so brightly in my memory of studios and coffee shops have become models for a huge section of the population. If they in turn can just stay alive in the face of power and terror, they may become the decisive section.

AN AUTOBIOGRAPHICAL NOVEL

CHAPTER 1

The standard reference works are probably right in beginning their biographical articles with a summary of the ancestors, background, and environment of their subjects. I certainly feel that this is the way to begin my own autobiography.

The Rexroth family is German in origin, and there are still a number of people of that name fairly prominent in Germany, although their connections with the American family must be remote. Every once in a while one of them writes to me or comes to visit. Immediately after the Second War I heard from a Gunther Rexroth who had been a district director of the Balkan area for the Agfo-Ansco Company in civil life. During the war he had been an officer in army intelligence in the Balkans. He'd been captured in Stalingrad, escaped to fight in Russia until the German armies' collapse, been captured again, and again escaped, worked his way west, been captured by the Czechs, escaped again, and finally surrendered to the British at the end of the war. I answered his first letter immediately and asked him if there was anything he needed. He replied, "Oh, no, we're doing very well." He sent snapshots of himself, quite a handsome fellow. As time went on I found his Nibelungen *Geist* rather repellent and dropped the correspondence. His story was that possibly as early as the thirteenth century the family had been Harz Mountain peasants who had come down into the Bavarian cities where the first Rexroth to take the name had been a scholar. The family became technical and professional intelligentsia, clerks and officials in the petty courts of West Germany. It is among this caste that the Latin and semi-Latin names in the Teutonic countries originated. Considering the activities of the earliest Rexroths, the first may well have been assimilated Jews. Christians of this sort were commonly celibate and did not found families. I have also corresponded with Franz von Rexroth, a poet of about my own age. He is a professor in Württemberg, an authority on Rimbaud, the translator of a considerable amount of Chinese poetry. During the war he translated the *Thirty-three Sonnets Written in Silence* by Jean Cassou, had them printed on an underground press, and distributed them himself. Immediately after the war was over everybody in Germany discovered that he had been a member of the Resistance, but few can document it as well as Franz von Rexroth. He sounds as about as congenial as could be imagined, but I doubt if I'll ever see him. I have an intense dislike of all things German. All my life attitudes are antagonistic to those of German culture. I have never been able to read Goethe with any pleasure whatever. I prefer William Byrd to Bach. I don't even like the Grünewald altarpiece. In fact, I loathe it. Another von Rexroth was a judge in Thuringia who was hung by the Allies after the war.

Hans Rexroth is a medieval scholar and a specialist in the Old High German poets and in St. Mechtild and Hildegarde of Bingen. This is the only expression of German culture that has ever appealed to me. Hans Rexroth is a thorough scholar and his account of the family seems to me the most reliable. It also agrees with the traditions preserved in America.

The family name was originally Reiksrada which means "straight-cut" or "well-hewn" as a furrow or a roof beam. They were ironmongers, not peasants, although they came from the Harz Mountains. Some of them became moneylenders, chancellors, and treasurers, but many of the family are still in the original business. The "von" was given by Bismarck to a family of minor steel barons in Essen.

The Rexroths in America were simpler people. At least three unconnected Rexroths migrated to America and founded families. According to my Granduncle John, the first was a member of the pietistic sect of Schwenkfelders who came to America before Penn. This branch of the family did not produce male descendants except through the one person who married into my own family. However, some were students of Schwenkfeld, Boehme, Valentine, and other pietist philosophers, and their papers survived in the possession of my granduncle.

Another Rexroth was a friend of Wettling, Marx, and Engels, came to America with Wettling, and settled in St. Louis. He was an associate of Carl Schurz. Today around St. Louis and in Oklahoma and Kansas there are Rexroths descended from him. Although there were many Socialists in my own family in Ohio, the two groups never knew of each other. I discovered their existence through Byron Rexroth, a poet and oil chemist at the University of Oklahoma.

There was a girl named Augusta von Rexroth who was a ballerina in New York in the Thirties, presumably she was herself from Germany and a member of the Essen family.

The founder of my own family came to Baltimore in the late eighteenth century. He or one of his sons worked his way west into Ohio and this man's son married Matilda Rexroth, a Mennonite and a member of the old Schwenkfeld family. Their descendants were my grandfather and his three brothers.

In Ohio the Rexroths persist as a typical German-American family organization with a family secretary and a great Teutonic reunion every August. There are still German-speaking members and people who dress and talk plain. Pietistic customs still survive even amongst the nonreligious members. I myself have strong prejudices in favor of modesty, direct speech, and lack of ostentation. Emma Goldman points out in her autobiography that the pietistic sects in America have produced an unusually large number of radicals, reformers, and revolutionaries. The specific sectarian religion dies out; the radical ethical social impulse endures and produces secular revolutionaries. The Rexroths I knew as a small boy were well-to-do farmers and professional men in central Ohio. My grandfather and his brothers were skilled mechanics except for John who taught German in a high school on the North Side of Chicago.

My grandfather, George Rexroth, had a plumbing shop in Toledo, Ohio. He was a simple man, morose and silent. He voted the Socialist ticket and read the Socialist press but in his old age stopped voting and called himself an Anarchist. Following him, my father never voted in his life, had nothing but withering scorn for politicians left or right.

In those days Toledo, Ohio, was not the depraved and brutal city that it became after the First World War. Golden Rule Jones had only recently been mayor and radicals were still a power in the city. The Ohio Group dominant in the Socialist Party before the war played an important role in the founding of the Communist Party. Charles Ruthenberg, a typical Ohio German, one of the first secretaries of the Party, was a friend of the family. He was only one of a large number of Exceptionalists, Single Taxers, Mutualists, former leaders of the Knights of Labor, and followers of Daniel De Leon whom my grandparents knew. It is interesting to note that none of these people ever became an orthodox Bolshevik. Stalin would have expelled Ruthenberg if he had lived a couple of more months. The rest of them became dissidents of one sort or another, leaders of the Proletarian Party or the more outlandish Trotskyite splinter groups.

I was about four when I first saw my grandfather. He was sitting at a scrubbed oak table in the buttery, a dark musty closet off the kitchen in a house that smelled of old people. A little window, high on the wall and covered with a spotted and peeling imitation stained-glass decalcomania, cast a dim light on an old man with immense mustaches eating a great stack of gray buckwheat pancakes and black sour gravy—cold. He informed me that I was a very bright little boy and if I minded my father and mother and didn't eat too much candy I'd become a great man, and then he returned to the gloomy, muddy Leaning Tower of Pisa before him.

My grandmother's name was Mary Moore, originally Mohr. Both her mother and father were part Indian. I suspect that the Pocahontas from whom they were descended looked a good deal like the lady on the pancake box, though I don't doubt there were authentic Indians mixed in. The Moores were traders who came to the Illinois Genessee Valley with the first wave of immigrants from the Genesee Valley in New York, where they had been connected with the Johnson family, descendants of the Great White Father of the Iroquois.

My grandmother was an improbable lady. She was dark as varnished oak and six foot two in her prime. She had a long neck like a Botticelli girl, a long, pear-shaped head, with thinning hair done up in a knot in back. After my grandfather's death she always wore the same black bombazine dress. Outdoors she always carried a cane. She had a goiter the size of her head suspended in a black net collar supported in the back with heavy stays. Her face was drawn and fleshless, her nose long and aquiline, her eyes a very pale blue. Before she married my grandfather she had been a teacher in a country college and she cursed in several languages including the dead ones, but she could be marvelously obscene in English as well. She might be said to be continuously flatulent, a dry, aged, leathery racket that went on night and day, even in her sleep.

She told me stories of her father's trading post in Tonawanda, Illinois, stories of Indian battles, of squaw men, and of women who ran away with Indian lovers, stories of her River French relatives, and of life in the villages along the Illinois waterways which remained French-speaking until my own youth. The sod of the long-grass prairie was still unbroken when she was a girl. By midsummer they could only see the top of an express rider's hat as he rode up to the post. She had stories of the Mohrs who were amongst the handful of Germans who settled in the Finger Lakes country even before there were Germans in Pennsylvania.

Of my grandfather's brothers, Granduncle John impressed me most. He lived in a noble Teutonic flat on Lincoln Park West in Chicago, one of the Bavarian Romanesque buildings which faced the park in those days with big round red brick bays and potbellied iron balconies. This was a Romanesque revival which preceded Richardson, examples of which still survive around Cincinnati and on the Near North Side in Chicago. The house was full of beautifully bound German books, black, intimidating furniture, and paintings of cuckoo-clock chalets set in the midst of virulent green meadows over which floated sentimentally dreaming cows, slightly out of perspective. The entire neighborhood was Bavarian and Catholic and life went on exactly as it had in Munich.

Nearby was the German-speaking St. Michael's Church where later as a young bohemian up all night I used to go to Mass. Granduncle John was not a Catholic, but the St. Michael's clergy were his friends and I used to see them at his flat, drinking beer and eating sandwiches of liverwurst, limburger, and raw onion and cracking German jokes. Compared to the Protestant ministers I knew they seemed military, alien, and more self-assured than anybody I had ever met.

Although my granduncle was fifth generation in America he was not assimilated at all. Life for him certainly went on exactly as it might in Munich. The most precious book in his library was as large as the family Bible, deeply embossed, and locked with a clasp. It was a history of the Rexroth family written and illuminated by himself. It was his lifework and, I suspect, largely the product of his imagination. He read me long sections of it, translating from the German—the obviously apocryphal legend that we were descended from Barbarossa, stirring tales of ancestors with the Hohenstaufens in Italy and at the court of Federigo Due and heroes of the battles of Wallenstein and Tilly. Except for the stories of the Thirty Years' War, which was recent enough to have some basis in fact, all the rest of it was certainly made up. It was as epic and contentious as an Icelandic saga and most awesome to a little boy—especially the many portraits which were as imaginary and as frightening as William Blake's.

My parents and I lived in this flat for a few months following Granduncle John's death. To me it was as vast and sumptuous and exotic as a castle on the Rhine. Lincoln Park West in those days lay calm and deserted all day long. Not a motorcar came past in two hours. I could cross the street to the park to play. Every morning and afternoon I could hear the animals in the zoo roaring for their food, louder than a storm at sea.

Mary Mohr and George Rexroth had two sons, my father, Charles Marion, and my Uncle Will, and one daughter, my Aunt Grace. Will was the youngest of the three with a wizened face in his late thirties, a little shrimp, the only small Rexroth I ever heard of. He owned the Senate Barbershop, opposite the State House in Columbus, Ohio. He was not a barber; my father said he acquired the place in some dirty deal. His Negro help cut the politicians' hair and shaved their faces while he glad-handed everybody and took in the cash. In rapid succession he married three brutal women. They used to knock him around even in public. On visits to us they'd pinch him or clout him and make him yelp. All three looked much alike and much like the Polish wrestlers Stanislaus Zybisko and Strangler Lewis. When my father died he left the funeral early and came to our home and stole all of his personal jewelry and other small valuables. At least his guilt eliminated him and I never saw him again.

My Aunt Grace looked much like her mother except that she was quite beautiful—tall, angular, aquiline face, long pear-shaped head, long neck, slender breasts, and long thighs. Her skin was ivory, not brown, her eyes deep dark blue, her features chiseled. She had a considerable amount of taste and intelligence and as a very old lady she still wrote me appreciative and critical letters about my poetry.

Through my grandfather's plumbing business she met and married a fat bald drummer for a wholesale plumbing house, a typical traveling salesman, the only Babbitt on either side of my family. Outwardly they lived lives of perfect equanimity, but twice when I was in my teens she sat with me on the chain swing on the porch in the evening and told me how terrible it was to realize day after day that she was married to a man with whom she had nothing whatever in common. She said she had been able to endure it only because he was at home perhaps two days in two weeks. He had one daughter, Vera, who lived with them, and my aunt had two daughters, Bernadette and Marcella.

I was supposed to marry Bernadette when we grew up. She was the first person whose death I witnessed. She died of diphtheria while we were visiting them, and her beauty and intelligence became a legend in the family. Cousin marriages were common amongst the Rexroths and I was destined for Marcella after Bernadette's death. But after my fifteenth year I never saw the family again. Marcella, too, was a very pretty girl, with black hair, deep blue eyes, and ivory skin like her mother's. She was a passionate youngster and each time we visited them in Toledo I fell wildly in love with her.

My mother's family were the same kind of people. Her father's name was George Reed. His father's name had been spelled Reid, one of the "Cincinnati Reids," some of whom were connected with the Rexroths. He'd come from Ohio as an itinerant horse trader, first to southern Indiana and then to Elkhart. He used to say he arrived in Elkhart with a cavvy of the sorriest-looking jackasses and horses ever driven into the town, in a pair of walnut-stained homespun pants and a torn deerskin jacket with nothing but a broken jackknife and two bits in his pocket. He became a successful livery-stable keeper, then a hay, grain, and feed merchant, then a lumberyard operator, and finally a grocer and a partner in the Bucklen Hotel and Opera House. He was a friend of Gene Debs and like him a heavy drinker. I remember the two of them sitting in their socks with their feet up on the railing of the front porch, eating roast chicken and drinking straight whiskey, each with a quart bottle beside him. Debs was unhappily married and he'd come

up from Terre Haute to visit old cronies like my grandfather for com-
miseration. Several members and friends of the family worked on the
railroad and had gone through the great strike with Debs. But grandfather had lived in Terra Hut—the way it's pronounced in Indiana—in
his horse-trading days. George Reed (both my grandfathers' names
were George and both my grandmothers' names were Mary) was the
son of a woman who went by her own name, a "Lucy Stoner" before
Lucy Stone. She wore what was then considered very masculine at-
tire, taffeta or broadcloth suits of Second Empire cut as some women
are dressed in a few early Renoir paintings, linen or flannel shirts with
studs instead of buttons, and a lavender, olive, or gray string tie. She
left me her studs and cuff links. I had them for many years. She smoked
little cigars or a beautiful painted china pipe. She had a small, powerful, masculine, but somehow also very feminine face. For a nineteenth-
century woman, her picture certainly looks determined and knowing.
She lived on past ninety-five crocheting by the fire. In her young days
she'd been an early Socialist and feminist leader.

I'd sit with her by the great stove with its glowing mica windows,
while she read me books, told me stories, and gave me sage advice.
Both her family and the Reeds were German—the Reeds were Scotch-
German with even more pietist members than the Rexroths. Her husband and her brother ran an Underground Railway line from Alabama
and Mississippi through Kentucky and across the river at Cincinnati.
Either her husband or her father and her brother were caught in Cov-
ington with a load of Negroes. The white men were hung and the
Negroes burned alive in full view of Cincinnati across the river. Her
son, my grandfather, was anything but a pietist, but rather a mild sort
of freebooter in the still partially frontier Midwest of his youth. His
family, too, was supposed to have Indian blood. My great-grandmother told me I was descended from Tecumseh, who I'm pretty sure
had no descendants. George Reed died of drink many years before
his mother.

My maternal grandmother's maiden name was Mary Newman. Her
mother, who died at her birth, was named O'Connor and *her* mother's
name was Pretty, a family that came to Roscommon from Bristol, where
they had been minor gentry. The extensive Pretty estate in Ireland
and Somerset descended through the O'Connors to Mary Newman as
sole heir and she died in childbirth in Sandusky, Ohio, leaving my
grandmother, her only child. Of course, old ladies are swindled all the
time by rascals in Ireland, lured on by imaginery Irish fortunes. This
estate seems to have been perfectly bona fide. The priest in the Roscommon village and various O'Connors corresponded with my grandmother and an impressive case was built up but nothing came of it. She

dreamed of her Irish fortune all her life, died planning how she'd spend it, and left me her most valued possession, a stack of correspondence and documents. Mary O'Connor's Irish blood must have been very strong. My grandmother, my mother, and myself all had chestnut hair and blue eyes—and a pert Irish gaze—and so has my daughter Mary and we would all be taken for granted in Ireland. Practically everybody else on all sides of the family is German except for a few French, Indians, and Negroes far back.

My grandmother's father, Charles Newman, originally Neuman, was the son of an Indian trader on Lake Ontario. His mother was a Huron named Mary Saturday. The Saturday family later migrated to the Winnebago reservation, where they are to this day. A picture of one of them in a Bureau of Ethnology report bears a striking resemblance to my grandmother. Like most Eastern Indians, he is obviously more white than Indian. My great-grandfather grew up in his father's trading post and came to run one himself at Sandusky on Lake Erie. Before the Civil War he lived with his cousin as a housekeeper, and when he was away on wagon trips my grandmother, then about seven or eight, was forced to do almost all the work. She clerked in the store and kept it clean. She waited table in the inn and made the beds and washed all the dishes and all the glasses from the bar—in cold water with homemade lye soap—and fed the pigs and chickens and helped milk the cows. If she broke a dish or made a bed improperly she was beaten unmercifully. When her father came home his cousin pretended to be a most loving foster mother. I accepted my grandmother's tale as the invariant fate of all orphans and was never surprised at anything that happened later in my own childhood.

This great-grandfather, too, was busy in the Underground Railway. His shop on Sandusky Bay was the last stop for runaway Negroes on their way across the lake to Canada. From my grandmother's stories it is apparent that an unusually large number of these were house servants or freedmen who had acquired an education before the persecutions which began in Charleston and Savannah after the slave revolts and spread all through the South when so many free Negroes were reenslaved, driven out of the South, or murdered.

Although she was a little girl she realized that many were as well educated and polite and the women as handsome as any in her family. They arrived late at night in disguise or hidden in hay wagons, and boats came in the small hours of the morning and smuggled them across Lake Erie. One beautiful brown girl died in childbirth in a secret room in the barn—like a Catholic in Cromwell's England—and I met the child, a schoolteacher in Clyde, Ohio, when I was a boy. Not only were the stories all more romantic than Eliza on the ice but one was almost an exact duplicate of Eliza's and for all I know could have been the original of Mrs. Stowe's tale.

In the winter the lake was frozen, at least in Sandusky Bay, and Indians appeared across the whiteness. Michigan was still a wilderness, although many Indians had gone from Ohio and Michigan to Canada, where there was more game. There was still enough game around Sandusky Bay and in the winter they lived on smoked deer, sturgeon, lake trout, and whitefish, and bears would come to the house and root in the garbage. It's been a while now since a bear has been seen on Sandusky Peninsula except in circuses.

This grandmother, Mary Reed, *née* Newman, was the person closest to me after my own mother's death. Before that she was a most devoted grandmother and took care of me most of the time after my mother's illness. She had an endless repertory of folk and ancient music hall songs, between which, like genuine folk singers, she was unaware of any distinction—"The Boston Butcher Boy," "Barbry Allen," "Little Mohee," "The Blue Juniata," "Careless Love," "Captain Jinks of the Horse Marines," "The Letter Edged in Black," "Little Musgrave," "My Heart's as Gay as a Young Sunflower That Nods and Turns in the Breezes." She was full of tales that I know now are the classics of folklorism and are spread throughout the world but which she localized on Sandusky Bay and peopled with Indians and Civil War soldiers. In my infant imagination Clyde, Ohio, became a wonderland east of the sun and west of the moon. I have seldom heard a ghost story since that was not supposed to have happened to a relative, and northern Ohio seemed fecund in monstrous births of scaly children that hissed and crawled like snakes or were blind and furry as moles or were marked in red with the silhouette of the Indian with his tomahawk who had scared their mother. There exists a learned essay on the sea beast of Lake Erie, a legend so common that it may have some strange basis in fact. My grandmother never tired of talking about the Lake Erie sea serpent. It laid great tracks through the wheat, smashed down whole rows of corn, and devoured pigs. She had a most circumstantial account of the time the menfolks cornered it in a wood lot and shot at it and the bravest got near enough for it to crush his skull to a pulp after which it escaped back to the lake.

She had stories of meteorological phenomena that would have delighted Charles Fort—who, by the way, was a friend of my father—rains of frogs, mice or blood, hail mixed with stones, colored snow and lights and visions in the sky.

Her home in Elkhart seemed to be advantageously sited for the witnessing of inexplicable happenings in the heavens and I witnessed two of them myself.

One sultry afternoon with thunderheads on the horizon but with a clear sky overhead, a fireball materialized in the attic, came down two flights of stairs, passed among a number of people without touching them, went out the front door, collided with a bicycle in the yard, and exploded, leaving nothing but a slight burnt smell in the air. It was sapphire blue, the size of a basketball, and seemed to be spinning at great speed. It floated about four feet above the stairs or ground and preserved that height throughout its course. As the folks said, it moved more like an intelligent being than an electrical phenomenon.

Another time on a similar clear, hot, oppressive day near enough to the Fourth of July so that at first we thought it was a fireworks display of some unheard-of kind, a curved fish-shaped hole filled with leaflike dull red flames opened up in the sky. It looked exactly like a photograph of a sun spot. It was about twenty degrees long, curved like a flattened "s," pointed at both ends like a laurel leaf. It stayed in the sky for about a quarter of an hour and vanished about as instantaneously as it had appeared. It was as though the sky was a blue skin with a sudden laceration in it. People ran screaming about the streets, the superstitious sank to their knees, and even atheists like my grandfather thought it might be the end of the world. There are undoubtedly people who lived in Elkhart in those days who still remember it.

From my grandmother I inherited the annoying habit of second sight which she in turn had received from her mother, Mary O'Connor, who was famous for it in Ireland before she ever came to America, and from her father's Indian mother. It is an exasperating gift, because, with the exception of premonitions of death or disaster, it is always quite trivial. My grandmother was always saying things like "We're going to get a letter from Aunt Vonie today" or "The cherries I put up last year have spoiled down cellar" or "When Minnie gets home from the dance she's going to discover somebody stole her amythest brooch" or "You'll find the ten dollars you think the clerk stole between the cash register and the sugar barrel." There was no question of coincidence or probability; she was never wrong and she was as annoyed by the triviality of her foresight as I am by mine. Once I was sitting with her by the great coal stove with its glowing mica windows while she was sewing for the woman who lived next door, one of the Saturday family. Hanging on a hook by the door were several of the old lady's nightgowns. My grandmother said, "Look, Mrs. Saturday's nightgown has just raised one of its arms and is waving at me," and so it seemed to me. She said, "Mrs. Saturday has had a stroke and is dying"—she had never had either stroke or heart attack before but was in bed with the grippe. We ran across the yard and there she was, lying in bed, quite dead but still warm.

My grandfather Reed and my great-grandfather Newman and my grandmother were famous horse-whisperers and I am pretty good at it myself. This is the ability to talk horse softly into the ear of a fractious beast and calm him down. People with this talent can often ride horses that no one else can even mount.

When the Civil War broke out, my great-grandfather John Newman put his business on wheels and went off with the armies as a sutler. He was an idealistic Abolitionist, and after Shiloh he decided that sutlering was a disgraceful occupation and not for him so he enlisted in the cavalry and got himself a commission in time for the first of Sheridan's fights in Kentucky. My grandmother passed on from him to me tales of Perryville, Chickamauga, Missionary Ridge, Yellow Tavern, Winchester—I knew them all as though I had been there—and of Libby and Andersonville prisons, the horrors of slavery, and the barbarism and depravity of the South.

My great-grandfather had saved a Shenandoah family from rape, loot, and Sheridan's scorched earth, and had fallen in love with one of the daughters and even courted her for a weekend or a few days as the army passed along. He had ridden up to a fracas just as some drunken Federals were about to shoot up the family and burn down the house. When he left he freed and armed their Negroes with squirrel rifles and shotguns and pistols, and gave them blue caps and papers to present to any Federal troops that happened to pass by. After the war was over and he was back in Ohio, several chests of white cedar arrived with linens, crystal, and a lavish silver service—some of which passed on to me at my grandmother's death, along with the girl's letters. It was the sumptuous hope chest of a plantation belle but she herself never arrived.

Possibly the reason why the marriage never took place is that a little after their meeting, at the battle of Winchester, John Newman was standing against a tree loading his carbine and what my grandmother called "one of Jubal Early's bums" hit the tree, exploded, killed his horse, and either a piece of the tree or a piece of the shell hit him on the head and caved his skull, so that they used to say that if he stood still with his head in the right position you could pour a cup of coffee into it without spilling it. This left him a little simple, not quite right, disoriented for time, person, place, and things, and when his head got to bothering him he fought the war all over again. He actually did get the shotgun and chase the gray-uniformed postman up the street under the impression he was a Reb coming to get him.

I was there when it happened and watched them take him away from Elkhart, where he had come home to die, back to the Old Soldiers' Home in Toledo, Ohio, where he had been for thirty years or more. I visited him there, one last time. He patted me on the head and told me that if I was a good boy I'd become a great painter and writer. It was a solemn moment, the aged man in his shiny, faded blue uniform, sitting on a bench in the sun, in the garden of the Old Soldiers' Home, and me in my white Buster Brown suit. He looked quite a bit like Eugene Debs in the last years of his life when Gene was very thin, his face flabby and his eyes tragic. The prophecy was that I would become a writer *and* painter, not *or*, and this made an indelible impression on my family, on my mother who devoted herself to making sure it would come true, and on my father who had a horror that I might go into his pharmacy business.

When her father came home from war, a little simple, my grandmother was left at the mercy of her cousins. They took her out of school and put her to work, and any further education she obtained by stealing up to the attic and reading her father's books. Even this ended when she was finally caught. She was whipped and the books were burned up. Out of such a Dickensian childhood she grew up to be a beautiful girl and at last a beautiful old woman, gifted with great courage, prudence, candor, and wit. Through the years she stood steadfast in all the family's tragedies, disasters, and sicknesses. I always knew that if I got a dope habit or was wanted for murder or discovered that I was a pansy I could go to Grandma and she could take care of me. I had no such occasions but she helped me through many lesser difficulties and even after I was long grown up it was hard to keep her from giving me money. A childhood which nowadays would be an excuse for neurosis and delinquency helped to make her exceptionally generous and wise with an irrepressible talent for enjoying life.

My grandfather, George Reed, was distantly related to my grandmother's cousins. One day he arrived in Clyde, Ohio, from Elkhart with a string of stock he was driving through the country to trade and sell. He put up at the inn where my grandmother was still in peonage to her relatives and took her off to a dance. The next day he married her, put her on a horse, and went back to Indiana. Until late middle age he was a successful merchant. The hotel and opera house in which he was a partner were frequented by the itinerant high life of the small-town Middle West—Chautauqua stars, harness racers, stock-company actresses, and opera singers known and unknown to fame. He played host to them till the drink caught up with him and after his third attack of delirium tremens, he died in middle age.

The important years until their children were grown were certainly happy for my grandparents. The rich, busy social life of an Indiana small town at the end of the nineteenth century was a vital culture in the anthropological sense if not in Oscar Wilde's.

CHAPTER 2

My grandmother had four children, Minnie, my mother, Delia, and twin boys, Clyde and Dale. Dale died in infancy and left a legend of great promise. A glass marble the size of a billiard ball, with a beautiful swirling insert in it, descended to me along with the responsibility to fulfill that promise. I kept the marble until I was thirty years old. My Uncle Clyde was haunted by his twin and told me that he often woke up at night with the feeling that half of himself was on the other side of the earth living a life he could sense—and that he felt there was someone beside and slightly behind him, out of vision, in all the important moments of his life. He was convinced that he would die young and did little to prevent it by becoming a silversmith. He ran away to Chicago in his first long pants and spent his adolescence as a pitchman, house-to-house salesman, burlesque actor, carney, general hustler, grifter, and gay cat of all work. For a short time he owned Cupid's Diary, the most ethical of the matrimonial agencies. Out of it he got a fine wife, a Mennonite widow with three children, and then settled down to silversmithing. Like most lesser skilled silversmiths of those days, he did a lot of electroplating and other acid work and died of scorched lungs in his midthirties. He was a gentle, cocky, wise little man, and in my own adolescence I often stayed with him and his Mennonite wife for weeks at a time. Through Clyde I first met people like Yellow Kid Weil and Yellow (Kid) Nunez and an assortment of carney, burley, circus, and early ragtime-jazz people. The women were big-boned, fleshy, florid, and moist. The men were like my uncle, little and lithe of step and finger, boosters, cannon guys, and operators.

My Aunt Minnie was eight years older than my mother. She was a handsome, tall, strong-willed woman with snapping blue eyes and thick black hair. She was smartly but severely dressed. Her shirtwaists were immaculate and unwilted at the end of a day's work. Her workaday hats were polished sailors or severe felts. Her dressy ones were piles of ostrich plumes or flowers. Her evening gowns were tailored of sumptuous materials, heavy velvets, crackling taffetas, slipper satin, with the maximum décolletage the custom of the day allowed. She was the head of the glove department in the local department store and the buyer of all their high fashions. She was incapable of boiling an egg. She had a succession of fellows, doctors, lawyers, engineers, architects, and heirs of the local rich. Periodically she would announce her engagement to one of them. Then in a month or two the man would stop coming around and the engagement would be broken. This went on until she was past thirty-five. Then one Labor Day at a picnic at Silver Lake she met an Irishman from Chicago and married him that week.

His name was Paul Monahan. He worked in the Chicago stockyards for very little money. He was a widower with five children, a silent, devoted man still deep in shock from the death of his first wife. My aunt came to live in the decaying frame house on Emerald Avenue, Back of the Yards, the neighborhood of *The Jungle,* overrun with rats and cockroaches and haunted by the dead woman's memory. She cooked, baked, cleaned, washed and ironed and mended and cared for her family through sickness and death while their economic situation slowly improved, and they moved every few years mile by mile south until finally they were living near Seventy-seventh and South Shore Drive.

This is the typical story of the rise of an Irish family in Chicago and is exactly paralleled in James Farrell's novels. Nothing could be less like her own upbringing. Paul Monahan was a fine man but he certainly came from an extraordinarily unlike world. My aunt never seemed to have any regrets for the life she had left behind her. Indeed, she seemed to enjoy making a success of her family on its own terms, however outlandish and bitterly hard.

From her girlhood she retained her two closest friends, a brother and sister. One was an engineer on the New York Central; the other, the administrative assistant to the president of the Bischer musical-instrument company. They never married but remained together in their parents' home in Elkhart long after both had retired. Finally the man became ill with cancer. My aunt went down to Elkhart and helped the sister nurse him till he died. At his death his sister revealed that all through her brother's illness she had known that she had had fatal cancer, too. So my aunt stayed with her until her death. They left her what little property they had accumulated and with that my aunt and uncle lived out their old age. What little they had been able to put by had been wiped out in 1929. Just before her death Minnie Monahan was received into the Roman Catholic Church. Only two stepchildren survived her.

My mother was eight years younger than her sister and about as much again older than her brother. She was christened Delia but was usually called by the what was then the more conventional name of Della. As I remember her stories she had an unusually joyous childhood. Her mother seems to have encouraged an exceptional range of interests for those days. She read widely, painted watercolors, played the piano, was mildly stage-struck, and had a passionate interest in nature study and the out-of-doors. I judge that most of this was learned at home. She graduated from a finishing school run by nuns in South Bend and went on to Oberlin for a term or two. At the sisters' academy she met a small group of slightly flashy intellectual girls who remained her closest friends for the rest of her life. She quit college and bought an interest in a wholesale millinery business in Joplin, Missouri, with one of these girls. One day a cyclone hit town. She was talking to one of her girls who was sitting at a sewing machine when half the building disappeared. The sewing machine tumbled off into space and the girl was left with her chair teetering on the brink of the abyss. My mother and her partner sold out the business at a loss and returned to Indiana.

To judge from her chest of keepsakes—dance programs, pressed flowers, one man's tie pin, another's ring, relics of boys at West Point, Notre Dame, and Northwestern—she had been a successful young girl with the men. I feel, though, that the most significant share of her early life was lived in her little circle of highly sexed, slightly hysterical suffragette but chic young women who were much more interested in one another than they were in men. They all made successful marriages of the kind that end in spectacular and immensely profitable divorces—except for one, the most beautiful, the idol of them all, who went on the stage. She must have been fairly successful, too, because letters used to come from her from all over Europe as well as America filled with ironic descriptions of the great and with sarcastic criticisms of her own leading roles. When she played Chicago she'd come down to see us, loaded with flowers and fantastic presents for my mother and me. I remember her hats, covered with plumes or flowers, heaps of lace petticoats, lace clocks in her stockings, higher-heeled slippers than I had ever seen—or walking costumes, an Italian felt hat with a pheasant feather, an unusually short, green velvet skirt, Scottish stockings and heavy brogans and a blackthorn walking stick. When we would go out with her at night in New York or Chicago she always had the most décolleté bosom in Rector's or Delmonico's. Then she had a disastrous love affair which ended in a shooting. She came back to Elkhart, gave away all her fine clothes, locked herself in her room for a year, and then entered the Poor Clares. My mother kept her friend's picture on her dresser till she died. After the actress entered the convent my mother's closest friend was the wife of a millionaire doctor in South

Bend. We saw a lot of her because she was always taking her two little boys and running away to stay with us. The doctor kept his mistress, a redheaded nurse (they always seemed to be redheaded, these nurse mistresses), in one wing of the house. Then he betrayed both nurse and wife and embarked on a scandalous affair with one of the country's most notorious professional beauties. We were in New York and his wife showed up and had dinner with us at our hotel. As we all came out to go to the theater the husband emerged from a cab with his ornate lady. His wife darted out from behind a potted tree and threw acid on the other woman's face. Fortunately she didn't know what kind of acid to buy so she didn't do much damage.

Daughters of manufacturers of musical instruments, patent medicines, plows, wagons, corsets, gas and steam automobiles and "electrics" —these girls differed little from their grander contemporaries in New York, Chicago, Newport, or the German spas; nor did they differ much, except in scale, from the actresses they adored—Duse, Ida Rubinstein, Mercedes de Acosta, or the roles those actresses played, the heroines of Ibsen, Strindberg, and D'Annunzio. They played Debussy and Scriabin on the piano with many mistakes but with many languors. They read Flaubert, Henry James, and Nietzsche. They smoked cigarettes. They read Shaw, Ellen Key, Havelock Ellis, Edward Carpenter. They believed in free love. They collected Tiffany glass, Art Nouveau woodcuts, Rodin sketches and Whistler-like etchings. The doctor's wife even owned a Pissaro and a Maurice Denis. Isadora Duncan, Emma Goldman, Mary Church Terrell and Irene Castle—they had them to dinner when they came to town.

After the Second War I went back to Elkhart and South Bend on a lecture tour and was amazed to find that the survivors and the children of this little band of small-town sophisticates were all campaigning for Henry Wallace. Howard Fast had replaced Flaubert, Rockwell Kent was preferred to Aubrey Beardsley. Satie and Busoni had given way to Paul Robeson, Pete Seeger, and Josh White. They were all progressives.

I have lived twenty years longer than my mother and look back on her airs and graces with amusement when not with admiration. Her life was not so fast as she thought but I am sure she enjoyed it. Her enthusiasms were genuine; her glamor provincial but real. She had a pretty accurate estimate of her own role in the scheme of things. I don't think she was a blue stocking, although she may have daydreamed of becoming an adventuress. I don't think she was a snob, although she used to say, "A snob is a person who mimics the manners of the class above him."

Generations back, branches of my family tree cross. Indiana and

Ohio were not densely populated before the War of 1812 and people of similar background and interest were drawn together. One day a very distant relative, a young pharmaceutical chemist from Chicago, came down to Elkhart to a family party and met my mother. In a few days they eloped to Benton Harbor. My father's father had been punished by his father and had run away from home, and then, just as in Gertrude Stein's *The Making of Americans,* my father and grandfather got in a row. My father refused to stay in Napoleon, Ohio, take care of the business, and go to a poor college. When his father tried to whip him he left and didn't come back until after he was married. He went first to Oberlin, which he didn't like, and then to medical school at Northwestern. He had formed a friendship with a Mr. Eliel who owned the oldest drugstore in South Bend and a considerable share in the largest wholesale drug house in Chicago, Kinsolving & Granisson. It no longer exists. He told my father he would put him through school and into the business and in no time at all he would be one of the owners because the original families wanted to sell out. To do this he should get a pharmaceutical chemist's degree and then a Ph.D. in organic chemistry. Since Mr. Eliel offered to finance both the education and the partnership my father allowed himself to be persuaded. He quit medical school and went into pharmacy. Time would prove it a fatal decision.

He seems to have had a good time at college. He went to Europe as a workaway, spent a summer wandering all over the Continent, and planned to spend the winter at Vienna, but he came home with a strong dislike of European scientific education, a small collection of art books, some photographs of beautiful girls, and fascinating anecdotes of the bohemian life of Paris, Munich, and Berlin in 1890. In his youth he was tall, fine-boned, with a thin face and oversensitive eyes and an extremely heavy mustache. His pictures bear no resemblance to the man I knew, who was portly, bald, usually smooth-shaven, with the look of a sad child. Young, he was handsome, romantic, and sophisticated and must have swept my mother off her feet. At forty he had become an Elk, a good-time Charlie at poker, drinking, and wenching parties, and on fishing trips with his brother Elks.

In the early photographs of their marriage, my mother looks blissfully happy; their surviving correspondence is passionate and devoted. As sales manager my father traveled all over the Middle West and occasionally to New York or the West Coast. My mother went with him on the longer trips. They went to the Derby, to French Lick and Saratoga, to the opera and theater in Chicago. Then my mother had a miscarriage and afterward was chronically ill. My father began to drink heavily and grew dissolute-looking and fat. My mother became chronically mildly hysterical. Her old girl friends, who all hated men on principle, reappeared. My father drank more and more and they drifted still further apart. Eventually he would stay away for weeks at a time and my mother would go out with other men. They quarreled little but something seems to have gone wrong with the marriage, possibly only alcohol. They were passionately happy together even at the end, but as I look back I feel that they were never able to recapture the idyllic, blissful character their marriage had had in its early years, and when they were apart the old loyalty was ignored by both of them.

CHAPTER 3

I was born on December 22, 1905, in South Bend, Indiana. My mother was well past her time. She was sitting in a cabaret, eating breast of chicken on whole-wheat bread with a piece of lettuce and drinking a glass of champagne, as she always did in cabarets, and wondering when I was going to show up when she began to feel labor pains. My parents were visiting in Elkhart, but they had the curious idea of hurrying up to Chicago for the baby's birth. My mother was taken off the train in South Bend, and I was born there.

My parents rented a house down by the river near a park. I can still dimly remember this park. A good bit of it has been pared away. Somewhere I have written that I can remember the statue of Chevalier de La Salle in the little parkway between the river and the boulevard. I'm told the statue doesn't exist any more. In the other direction there was another park and the Oliver Hotel and our friend Mr. Eliel's drugstore on the square. He lived near us with his aged sister, both of them in their eighties.

I remember our house as substantial and comfortable, one of the homes of the moderately well-to-do, built in early settlement of South Bend. It was in a neighborhood something like Euclid Avenue as it once was in Cleveland or Hyde Park in Cincinnati—but not quite so splendid.

My earliest memory is of being with my parents for a Fourth of July celebration and seeing the fireworks. I can remember being held up by my mother and then by my father turnabout in the night and a great crowd of people and the rockets bursting overhead and the fire fountains and wheels. I was six months or a year and six months old. Another very early memory is of a white fur cap with little mice heads on it. I remember I saw it up in the attic later when I was seven or eight years old, and I remember my delight at seeing it again.

They used to wheel me around the park in South Bend over the bridge and let me watch the fish in the water underneath. I remember a winter day, me all bundled and with the white fur cap on my head. For the next two years I kept this cap as a mascot.

My Uncle Clyde never had any children, nor did my aunt. At that time neither of them was married, so I was the first and, as it would turn out, the only grandson. I got a lot of attention from my aunt, uncle, grandfather and grandmother, and from my mother's whole side of the family.

I have no other memories of that house, only of a visit to it once as an adolescent to see the place where I was born. We moved to Beardsley Avenue in Elkhart. This was a quiet residential street above the river where all the best homes in the town were in those days, where the patent-medicine people, the musical-instrument people, the buggy-works people, the corset people, and all the other leading citizens of the town lived in their wooden, sometimes Palladian or Romanesque mansions, and we had our own little Palladian house. I've always retained a great fondness for columns and porticoes. We used to call it the White House, after the one in Washington. It's no longer there.

We had a great expanse of lawn, trees, quite a little park, and beautiful gardens behind. Until I was grown I still had a picture of the house. It was really quite an impressive place. I imagine it represented the height of my father's career. He was not yet a drunkard. He had become vice-president of his business. Although later when I went to work for the firm it turned out to be ramshackle and run-down, still it was the largest wholesale drug company in the Chicago area, which is nothing to sneeze at.

He had an attractive wife, well known all over that part of the country. They used to give big parties. They went to the Kentucky Derby and stopped off at French Lick for the Derby Ball and went up to the best Michigan lakes of those days, which are now dreadful places. They spent much of their time enjoying themselves. Some of their clothes from their early days survived in a trunk in my aunt's attic for years. Certainly they were remarkably well-dressed people for their time.

We had a honey-colored horse, a buggy, a dogcart that was about the same size as my father, and two ponies that were slightly less fat than he but somewhat bigger. I was devoted to one of the ponies. We used to take him from the livery stable and keep him in the vacant lot next door during the day, and he used to wander around and graze on the lawn and play with me. The other pony was insane. He once bit my mother on the breast. He didn't actually do much damage. Horse bites are seldom very serious, because I guess they never really mean them. A horse ought to be able to inflict a very severe sincere bite. But he certainly terrified her.

His worst insanity was that he was queer for railroad tracks. Whenever we crossed railroads he would turn slightly off the crossing to where the tracks were exposed and lie down in the harness. Then my father, who was at that time very fat indeed, would get out and whip him and pull his tail and pull his bridle while my mother pushed and prodded. Once we lit a newspaper under him. Usually we would get him going. But finally his insanity was too much for him. He was lying on the tracks, and we managed to get the other pony unhitched and almost got the dogcart free. My mother stood sheltering me on the embankment about twenty feet away, and my father toiled on trying to get the recumbent pony out of the traces. Down the track came the train. The pony was made into hamburger and the dogcart into matches by the Twentieth Century.

The other pony survived as a saddle animal for me for a while. Then we got a wise and gentle donkey. There is still a picture of me on that donkey. I don't know what happened to the pony. I think we got too poor to keep him. But we kept the donkey for a long time in the vacant lot next door. I sit in the picture in the family Bible in my Dutch bob and velvet suit, very serious on the equally serious donkey.

I spent a great deal of time outdoors. Beside the house on Beardsley Avenue there was a large vacant lot. The next house belonged to a family called Fernault. I presume they were River French ultimately, since they were one of the founding families of the town. They had a large vacant lot completely overgrown with trees and bushes and high grass, and this was known as "out in the woods by Fernaults' house." I had a cabin built of a grand-piano case. It was stood up on one end, had roughly the shape of a grand piano, and was painted by my parents a little like a Russian church or a bit of the Kremlin. There was an entrance built out in front of it like an igloo passage. It was completely hidden by bushes with its own play area. I would spend many hours, sometimes the whole day, there by myself.

My mother taught me to read between the ages of three and four. When I was four she got me a library card. I remember the first book I got on the card and read through with great excitement. It was called *The Turtle Prince*. In the course of time in early childhood I read the whole series of Lang's colored fairy tales and several children's sets of science and history books. Later I went through all of what F. Scott Fitzgerald called Henty's perversions of history and the American Henty, Altsheller, who managed to play both sides. I've forgotten Henty's prejudices—it seems to me he was a Whig—but Altsheller managed to be a hack on both sides. He wrote stories about boys in the Confederate Army and about boys in the Union Army. He wrote stories about the French and others about the English in the French and English wars. He was doing that after the First World War broke out, writing alternately Allied or German boy's stories, and unfortunately had to switch to our side suddenly and exclusively. From him I learned first of the natural venality of authors. There was a German novelist, Ebers, who wrote dozens of books about Egypt. There was a series of the "Boy's Historians"—simplified Livy and Froissart and Parkman and Prescott. By the time I was ten I had read a huge mass of adventure and history, which for me shaded into each other, and elementary science. Early on I read *David Copperfield,* and somewhere about twelve, all of Dickens.

I used to take the books out to my cabin, and I'd be given food and have a little picnic by myself. My father was away traveling for a week or more at a time, and my mother and I hiked over the beautiful northern Indiana landscape. We roamed the woods and pastures of the Bristol moraine, where clear, sparkling streams ran over colored stones, something not common in clay-covered Indiana. She had a considerable knowledge, which I suspect she had acquired for the purpose of educating me, of birds and flowers and every edible variety of mushroom.

For a small child I lived an elaborate social life. I went to that thing which all well-off small boys were supposed to go to in those days—dancing school—and was taught formal manners of the kind that no longer exist. We had parties at every imaginable occasion: big birthday parties for each of us, Fourth of July, Christmas, Easter, Washington's Birthday, Halloween, and St. Patrick's Day celebrations. All the holidays of the American calendar were occasions for a party.

Depending on the season, some of the parties would be picnics on the lawn, some would be ice cream and cake inside, some would be snow parties, sleigh rides in a wagon box full of perfumed hay. I have a picture given me by my childhood sweetheart, Helen, of the children at one of the parties which was, I believe, given by the Beardsley boy seated in the center. About fifteen little rich kids are there—the boys all in Buster Brown suits, wide-collared blouses with a dickey and short pants, all white; the little girls in white dresses with Mary Jane shoes (Mary Jane was Buster Brown's sister) and some in curls like Esther Staring (who remembers her?)—all sitting under a vast white umbrella.

There were evening parties with Chinese lanterns on the lawn and parties at nearby Silver Lake out in boats. Whenever the adults had a party, the children usually had one of their own. The adults would have a lawn party out in front, and in the backyard the kids would have theirs with lanterns and sparklers.

I don't remember any of the violent rumpuses that would take place at such a party given by middle-class parents today. I think it would be almost impossible for children between the ages of four and ten to live the kind of social life they led in the first decade of this century among well-established, older, middle-class Americans. I don't think a party like ours is possible any more. Children would get set on fire, things would get stolen, little girls would get raped, and all sorts of mayhem would take place. On the other hand, I don't remember a single fight from those days.

One of the things that impresses me most, is the disappearance of children's culture except among Negroes. Children all over the world have songs and games and activities with which they fill their scanty free time. They have their own kind of organized play kept secret from adults. If you question children of the game-playing age, around ten or eleven, you discover none of the boys have heard of "Run, Sheep, Run" or "Pom, Pom, Pullaway"; none of the girls of "What's My Trade?." A certain number of songs, the skip-rope, and counting-out rhymes are coming back, due to the fact that they are taught in schools by women who have read them in a folklore book, usually women with no children and no desire for any.

Northern Indiana, as you know if you've read any folklore, had a rich child culture. There's a book called *The Play Party in Indiana,* one of the best folklore studies. The play party, originally an adult activity, survived in my time amongst children even in the upper middle class, although it had lost its puritan character.

CHAPTER 4

My mother took over the billiard room and moved the billiard table down to one end. At the other she built a one-teacher, one-student schoolroom with blackboard, desk, pictures, bookshelves, and cases of what are now called educational toys. I had a separate playroom with more shelves, cupboards and blackboard, lots of pictures on the walls, and all my books as I accumulated them. In the early morning, and on rainy days in the afternoon, too, we had our own school.

Winter evenings by the fire my mother told me long stories which I recognize now were educational in intent, about various aspects of life and science and how the world is run, how foods are produced, what makes the electric lamp give light—the things you find now in textbooks for young children. In those days such methods represented the most advanced theories of education. I also got plenty of mythology —stories of the Norse gods, the *Iliad* and the *Odyssey*, the *Ramayana*, the *Arthuriad, Robin Hood,* the *Mabinogion, The Arabian Nights,* and Lady Gregory's two collections of Irish folklore. She read me stories and I early had books about foreign children—Bushmen of Africa or Australia, Chinese, Japanese, Eskimos, and Indians. Like all children I had an especial fondness for the Eskimos. I now understand that my mother put a special emphasis on Indian folklore and factual information, and I understand why. In America we have nothing that takes the place of the gods and goddesses and heroes and demigods of the ancient world. There is nothing to connect us with the soil. We have no mythology. It has never been possible to construct one. The mythology of the founding fathers, of George Washington's cherry tree, of Johnny Appleseed, and of Lincoln studying by the firelight is not enough. The Indian connects us with the soil, connects us with the earth of America. Pan and the satyrs and nymphs and the Artemises with horses' heads or with many breasts or shaped like fish and the other strange pre-Hellenic local deities fused the inhabitants of the classic world with the rocky bones of Greece. The Indians and their ways are our mythology, our gods of the fields and springs and high places. For that reason, before my daughters knew anything else about American history, they knew a great deal about Indians.

My mother and father made me toys which somewhat resembled Montessori apparatus. Some of them probably were Montessori or Froebellian toys, although I cannot remember any of those things that button and unbutton and lace and unlace that Signora Montessori was so fond of. I do remember graded and weighted, carved and textured blocks painted in spectrum colors, of the kind now obtainable in any good toyshop. They were quite revolutionary in those days. Tasteful and carefully planned educational toys were used by few people and weren't bought in a shop, but made at home or imported from Switzerland.

I learned elementary arithmetic and a considerable amount of natural science. The nature study was all done in the fields. The schoolroom filled up with collections—herbarium, aquarium, terrarium, minerals, shells, rocks, fossils. Eventually we called it "the museum" rather than "the schoolroom." Gathering and studying these things with my mother, I spent what still seem the happiest, most lyrical hours of my life. I still make collections in every strange country that I go to. Now I do it with my little girls. We collected butterflies and insects by sight, never by catching and killing them. On this subject my mother was quite fanatical.

A few years later, in front of our second house, there was a slight rise in the road. A man with a team of four horses and a flat-bed truck loaded with stone came along. The horses were unable to negotiate this very slight rise—Elkhart, Indiana, is on a perfectly flat prairie—and he whipped them until one of the rear horses fell and there was quite a tangle. The front horses broke half free, rearing and snorting. Instead of getting down, the truck driver continued to whip them. My mother went into the house and got a pistol, came out and shot at him until she emptied the chambers. When the sheriff came round he said, "Del, what on earth got into you?" She said, "Bill, I just shot over the son of a bitch's head to frighten him." I don't think she could aim a pistol at all. I remember her holding it in both hands.

She had a great capacity for joy, and I never see a Kate Greenaway dress or one of her pictures of little girls dancing in their characteristic gowns and little slippers without thinking of my mother and the innocent, graceful handling of the body that Kate Greenaway drew so well. That physical grace was probably the expression of joy and contentment with her life at that time, her happiness as a mother in relation to her child.

Many of her stories not only were about Indians, but they stressed the Indian past of our own family. Unfortunately, although I was taught to be very proud of this strain in my own blood, I have forgotten most of the anecdotes. She was even more proud of the family's past relationship with Negroes. Incidents that took place in the Civil War and in the work of the Underground Railway I do remember somewhat better.

The towns in northern Indiana lying along the Michigan border had been the last stops on the Underground Railway. They had a good many Negro freedmen living in them. Elkhart became one of the centers of the Ku Klux Klan only some fifteen years after that, but in my days there if you called a man a nigger in the street a white man would very likely walk up to you and knock you down. People today have no idea how living a thing the Abolitionist spirit was as late as 1914. We can no longer gauge the destruction of native American radicalism and liberalism in the First World War. In those days people like my family were still animated by the spirit of a won revolution.

"If you want to know what America would be like if the South had won the Civil War, look at France." The French have lost all their revolutions and the modern French of all parties are severally defeated groups of partisans. In the course of the last two hundred years everyone has managed to defeat and betray everybody else. Nowadays it's hard for people to find out that the Civil War was not the sort of thing you see in the movies or read about in the *Sewanee* or *Kenyon Reviews*. The Civil War was America's great revolutionary war, and it was a revolution which was won. It was from several generations who had won all their revolutions and expected to go on winning them that I came.

I spent a great deal of time at my grandparents' house. They lived a little way across the river—over a long railroad trestle and over a wooded river bottom, then a low bank, and then my grandfather's house, which was still on a dirt road although just a few blocks from Main Street in Elkhart. To this house came a wonderful new member of the family, a more delightful visitor than Santa Claus.

At the junction of the St. Joe and Elkhart Rivers, there'd been a Potawatomi village in the early days. An old Indian who had lived there as a boy came back one day, working his way across from Oklahoma. He was a man long past eighty. His name was Billy Sunlight or Billy Moonlight, I've forgotten which, and he was known around Elkhart and to the family as Old Billy. Although he was very old he was very spry. He came down the dirt road past the house when my grandmother was working in the garden. He stopped and put down his bundle of herbs—he was a herb doctor—and he asked my grandmother if she could give him any work for dinner and a place to sleep and feed for his horse, which he had hitched off somewhere as he went from door to door with his pack of herbs on his back. She said certainly, he could help her with the work she was doing in the garden that afternoon, and that night they fixed him up a shakedown in the chicken coop and put the horse in the barn.

I don't want to give you the impression that we put the Indians and the lower classes generally in the chicken coop. I used to play in it before Old Billy took it over. It had a wonderful smell of fresh clean lumber. It was quite spotless and had windows all along one side. Once they planned to have a lot of chickens, but they gave it up and had just a few chickens, enough for eggs for breakfast. These were off in an old coop which left the new chicken coop unused; it was built to house maybe a hundred chickens on the other side of the garden, and was back from the house about a hundred and fifty feet.

In the morning very early, Old Billy was up cooking himself breakfast on a potbellied stove that had been put out in the backyard to boil soap. He stayed for several years. He kept a garden that was the wonder of Elkhart. He didn't seem to do much work on it. He would go out and putter around for a while and make magic over it. The weeds disappeared; the tomatoes were the biggest in town. This is so much more remarkable because Indian men commonly do not believe in working the earth. They believe that only women can do that without destroying the fertility of the soil, which is the reason why the Indian Bureau has never been able to make farmers out of most of the Indians of the United States, except those of the Southwest, which has a different culture.

The rest of the time Billy spent sashaying around in the woods looking for herbs. He took me with him. Like Hiawatha, at the age of five or six I knew the names of all the birds and beasts and flowers and roots and plants, but unfortunately I knew them in Potawatomi. And the only Potawatomi I ever knew slipped from my mind within a few years. So I wasn't what could be called a trained botanist. My knowledge didn't have much to do with Linnaean classification; its taxonomy was of an older and stranger culture. I gained, more important than taxonomic order, a living experience of what was then still, particularly along the river bottoms and some of the moraine country, quite wild woodland and meadow with small animals of all sorts—mink and otter, muskrat, skunk, and coon—though not possum, which in those days I don't believe crossed the Ohio River.

There were lots of woodchucks and weasels, and I remember the first time I ever saw otter play and slide down a slippery bank into the water. Old Billy knew where they were and took me to them. We sat down silently behind some bushes on the bank of an Indiana stream and pretty soon out came a family of otter and climbed up on the bank and slid down the mud slide over and over again like little children. Nothing looks funnier than an otter having a good time, unless it's a sea otter, which looks even more cherubic.

Then somebody, for some reason or another, perhaps just for love of nature, imported some beaver into a nearby brook, and we watched them, Billy and I, build their dams and lodges. I sat for long hours quietly by the side of the pond. I still think sitting still by a beaver pond in the sunset and early dusk is about the finest activity of man.

Billy had an old horse and a buggy with a little canvas cover with a pucker string over the box on the back. It was like a miniature prairie schooner, just big enough for him to curl up and sleep in in bad weather.

The horse was as aged for a horse as Billy was for a man. He was the first Indian horse I had ever seen. He was a real Indian horse that had come up from Oklahoma—then Indian Territory—a Palouse, and I'm quite sure he was then the only Palouse in that part of the country. In a small stable in the back of the property, Billy kept his horse along with my grandfather's, and he took care of them all. This again he did without seeming to do any work.

One of the things you discover about Indians if you live with them, as I was to do later, is that the mountain men who despised them were perfectly right. The other mountain men who liked them were perfectly right, too. Most Indians who live any distance from water, or where there is any inconvenience about water at all, are terribly dirty, and Indians demoralized by life near white men or on poor reservations are even dirtier. They may have sterling virtues but cleanliness is not one of them.

Old Billy was fanatically neat and clean. He was a regular Swiss watchmaker of an Indian. He rebuilt the inside of the chicken coop, and on the rafters he hung his herbs. He had a built-in bunk and a little stove, wall cupboards, magnifying glass, various pots and even glass flasks to cook up some of his mixtures in, and a Bunsen burner. He probably would have been a fine pharmaceutical chemist if he had had the chance; perhaps he was anyway.

He covered the coop with insulation and then with shakes which he split with a frow. It's the first time I ever saw a frow used, and I was permitted to help him. It gives me great pleasure to this day to sit on a warm late-summer afternoon and sock a frow and split off shakes. I've forgotten the name of the mallet like a one-handled rolling pin that you hit a frow with. I wish someone would tell me. It's a fine name like those old British names for parts of windmills and tails of animals.

Billy's cabin was warm all winter long and cleaner than my grand-mother's home, which was spotless. He did his own washing and mending, and in the wintertime, when he wasn't busy, he was always grubbing around in the house getting stuff to take out and mend for the family. He was an expert seamster, much better than any woman in the house, and he never used a sewing machine. He had many other talents of this sort. He could cure leather and make beads and do all the things Indians are supposed to do. He had all the female talents as well as the male talents. He was quite an Indian.

I was willing to spend all my time with Old Billy, and I did spend a considerable amount with him. He couldn't read, but he used to give me long lectures. He spoke perfect English with no trace of an accent. Indians like him had been in contact with white men for generations. As far as anybody in Elkhart could tell, he spoke perfect French.

In those days Indians used to travel around like gypsies and sell baskets and leatherwork and beadwork from door to door, and some of them traded horses. Whenever they camped, if they were good Indians, Billy would take me to see them. A lot of them were more like gypsy bands. These "bad Indians" would never speak to Billy in the street; they would look at him with sidelong faces and they would never come to the house. There must have been an Indian sign on the gate, for we were never bothered by bad Indians or bad gypsies.

Billy knew almost all the gypsy bands that came and went through that part of the country. As an itinerant herbalist, he had been in contact with them all the latter part of his life, and if he approved of them we would go and visit them. He had them classified, too, and he had a rather low opinion of all of them, graded as untrustworthy, thievish, and evil. We spent many hours by gypsy fires, the gypsies singing and dancing and Billy and me sitting grave and silent with the gravity of five years and eighty-five years.

And as I said, Billy used to give me long and slowly delivered and dramatically illustrated lectures teaching me the ways of life. The relationship between me and Old Billy, I would say from reading about and living with Indians relatively untouched by white men, like Northern Utes, was that which prevailed in the average Indian tribe in an uncorrupted state. The middle generation, the fathers and mothers, are busy, but after an Indian gets to be fifty-five or sixty, if he's still alive, which is unlikely, he's really out of affairs altogether. So the old men sit around and teach the young and are otherwise only called on for counsel in serious situations. The basic educational relationship was that between the grandparents, or even the great-grandparents, and the children in most Indian tribes.

When I was about seven, one day I went out to the cabin—it was called Old Billy's chicken coop still—to get him to go on a trip. I opened the door, and he was lying dead in his bunk, his hands crossed over his chest and a luminous look to his face. I wasn't afraid or upset. Old Billy by then was, I guess, over ninety, and I knew that he was going to die at any time. He had talked about his death to me, and it seemed just as it should be. I walked back up to the house and told my grandmother, who was surprised at the way I took it. Then as the days went on I felt lonely and I used to cry for Old Billy, but not because he was dead really, only because he was gone from me and from the woods we loved.

CHAPTER 5

My grandmother came to South Bend and helped take care of me when I was a baby. In later years she spent a great deal of time with me. After my parents' death she spent even more. Even in those days it seemed to me we were always going places with my grandfather and grandmother or visiting at their house.

The extended family of three generations or more was still a living thing in my youth. My grandfather and grandmother, my uncle, my aunt, my father, and I, even my great-aunts and second cousins, were all just as much an emotional unit as though we were living in one of the long houses of the Iroquois.

The period just before the First War witnessed the last flowering of Western European man and the last days of the old Western European family structure. As we look back upon the architecture and interior decoration of the Edwardian and Victorian periods, there is one thing very obvious about them. They are homey. Nothing has ever been homier—the physical embodiment of a domestic life that was vanishing.

Although my father was hardly an Atlas to shoulder responsibility in the last years after drink had caught up with him, in the formative years of my life he was quite the opposite. He was handsome and successful and well liked, and what he said in the family went. He was a well-educated man, and he knew what he was talking about. I spent a great deal of time with him. We used to go fishing together, out in a boat on Lake Michigan or fly fishing in the streams which were just then being planted with sport fish. And we took trips up into the forests of Wisconsin and Michigan.

We once took a trip far up into Canada. My father didn't believe in hunting but he brought a rifle for good manners. Once they'd all gone off fishing and left their guns near camp. I came down in the early evening through a logged-off clearing. My father's rifle was there and I picked it up and started walking back toward camp. I couldn't have been more than nine. All of a sudden in the middle of the corduroy road there was a moose. I raised the rifle and fired it, and I hit the moose smack between the eyes. He lunged at me and fell down on his face. Blood exploded all over. The gun knocked me down. I ran screaming into camp and said that I had just killed a moose. No one believed me, but there was the dead moose. That was the only hunting I've ever done in my life.

I had a dog, a large brindle bull named Rex. He was an adult dog when we got him. He had been passed from hand to hand because he was a notorious fighter. Four other people had owned him, and a brother Elk or Mason gave him to my father. His name was already Rex before he entered the Rexroth family, where all dogs are named Rex whether male or female. We acquired him when we first moved into the Beardsley Avenue home while I was still a baby. He immediately became a devoted guardian, took care of me, and played with me all the time, but he remained the most notorious fighter in Elkhart. It was amusing to watch the other dogs in the neighborhood come down Beardsley Avenue. Rex would shift his weight and growl and they would cross the street rather than pass in front of our house.

After having been pulled and beaten out of fights and having had pepper thrown in his eyes and having been in all sorts of uproars in Main Street with all the dogs of all the leading citizens, he got into a fight with another bull which belonged to the man who had bought my grandfather's coal and lumberyard. This man came along with a stake truck, pulled one of the stakes out of the truck, and drove it down between the fighting dogs. He smashed Rex's skull and killed him and hopelessly crippled his own dog so that he, too, had to be killed.

Rex had been a friend of all the family and a companion to my grandfather and to Old Billy. Old Billy saw the whole thing from horseback and took after the man, who left his truck and fled to the lumberyard and ran upstairs to his office. Old Billy called up my grandfather, who was at the grocery store, and he came over to the lumberyard. The office building was one of those little two-story things peculiar to lumberyards with an office downstairs and a watchman's bed, I presume, upstairs. The murderer of the dog locked himself into the upstairs compartment. Billy was downstairs at the telephone holding guard, and the horses were coming into the gate of the lumberyard with the abandoned lumber truck when my grandfather came tearing over on horseback. This all sounds very Wild West, but normally nobody in my family rode horseback very much although we had saddles for everyone and all my grandfather's horses could be ridden. He came over with a Civil War musket, drunk. My grandfather stormed around downstairs, finally fired all his ammunition through the floor into the upstairs room. The other dog dragged himself home, badly torn by Rex, with his

shoulder bone and front leg broken by his master, and had to be chloro-
formed.

The friendship between the two men had been close, and a great
strain was put on it by all this dog killing and shooting. Nevertheless
the death of the other dog, particularly since he had been killed by his
own master, so upset everybody that the friendship was made up,
mourning over the two dead dogs.

That's the only dog I had in my childhood. I have a memory of other
brief periods when dogs were brought home or I found a dog that
maybe stayed a week. We never had a regular pet after Rex and nothing ever took his place. There were other dogs around my grandfather's,
though, until he died from drink and other ailments brought on by his
own modest high living.

Just before his death the grocery store burnt down. The store caught
fire while my grandparents were living above it for some reason in an
apartment that was usually rented. I think their house was being remodeled. For years afterward I was told how Aunt Minnie threw the
china out of the window and carried the pillows downstairs. Everybody was quite hysterical and everything burned up. Although I imagine a bit of money was made on the insurance, everything, upstairs
and down, burned up.

Only those things which remained in the home in a different part of
town were left. Eventually most of them descended to me, so that at
one time I had a large collection of early nineteenth-century furniture.
I still have some magnificent patchwork quilts, although I've lost the
cashmere and Paisley shawls, the beautiful glassware and china, the
silver service and china-handled knives, the whatnot loaded with
Mound Builders' carvings, fossils, punitive hardware of slavery, and
a small iron meteor.

Shortly after that a large musical-instrument factory caught fire and
burned to the ground. It was most spectacular—two blocks of industrial
buildings burning up, the whole town standing around, and horse-
drawn fire departments from as far away as southern Michigan managing to get there before it was out. The place wasn't far from my
grandfather's home. For many years after it was my favorite playground. The factory was not rebuilt on those grounds. Deep under
heaps of rubble were buried clotted masses of melted brass and silver,
all overgrown with berry bushes, a playground with real treasure in it.

At this great distance the experience seems to be perfectly intact. I
can see the huge fire, over two city blocks long; the great buildings
glowing like coal; the black waffle pattern of the walls showing in
places against the interior fire; the exploding roofs and collapsing
walls. Fire engines from all around helplessly squirted what seemed

like tiny streams of water that went up in steam before they ever touched the heart of the fire. I see the firelit faces of the people who, although many of them owned stock in the company, were sitting in rapture in their own rigs looking like a crowd at one of Nero's circuses; the horses puffing and blowing and snorting and rearing as the blazing embers flew through the air. I sat in my grandfather's buggy and looked out over the heads of the crowd until at last the buildings burned to the ground in the early hours of the morning.

CHAPTER 6

About my fifth year something must have happened to the family finances, because we moved out of the White House. I should have
imagined that at this stage in his career my father's income would have
gone up rather than down. Possibly unbeknown to me, my mother was
already ill and unable to keep up such a big home. We had servants,
usually two Mennonite girls. The country surrounding Elkhart is still
settled by Mennonites, and they are still the commonest source of
servants. I guess they were always a problem, in spite of—or perhaps
because of—their extremely strict religion. My father would slowly get
familiar, treat the girl as one of the family, as they say. Then one day
she would disappear, to be replaced by another, and the process would
start over. I don't remember much about these girls; they struck me as
rather inert, and I had not developed at the age of five the blasé tastes
of my father, who seemed attracted by the six petticoats they wore
winter and summer.

We moved to a duplex house on Franklin Street. It was all strange to
me, ultramodern for those days. It even had some of the first electric
utilities. There was a blacksmith's shop across the street and down a
block and this was the finest thing about the place. Next door was the
family home of Ambrose Bierce.

In the neighborhood I began to meet more children. All around us
were fairly well-to-do middle-class people with moderately wholesome
children. About two blocks away the neighborhood became poor;
there on the corner was an old tumbledown yellow house with the
paint peeling off, which was occupied by two families who I imagine
were from the South, because they seemed to me to speak very oddly.
The older children wouldn't let me play with them, which was all right
with me because they frightened me with their violence. But the
youngest little girl attached herself to me and it was with her that I
had what books of child psychology call my first sexual experience.

I do not remember ever having had the typically Freudian develop-
mental pattern of child sexuality, but she certainly did. I didn't lose

my virginity, except conversationally. She was what in adults is called a coprophiliac and an algolagnist, addicted to all those varieties of human pleasure which cost so much money in brothels. I was baffled by this, not just by the fantastic character of the games she wanted to play but by the terrific head of steam her fantasies engendered in her. I have a clear memory of sitting on the curb on a sunny afternoon while she whispered to me, and of her rapid breath and shining eyes and moist lips—in a six-year-old girl all the behavior of a woman overcome by passion and overpowered by guilt.

I had never encountered anything remotely like this. My own parents, who were not any too circumspect about their lovemaking, gave it the aspect of a wonderful romp. This great charge of affect and effect did not make her proposals at all attractive. I wasn't just repelled, I was puzzled and exasperated. I don't want to give the impression that at this instant I was forever cured of all childish—or adult—impulses of inventive sexuality, but this time I was not stimulated. Her reactions were not in my vocabulary, and I found nothing attractive about guilt.

I went home puzzled, and consulted my mother. She, I guess, had not expected me to become aware of sex that early, and seemed for a moment just a little taken aback. But she sat me down in front of my blackboard and drew pictures of male and female anatomy, and explained to me how people make love and how babies are born. There wasn't anything about how the little butterflies and flowers made babies; it was a perfectly straightforward description illustrated with drawings as accurate as she could make them. It was not delivered in an affected vocabulary. I think when children are told about the functions of life and the human body in a special vocabulary they sense that there is something wrong and the whole subject starts off under an aura of guilt.

My mother explained to me that for each function or part there was a scientific word derived from the Latin, which was used just like the Latin names of plants and animals so that everyone everywhere could understand them. And then, she explained, there was a common word, part of the language like the word "robin" or "sunflower." I remember I said, "What's the name of these?" and she said, "It's on the tip of my tongue but it's slipped my mind. Just call them balls; everybody will know what you mean."

Then she said, ending the talk, "Everybody is not like our family. You can talk about these things at home, and to some of our friends, but you can't talk about them to other people, and you must be careful not to use these common words. Most people are a little crazy about these things because they have been taught a lot of crazy ideas in their churches, and their churches are now run by crazy people, and were started in the first place by crazy people. You must learn now that there are two kinds of people in the world—people like us, and 'common' people. The word for them is 'vulgar,' and one of the things that makes vulgar people vulgar is that they are dishonest about life and about themselves. They pretend that many of the things that happen in life and many of the things we do with our bodies don't exist, and if they talk about them they talk about them in very funny ways. Things like this make these vulgar people sick and crazy, and that's what is the matter with that little girl. Her parents have taught her that it's bad to go to the toilet, and so when she talks about it she gets very excited. Think of how silly that is! Think of how sick you'd get if you didn't go to the toilet for a couple of days. If you didn't go long enough you would die. So you can see that it isn't something bad; it's something good."

What I learned from this first experience was rather the opposite of what I might be supposed to have learned. I learned that other people were not as we were, but slightly demented, and demented in such a way that they could easily become dangerous. And I learned that we, as more responsible members of society who knew better, had to take care of them as though they were sick. In fact, I gained the impression then that the society which lay over against my family—*les autres,* as the French say—was a helpless and dangerous beast that we had to tend and save from its own irrationality. I rather doubt if anything in life has ever caused me to give up this attitude. I don't see anything wrong with this. The British educational system just a little while ago was based on Plato's *Republic;* the children of the upper classes were taught that they were Platonic guardians whose sole mission in life was to tend, guide, and nourish the classes without their advantages. Alas, this caste education no longer exists. Nobody today cocks his stick under his arm, screws his monocle into his eye, and leaps over the sandbags to lead the last charge against the Fuzzy-Wuzzies, with a quotation from Horace on his lips. Still, in a sense this kind of social responsibility has today diffused over a much wider section of the British population and is slowly bringing about a society in which civilized conduct is no longer the burden and privilege of a small caste.

I suppose my parents had the same ideas and the same motives as the great British schoolmasters. It was impressed upon me again and again that there were things that other people did that we never did, and conversely things that we did that it was best to keep to ourselves, because ordinary people wouldn't understand them. Later, really not much later, I was to recognize my parents' philosophy of caste responsibility in H. G. Wells's *The Research Magnificent,* and that was undoubtedly why it became one of the determinative books in my life.

This first sexual episode therefore led to a sharp development of a sense of my social role. I am sure that the Freudianized Deweyites who run around everywhere today would say, "See—just like Freud says, his first sexual experience was so traumatic that it made him a lifelong snob." Soon I had other and more active childhood sexual experiences. They were just fun. What I learned from this one was the contrast between social reality and the Social Lie.

While we are on this subject I should get out of the way some of the other things the analysts consider terribly important. For their benefit: I was half-weaned early. My mother was at the time an extreme feminist who believed in nursing her baby; the ordinary ones of course abhorred the idea. After about four months something happened to her milk and it became insufficiently nourishing. Then for about a month there was a lot of trouble finding a supplementary formula that agreed with me. Finally we settled on Mellon's Food, which in those days was prepared in a most complicated fashion. So from then on until I ate regular food, I was fed both at the breast and by bottle. I not only throve, I won the prize. For years I had a page out of a picture magazine which looked rather like the *Illustrated London News*. There were dozens of pictures of little babies, all of whom had won second, third, or fourth prizes. In the middle was a large oval of a fat and regal infant—me, the first prize. Whether of Indiana, the Middle West, the United States, or the world, I don't know.

The bottles and racks and siphons and funnels and sterilizers were a formidable array. The formula was not actually just Mellon's Food, but something very complicated—I suspect invented by my father. It disgusted our Irish maid, who said, "Sure, Mrs. Rexroth, and ye take too much trouble with himself. My old mother didn't have good milk, and me and my four brothers sucked on a straw stuck in a beer bottle." The apparatus was kept for the next baby which never came, and even the complicated formula directions survived amongst keepsakes for me to read in my adolescence. So two contradictory Freudian determinants operated at once—breast feeding and bottle feeding. I suppose it producted a schizoid personality, helplessly suspended between oral-retentive and oral-rejective fixations, much as Paul Tillich likes to describe himself, hung like Muhammad's coffin midway between all the basic contradictions of civilization.

I realize now that my parents concentrated on developing autonomy: not only did I spend long hours by myself in my remodeled piano box in the vacant lot next door, but I had a specially built functional playroom, with built-in shelves, tables, bins, drawers, blackboards, and other apparatus, rather like those ultramodern closets that women make fortunes designing for the rich. Although it was built-in, it was detachable and movable, because it followed us around until we left Elkhart and I was too old for it. Each of my things had a place, and when I got through with playing it never occurred to me to do anything with them but put them back in it. I suspect that children, who are rather compulsive about their behavior anyway, are naturally scrupulously neat and have to be taught disorder. I would go into my playroom and shut the door and spend a whole morning or afternoon by myself quite content. Today my two daughters do the same thing.

Sometimes other children would come over, and I realize now that I was taught to be rather formal about playing host. The atmosphere of our house must have been intimidating, because looking back I can feel that the kids who visited us were impressed and felt that something special was happening. This was true even though our neighbors along Beardsley Avenue were the richest people in town. The other children went to nursery school or kindergarten; I didn't go. There were many more books in our house and Medici prints and etchings on the walls, and the furniture was in a different taste.

I liked to be a host but I was perfectly content by myself. I learned to clean my room myself. The breaking of a toy was quite a disaster. When I grew older I had most of my toys and all of my books from the very beginning. This is true of my daughters today. We do not give them cheap, flimsy toys, and they have kept unspoiled almost everything they have ever been given. This is beginning to be a bit of a problem, until even my daughters are persuaded that the time has come to unload some of them onto charity. All this sounds as though I were just a mother's darling, but I think children have to learn disobedience and combativeness. I think these are reflections of the conflicts in society and of conflicts in the home which are social in origin. I think that anger and disorder in children are expressions of conflict between the parents, and although my parents' marriage objectively came to a sad end, I never felt that sort of conflict and never learned that kind of response.

I had various toys that accumulated from year to year. One was an Erector set, for which I got a big new box of parts each Christmas until finally I could build bridges, on which my father could stand, clear across the room. Later I had a chemical set—not the ready-made one which the people who made the Erector put out, but one assembled by my father from stuff from the drug house, real chemicals and real utensils. This grew from year to year until eventually it became a well-equipped little laboratory of electrical, chemical, and physical apparatus.

I had a microscope quite early, when I was about five years old, and I can remember the first microscopic plants and animals that I gathered out of the aquarium, rain puddles, the soil, and off moldy vegetables. Some of this activity was guided by my father or mother, some of it I did independently. I suppose a good deal of it was meaningless, but in the course of time I learned a lot of natural history, and eventually I came to have a large collection of rocks and plants and birds' nests and shells, which became quite a nuisance because they took up so much room.

Another toy, more normal or at least usual for a child of my age, was a circus set. There was made by a German firm called Schoenfeld a practically illimitable assortment of figures—acrobats, trapeze performers, jugglers, animals, clowns, bareback riders, horses, wild men of Borneo, elephants, tigers, rhinoceroses, ringmasters, and all the equipment and furnishings for the circus. They were made of spool-shaped joints of wood, held firmly together by elastic. The feet and hands were slotted, and you could put trapeze bars, ladders, chairs, and the ringmaster's whip tightly into them and arrange the figures realistically in all the postures of the circus. They were perfectly balanced, and any of them could be stood on one rather large foot, not only the people but the animals, and with a little care even the elephant could be balanced on one leg on the back of a chair which was balanced on a ladder, and that on a barrel. His trunk could be curled up, and the equestrienne could be made to stand on the tip of it while he stood on one hind leg. All this involved a most delicate sense of balance. I remember the first elementary set, which came in the fall some time before Christmas. It consisted of a clown, a chair, a barrel, and a ladder. Nobody could work it except my Uncle Clyde, who had learned skill of that sort as a street-corner prestidigitator and pitch artist. After a while we all learned, and when Christmastime came the clown was joined by a donkey, an elephant, a horse, and a beautiful lady bareback rider. As the years went by, this was added to until finally it was an enormous circus. Buffalo Bill and the "101 Ranch" Wild West shows were still going, and eventually a Wild West division of the "Humpty-Dumpty Circus" came out with cowboys, Indians, spotted ponies, and a stagecoach. I got my first Erector set and the first electric train the same winter, and the three sets grew up together, until at last they turned the parlor floor into a crowded city.

My grandmother taught me knitting, crocheting, even tatting. Like the philosopher, nothing human was foreign to me. Best of all, she taught me to sew. In the first instance, new costumes for the figures in the Humpty-Dumpty Circus. Eventually this led to another activity because, as I made more elaborate costumes, they outgrew the circus, so I built a stage and used the figures and put on plays. This was before the days when anybody had thought to make marionettes for children. At first I used fairy stories or episodes from books like *Tom Sawyer*, then I began to write plays for myself. I learned to make dominoes and ruffs for the clowns, cutaways for the ringmasters, and *tutus* for the equestrienne, as well as, later, fancy costumes for plays about King Arthur and his knights or Long John Silver and his pirates. This knowledge never did me much good until much later in life I came to marry modern women to whom the needle is a symbol of bondage. In the weeks before Christmas the whole circus had to be freshened up with new clothes to welcome the new arrivals. We had a large crèche, and all those figures, too, had to be repainted and newly dressed.

Holidays were all important events; even minor ones like Washington's Birthday got all the ritual. Christmas was tremendous. My parents had the wise habit of giving at Christmas permanent things that would be used throughout the year. We had the largest Christmas tree that we could get in the house, and as sumptuous a dinner as we could afford. As a wholesale druggist and liquor dealer, my father got all sorts of booty from his suppliers. No matter how much trouble came on the family later nor how hard life became, they always, except once, seemed to manage to make Christmas pretty splendid.

I had a birthday three days before Christmas, so I really had a double Christmas. Unlike some unfortunate children who are born near Christmas Day, my birthday was never slighted. We have gone on doing these things all through my life. My own children have more elaborate Christmases than most children do, and this year, when we were living in Aix-en-Provence, we had by far the largest tree in town and the children had all the toys and books and clothes we could afford. As you know if you've ever lived in France, compared with the Germans or the Americans, the French don't think much of Christmas and, in fact, don't really like children. Now the Christmas tree has come to France, but it is just a little bitty thing, and the French give few and flimsy gifts. We were in Italy at Eastertime, and the contrast between the Italian Easter and the French Christmas was a rather startling comment on familial love in the two countries. Anyway, I am sure we scandalized our neighbors and our *bonne*. All this doesn't cost very much if you give the child everything he's going to use in the course of the coming year. However, if you have badly raised children who have broken everything they have received by the morning of Boxing Day, then I suppose it can be expensive.

This play world of mine I know now was organized by my parents in terms of self-sufficiency and autonomy, and then of hospitality. I realize that I learned then while playing that only the autonomous can be hospitable, and that these two virtues add up to magnanimity. It wasn't deliberately taught to me, cordiality was simply the way we did things.

In my infancy, television, murder, and sadism for infants were unknown—for better or worse. I can still remember one of my first movies, *The Squaw Man*. It seems placid enough today, but I remember when its violence and horror made me so physically ill I refused to go to a movie for many months, and then only to John Bunny. It's only in adult life that I have ever acquired a taste for Westerns. Many of them are rather true to life, as I was to find out when I went into the West. But still today I tend to think of movies—even the best—as fare for the miserably bored, the frustrated, and the feeble-minded.

I began to travel with my father. He used to take me over the Middle West visiting the drugstores of his customers. Living in Europe, I never go into a drugstore in Italy, especially in the beautiful Venetian ones unchanged since the Renaissance, or even much more modern ones in the South of France, without remembering the drowsy perfumed pharmacies of my childhood. It seems to me that the drugstore before the First World War was the most beautiful interior in America. The armamentarium in those days did not consist of wonder drugs made out of coal tar but of an endless array of natural substances whose entrancing odors seeped out through the ground-glass stoppers of tall, gold-labeled jars. The atmosphere was dim and marvelous, and the druggist in his linen coat had the dignity of a priest of Aesculapius. My father didn't have to take any orders. His traveling consisted largely of emanating good will over the whole Middle West, which is one of the things that killed him. We were always welcome, and our visits were always leisurely. I was treated to mint placebos, chocolate cherries, and Iceland moss lozenges. As I grew a little older I was initiated into the mysteries of the art. Pills were still rolled in those days, and I learned to roll them on a grooved slab, cut them up, and coat them. Not only were they still rolled, but often they were still coated with some kind of edible gold or silver, like the shot on cake. I learned to make wafers of acetic-acid ester of salicylic acid, a form in which it no longer comes. I still remember the first time I was permitted to mash up opium and camphor in a mortar and watch them suddenly react and change to a pale brown sugar which, with the addition of alcohol and water, became paregoric. I remember the large-bladed overhead fans slapping the air in Three Rivers, White Pigeon, Dowagiac, and all those other towns whose names Carl Sandburg loves so much. And the horses in yellow net negligees, with their ears sticking out of straw hats, nuzzling their feed bags in towns that have since become hideous centers of the automobile industry.

Recently I went with the children into a drugstore in Vicenza, and the druggist got down a big brown bottle with a blown-glass label full of ten-grain mint placebos. I don't think these exist any more in the States. Their place has been taken by steam yachts, evening dresses, roast turkeys, tame bears, and all the other things American drugstores sell. I asked if I could have one, and as I ate it my overwhelming nostalgia was at least as strong as that Proust got out of his madeleine. Soda fountains were just coming in, and I was encouraged to help myself. I aided in the construction of the most elaborate parfaits, frappés, and sundaes. Then, as we left, the druggist would pull an egg out of my ear or a half dollar off the tip of my nose, or the jack of hearts out of the back of my collar. And I always got to keep the half dollar.

CHAPTER 7

Here in Vicenza, where we are living as I am dictating this, the river runs under a Roman bridge, and nearby there are several waterwheels and long narrow sluices or millraces in stone-lined channels. One is a horizontal wheel of the kind that never became popular in America. There are three undershot wheels in one sluice all covered with moss, and one huge overshot wheel with sparkling cascades of water dropping from every bucket. When I was little there was a similar battery of waterwheels in the Elkhart River. One went to some factory which I've forgotten, one worked a saw-and-planing mill in my grandfather's lumberyard, the overshot one turned the machinery in a tannery, and a group of them went to a large flour mill.

I was specially fascinated by the flour mill. The air was powdery, the place was full of flying machinery and mysterious noises, and yet the process of making the flour was simple enough for a little boy to understand. And all the people were fat and covered with flour. They used to give me something fine whenever I stopped on the way by. It was a handful of hard wheat, and if you chewed it long enough and spat out the flour and bran, the gluten would stay in your mouth, a sort of cross between chewing gum and nougat but with a more subtle flavor. You can do this by chewing green hard wheat, too, and I've done it many times in fields all over the world. I always like to think that's what Jesus and his disciples were up to, snapping ears of wheat and eating them on the Sabbath to the consternation of their co-religionists. Anyway, that's what I was sure they were doing when the story was first read to me. I remember the first day we went to the mill—the peculiar smell of the floury air, the huge millstones, the roaring blowers, and the smell of the coarse bran. Later I used to go by myself to get feed for the stock, and drive off with the buggy stacked with bags of fresh bran or rye grits.

We were coming up the road one hot day at the height of a long drought. Although it was extremely dry, there was thunder in the air. The mill was very busy, banging away. Inside, the air was full of flour which drifted out of the windows like a faint smoke. Suddenly the whole building blew up. The flour in the air exploded, blew out the walls, blew off the roof like a firecracker, and killed everybody in the place. We were near enough so that a piece of corrugated sheet iron went sailing through the air over our heads. The horses reared and screamed, turned, and by some miracle the buggy turned with them, and set off for home at a dead run. I have a clear picture of the bodies of the horses running, and I am sure that they often assumed the all-legs-out position of the "flying gallop" which was considered to be an artistic convention until *Life* snapped a horse in that position crossing the line at the Derby. I have never seen horses run faster, and theoretically it should have been impossible for the buggy to stay behind them and upright. But we got home, and when we got in the barn one of the horses keeled over in a faint.

The explosion damaged the bridge, so they built another, the first concrete bridge for miles around. While it was being built, you couldn't walk on the old iron bridge alongside, but had to use a little wooden footbridge, which at night was lit with coal-oil lanterns and which I can remember crossing in the windy darkness low over the rushing river. The engineer of the bridge fell in love with my Aunt Minnie. He spent all his free time with her and they were to celebrate the opening of the bridge with their marriage and then go off to some romantic place like Wyoming or Brazil, where his next job was coming up. Of all my aunt's romances, this was the one which came nearest to fulfillment.

The engineer had a most beautiful stickpin; at least I thought so, because I had one just like it. It was a little fly; the eyes were emeralds, the wings were crystal, the body was some dark blue stone. My father had one, and because I admired it so much he had found one for me. I was thrilled because the engineer had one, too. It was as if we belonged to the same secret society. It seemed to be a passport to a world of immensely competent adults who built bridges and waltzed with Aunt Minnie and kissed her in front of everybody.

One day he was working on the wooden forms for the concrete, helping one of the workmen. He got a long sliver in his hand. He took his stickpin, opened the skin, took out the sliver, washed the tear in river water, and went on working. That night his hand and arm swelled up with blood poisoning. Lockjaw set in and in a few days he was dead and my aunt was out another husband. You would think that this would have conditioned me against stickpins, bluebottle fly or other, but when I grew old enough to wear a four-in-hand tie, I still had mine and my father's as well, and I wore them till stickpins went out of date. Long afterward, just before my aunt's death, after the Second War, she sent me a box of jewelry that my mother and grandmother had given her before their deaths, and in the box was the engineer's stickpin.

What I remember most poignantly from this incident is my first experience of the terribly accidental character of life; not just of death, not just of the realization that some random accident may strike anyone down at any second, but the accidental nature of life itself. I pondered over and over the fact of the appearance of the engineer. He had come out of nowhere and nothing, and vanished again, and I realized that this was true of everybody. I looked at maps of India and South America and strove to convince myself that they represented immense countries full of people living and dying. I suppose it is at this time that a child first faces the solipsistic dilemma to which we can never know the answer. Are the other people there or is the world just something going on in my own head? Even more, I realized that this applied to myself, that it was by the most extraordinary and absurd chance that I was here at all.

My aunt was prostrated and went somewhere for a month or more. I have never crossed that bridge, even in adult life on visits back to Elkhart, without thinking of the whimsical appearance and disappearance of the engineer. The other day when here in Vicenza I came to the same-sized bridge over the same-sized river—with waterwheels in the same situation and men fishing above the dam with their Italian basket nets—I remembered the engineer teaching me, the Sunday before he died, to snare pickerel from the bridge with a copper wire noose on the end of the line, using a very long pole so that I could snap the fish up out of the water.

In these years we used to drive out on weekends to visit an aged great-uncle and aunt in nearby Bristol. They lived in a white board house with a wide veranda, under the largest cherry tree I have ever seen, certainly the only one I ever heard of that was taller than a house. In the spring the cloud of blossoms was visible down the gravel road as we drove up from Elkhart, and all the air about the house was loud with bees. In June the tree was loaded with bushels of dark, black, tart cherries of a kind that have vanished from the earth. We took home huge baskets of them. My mother put them up, my father made wine, and we ate cherry pie every night. Uncle John and Aunt Mary made cherry ice cream, and I sat on the back porch with the Irish setter and cranked the freezer until my arms ached, while my Uncle John told me stories of the Civil War. He had been an aide to Grant, and I thrilled once again to all those sumptuous names—Chickamauga, Antietam, Wilderness, Shiloh, Appomattox. I remember his descriptions of all the battles of the war, and the detailed realism with which he described the last night—the cold chill coming out of the low ground at Appomattox, the bivouac fires growing dim in the distance in the mist, the buildings with their twin chimneys at the gables, "like arms raised in surrender." Uncle John talked of the war as though he had taken part in a noble crusade, as though he had fought with Michael and his archangels. The enemy were always "the Rebs," and he spoke of them as ignorant, misguided fools, pathetic beings whom it was necessary to kill. Whatever economic interpretation of the war I was to learn later, I learned once for all from my Uncle John in my heart that *we* fought it to free the Negroes. Modern historical writers, whether they have been Southern sympathizers or not (and most of them have been), have destroyed our memory of the dedication of the Abolitionist soldier, and plenty of soldiers were Abolitionists. After all, you could buy out of the draft. Uncle John was one of the first people I ever saw dead. I can remember him in his country parlor in his coffin —his thick, pure-white hair, his bright, waxy skin, his folded, aged hands, and an expression on his face as if he were dreaming a difficult and complex dream.

I have the feeling that my education was considerably stepped up about this time. I first realized the importance of reading, and began to read on my own initiative. I could go to the library by myself and take out books. My mother started teaching me French but decided that she didn't have a good enough accent. So she hired the younger daughter of the French milliner to give me lessons. The older was my mother's actress friend. I have always had an abominable French accent, but whenever it does slip over into authenticity I suspect it has the distinctly female intonation of the language, the lilting speech of the lady shopkeeper.

Soon we moved from Franklin Street to a place on Second Street, just off Marion. On the corner there was an ornate red brick Victorian mansion which was used as an undertaker's parlor. Next there was a vacant lot, which was mowed and tended and gave our house an extremely large lawn. Next up a little embankment was our house, gray, with Victorian millwork and rather shabby. It had been unoccupied for several years. Next was a low, rambling yellow house where lived a family named Carpenter, and then something of a small mansion, timbered brick with wide eaves, the home of an elderly couple named Knickerbocker. They manufactured a purported galvanic battery health device which had made them a fortune. Theirs was the type of house fashionable at the end of the last century, out of which Frank Lloyd Wright developed his first style. I suppose this is the first time I was ever conscious of architecture, because it seemed to me to be so much more homey than any place I had ever seen, and I loved to visit the Knickerbockers and play on their dusty red woolen Oriental rug with the toys of their children who had grown up and gone away.

The Knickerbockers themselves were Christian Scientists and had no belief at all in their device. It was one of the many descendants of Dr. Hercule Sanche's Oxydonor. It was a metallic cylinder about the size of the cardboard core of a roll of toilet paper. Inside was a stick of carbon, the same as was used in arc lamps in those days. From each end came a wire, and on the end of one wire was a copper disc, on the other a zinc disc as well as elastic straps on each. For maximum results —cholera morbus, rabies, paralysis, galloping consumption, or cancer— the patient put his feet in a tub of strong cold salt water and strapped a disc to each wrist. Less lethal ailments were instantly cured by putting *the tube* in a pan of cold salt water and relaxing with a good book —*When Knighthood Was in Flower* or *Three Weeks*. The Knickerbockers were not at all unctuous or hypocritical; they were quiet, grave, considerate, and very civilized. It was hard to believe my father when he said that in a few years the government would pass laws that could put them in the penitentiary. They didn't look at all like it.

Now the undertaking parlor and our house have been torn down, the embankment leveled, and there is a gas station there. But Helen Carpenter, the little girl who lived next door, still lives there. She was the greatest thing about our new home. I immediately fell madly in love.

The first childhood sweetheart always remains one of life's principal mythological figures. In a sense I have never ceased to be in love with this little girl. This is a bad habit of mine, not just with childhood sweethearts. I almost never fall out of love and it must make the women to whom I attach my affections uncomfortable as the years go by. Anyway, today, fifty years later, I can still feel the resonance of that old devotion. She was a slight girl with an ivory skin, dark brown hair cut in a Dutch bob, a beauty mark on her chin, a small black comma just under her lip, which made her very fetching but which she had removed before she went away to college. She was smaller than I although she was a year older, and had an intense fragile sensibility of the sort that distinguishes many children but which most lose by their tenth year. When I met her many years later it was instantly apparent that she had not lost hers, so probably I was choosing, at the age of six or seven, more wisely than I knew. We became inseparable. Her mother was a strong, big-boned woman and there was a great-grandmother who lived in the house until she died.

Helen and I discovered a great deal of childhood together. We took trips and went on picnics with our mothers in the woods outside of town and in boats on the Elkhart and the St. Joe Rivers, and together read our first real books. Almost everything we did we did together so that it was a kind of infantile matrimony. Nowadays when young-sters faced with the draft and imminent extermination by their elders enter into what are really marriage relationships in grammar school, I can sympathize with them. I look back on my own life and realize that in a sense I have been married ever since 1911, and that's a long time ago. This devoted and shared life was for me a foundation for all future experience. It shaped my method of dealing with life. This makes it sound like an adult sort of thing, but of course it wasn't. It's just that I responded to a playmate in a special way, and so I think did she to me. She was just the little girl next door, but my response was one of extreme identification and the formation of a set pattern of life —the need for duality. Of course at that age it was not an idea derived from Plato or romantic reading, although it may have been derived from the ideal, if not the fact, of my parents' marriage. With Helen and me it was simple fact. From what I can make out of other people's accounts, it bore few of the characteristics of puppy love; nor on the other hand did she look like or in any way replace my mother or fulfill any of the other Freudian obbligatos. She was pretty and sensitive and well bred, but primarily she was the little girl who happened to live next door. Proximity and availability have more to do with love than any other factors. Some people seem to be born with great talents for making the most of their proximities.

Backyards in Indiana in those days were not fenced off, so that the children played on the entire inside of the block. It was like the back gardens in certain parts of London where all the houses back on their own little communal park. After the duplex, which had just a clothes-drying place in the back and a tiny garden in front on a busy street, our new garden seemed immense. Right away we went to work on the lot between our place and the undertaker's, and I remember the ex-citement of digging and planting with my parents, Helen, and her mother. We lined the back wall with quick-growing vines—wild cu-cumbers, climbing nasturtiums, butterfly vines, morning glories, and scarlet runner beans which were up and all over the place in two weeks. In amongst them we set our perennial vines to grow through the years. Most of the space was turned into a croquet lawn (it had been a tennis lawn before) and surrounded with a border of flowers. Although I had planted and worked in my grandmother's garden with Old Billy, I scarcely remember it, but I have the most vivid memories of the enraptured excitement as these flowers came up. Perhaps it was due to Helen's company. In the backyard we made a badminton court and by early summer we were ready to give garden parties with Japa-nese lanterns—both adult and children's parties. The Knickerbockers and the Carpenters both had fine gardens so that the whole block, now so drab, was then splendid with lanterns, fiddlers, waltzing couples, and romping children.

Most of the houses we lived in we rented, but we must have owned this one, because my mother remodeled and redecorated it extensively. It was a run-down Victorian house something like the place in San Francisco where we live now, with lots of millwork and ornamental plaster, a very functional place of the type that functionalist architects despise. It didn't look in the least like an operating theater, a dairy, or a cooky factory. My mother went through it room by room and rehabilitated it. Our furniture that had been in the White House and had been stored somewhere came back. My mother and father worked painting and papering and sandpapering floors. There was a French boudoir with panels framed in rococo sprays of rosebuds with aquatints of Fragonard or Boucher in the center and an apple-green Aubusson carpet with a border of gold scrolls and rococo sprays of roses. There was a den with heavy leather furniture, a desk, and the rest was all in what was thought to be Turkish style, with my father's water pipe on a mother-of-pearl inlaid taboret and his Félicien Rops collection on the walls (a collection which had to be taken down when we had certain guests). There was a heavy oak William Morris dining room with imitation Whistler etchings on the oatmeal paper—or maybe they really were Whistler etchings. The old playroom was set up new with all its clean wood drawers, bins, and shelves.

Finally there was the room which brought doom to the family. They decided to do the living room and the adjacent music room in Art Nouveau. My mother made long brown paper stencils of water lilies, irises, and tendrilly vines all with a certain Japanese air about them, and paneled the celadon-green walls with wandering vegetation. She had a Tiffany blown-glass lamp of poppies which was kept in the family until my aunt's death and which always depressed me to see. There were coarse, unbleached linen curtains painted with iris, and furniture which looked like it was made of slightly modified grapevines. There was a large color print by Puvis de Chavannes. For the piano we got a new piano player and two large beaten-copper Art Nouveau vases. On their side were Adam and Eve emerging nude from the foliage—rather like Baizeman's work today. She bought them from some artist friend in Chicago and we waited for them in a state of great excitement. When they came to the railroad station just down the street, she wouldn't let the baggage man, Ambrose Bierce's brother, deliver them, although they were absolutely unbreakable, but took them out of the package in the freight room and carried them home one on each arm, like water jars. I walked alongside her in the warm early morning sunlight under the blooming catalpa trees. She smiled, but talked very little. When we came to the house, she put the vases down on the sidewalk and sat quickly down on the carriage stone and I saw that her face was terribly white. At first she couldn't speak, then she said, "Get Grandma, I think I'm going to faint," and then, before I could turn away, a fountain of bright red blood spurted out of her mouth. The blood flooded over her dress and the carriage stone, and splattered on the ground.

I ran into the house, blind and screaming, bumping into the doors and furniture, and my aunt and grandmother ran out, pale with terror. My mother had a friend, a dentist, who had an office across the street, and he was just coming back from lunch. He and a passer-by carried my mother into the house, by this time unconscious. Although she had fainted, she was still hemorrhaging as they carried her in. Her body was limp, her face white as paper, her long auburn hair dragged the ground, and the blood ran out of her mouth like water out of a faucet. A local doctor was called and stopped the hemorrhage, and then the husband of her best friend, who was supposed to be the best doctor in that part of the country, raced over from South Bend. My father was phoned in Chicago and he got there by nightfall. They spent several hours phoning around from Chicago and he turned up fairly near Elkhart and came over in a rented car.

My mother remained unconscious all that day and the next. She'd lost a tremendous amount of blood. It seemed to me to be more than a human body could hold. There were no transfusions in those days, as I remember, so she was very weak and was a long time recuperating. After this, all conversations about the little sister I was going to have stopped. Probably the new house had been taken to provide extra room for the new baby and for my grandmother, who had planned to live with us temporarily. My grandfather was dead by that time. She did move in, but to take care of my mother, not the new baby.

My mother just barely squeaked through. For several weeks she was expected to die, but by fall she was apparently almost well again. No one could diagnose the cause of the hemorrhage. There was no evidence of tuberculosis or any other lung trouble.

My father became very attentive and careful, but he also took heavily to drink. It was the first time I could remember my father being helplessly drunk, or having any other trouble connected with liquor. He not only drank a great deal, but slowly went to pieces morally and became a different kind of man, weaker and no longer sure of himself. An expression came into his face, not just as though he had had a great fright, but as though he was still being frightened. It never left him.

Tragedy and strain, not mistrust and lack of love, but remorse and fear, entered into the marriage. They went on loving each other just as passionately as ever, but they were never happy in the same way again, and from then on the relationship deteriorated, into drink on my father's part and into flirtation and eventually promiscuity on my mother's. She seemed well all fall, and then in the winter she got a cold and began to spit blood and to show symptoms of consumption. We had one doctor after another, but none of them could make a sure diagnosis. The Knickerbockers gave us their best electric machine, and my mother sat with wire wrapped around her as though she were going to be electrocuted, with her feet in a basin, and laughed at herself. In the spring she got much better, just in time for a new development.

Kinsolving & Granisson merged, not in buildings and plant but financially, with another company, the Herkimer Wine Company. This was then the largest wholesale liquor house in Chicago, and the importer of all sorts of liquors, wines, tobaccos, cigars, and cigarettes. They also ran a fancy bar and free lunch for publicity purposes, which was the hangout for the Indiana gang—James Whitcomb Riley, Eugene Field, Ted Dreiser, George Ade, and others of that first Chicago renaissance, which consisted almost entirely of Indiana-born newspapermen. They were all friends of my father's. He had already spent plenty of time in their company. Now he was able to play host, to his delight and destruction. Then, too, it's one thing to go around Indiana, Michigan, Ohio, and Wisconsin and glad-hand druggists, and it's another thing to do the same with saloonkeepers and liquor dealers. Even without the disaster that had struck the family, the conditions of my father's work probably would have turned him into a drunkard.

There had been some connection with the Herkimer Wine Company before this merger, because we had always had a superabundance of wines, cigarettes, cigars, which were sent to us as promotional gifts from all over the world. We had the most fantastic good-will cellar, containing not Mouton-Rothschild but the wine the Rothschilds themselves drink, and not Château Lafite of the best year but wine that never left the Château except as gifts to royalty and wholesale liquor dealers. The rare wines that are hard to get now, like Château-Ausone, which has remained my favorite wine, and the wines of the Côte de Cher, the straw wines of the Jura, and inky ones of Provence, unknown in America in those days, and "five basket" Tokajs and green Hungarians in tall flasks. There was every sort of champagne and great racks of German wines that I never liked and don't to this day. The most expensive wines still are German wines, which taste like pop to me and cost ten times as much as the best Château-Yquem. We had all sorts of them and could have washed our feet in them if we had wanted to, and guests always left the house with a bottle or two under their arms. There were great cabinets of cigarettes from Turkey and

Egypt and Greece, and cigars from Havana and Germany in elaborate humidor arrangements that made marvelous, sweet-smelling boxes of beautiful woods for me to play with when they were empty.

My mother got well enough so that I guess my father thought he would break with the old connections and patterns that had led to trouble. They would have a vacation and jollification, and fall back into the old honeymoon love that had lasted so long and was gone, and maybe my mother would get well. We went to Europe. One of the reasons for the trip was that my father wanted to meet the people whom we imported from and hunt up new suppliers, particularly for essential oils. A great many pharmaceutical essential oils and perfumes and herbs are produced in the Balkans and the Danube drainage. All that country was still pretty primitive in those days and commercially underdeveloped. The Baghdad-Berlin railroad was just going through, making itself into a *causus belli,* and it was in the Balkans, I remember, that we spent most of our time.

We came into Amsterdam, Rotterdam, or Antwerp, some big town in the Low Countries, up a long estuary with electric signs on either side that flashed "Bols" and "Föking" alternately from side to side, my parents tipsy and laughing at a joke that I vaguely understood. We went on to Hamburg and then north to Copenhagen and on to Oslo and Stockholm, and then down through Berlin, Frankfort, and the Rhineland to Munich, Vienna, and Budapest, through the Balkans, and out to Constantinople just ahead of the second Balkan war. Some of the trip was made by rented carriages, my father driving a pair of horses over the hair-raising Balkan roads through villages full of savage dogs that ate up peasants who fell over drunk in the mud at night, Muslim villages with man-eating dogs, and Christian villages with carnivorous pigs as well. I'm always amused nowadays when people talk of trips over the same roads. You couldn't have got a jeep through. It was all we could do to get through in a carriage. Soldiers were marching all around us, the population was in panic, there was even cannonading off someplace. We drove through it all, unperturbed, to Constantinople as the country closed up behind us.

We took a boat around Greece to Italy and came back up the peninsula, through the South of France, and then to London, Liverpool, Ireland, and home. Now this was quite a grand tour and must have been done fairly fast. Not so fast as people can make it nowadays, but fast enough so that I have no memory of ever having very cold weather on the trip. It seems to me that it was cold in Constantinople and then warm in Paris, and warm in Stockholm before that. Constantinople has miserably cold winters, but this was probably a storm. I'm pretty sure that it was all the operation of one summer.

Curiously enough for a child, my clearest memories were of the *monumenti;* the statues, the churches, the monuments and ruins, and the paintings in the galleries. I was never to go back, except to Paris very briefly, until after the Second War, and yet thirty-five years later in Paris and Rome and Venice I was pretty well oriented. Most of it all I've forgotten except as a memory pops into my head. People will be sitting around talking about something, or we'll be traveling in Europe, and I'll say, "Oh, I remember that, I was there," but now I can't remember any incidents of that European trip of any importance.

I remember the Swedish countryside; I remember how calm and peaceful and bucolic the German countryside looked, the least warlike landscape on earth; I remember the Alps, which were the first snow-covered mountains I had ever seen; I remember the homes of the German businessmen, most of them intellectuals, which were so much like my Uncle John's apartment in Chicago. I remember, I think it was on St. Stephen's Day of 1912 in Budapest, the spectacular procession of the Blessed Sacrament with the Emperor Franz Josef in an open carriage and, facing him, two princesses in beautiful white satin gowns and big hats with long white ostrich plumes. The old man had mutton-leg, not muttonchop, whiskers, and the archduke was mounted, riding with the Hungarian Guard. I have the clearest memory of that body-guard around the carriage. They all rode white horses with dyed tails. They were cuirassiers, and they had tight white pants and high boots, and then gold-brushed steel cuirasses and a peculiar round Bronze-Age-looking metal cap. Hanging from the cap was an immensely long red horsetail, and around their shoulders a whole wolfskin, with the wolf's head up on the left shoulder and his hind paw in his mouth, and they carried long-bladed lances with horsetails hanging from them. Now this is how I remember it; it may not have been exactly that way, but it was certainly the Hungarian bodyguard, so I think that this took place in Budapest. I have a memory of a spa in Budapest on an island in a river, and all the fancy swimming pools, with artificial waves and waterfalls and different temperatures and flavors of waters.

I remember the barren, windswept character of Constantinople, and the immense, ruinous hotel of wood and plaster which was falling apart, with wombats and armadillos and such coming out of the wains-coting. I remember Italy as one long, beautiful landscape, so beautiful I couldn't believe it, like Oz or the Land of Lyonesse, and the pictures and sculptures in the galleries.

I remember London as almost everyone from a civilized country re-membered it in those days. I remember the appalling poverty. I was prepared for it by a little experience that comes back to me whenever I read *Through the Looking-Glass* and see that extremely frightening picture of a sheep that kept a shop, that Tenniel drawing that other people have told me scared them into fits when they were children. I remember how Alice bought one egg. In those days in Elkhart eggs didn't come by dozens but by baskets, and you paid ten or twenty-five cents at the most for a basket of eggs, and here was a little girl buying one egg, and in all *Alice* this was, by far, the most fantastic thing. I asked my mother what it meant—I thought it was a flight of Lewis Carroll's fancy—and she said, "No, you must understand that in England people are very poor and many children never eat eggs, and most people just buy one egg apiece, one at a time." Well, this shocked me, as though I had been shown a sudden vision of the slums of Calcutta or Shanghai or Singapore. Very few things in my life have ever impressed me as much as the contrast embodied in that one little dark picture between my own opulence and the poverty that was hidden from me.

When we got to London we lived with some friend in a neighborhood that was very classy but completely surrounded by slums. I have no idea where it was, but nearby there were horrible children in rags with bruised bodies and sore eyes and bare, broken feet. My grandmother had given me Doré's three Dante books and the Chateaubriand book and *Paradise Lost* and *Aesop's Fables* and *Don Quixote*. I immediately thought that London's scenes were like Doré. Just in recent years Marthe gave me a copy of Doré's *London*, certainly his greatest work and a realistic documentation of what the city's horror was in those days. I look at it and think of what most of the big cities of Europe were like in my childhood, and now even Naples is not that bad.

In recent years the English intellectuals and poets who hang around Chelsea and Soho pubs, and the fashionable pederasts who hang around the intellectuals, complain about how the Labour Party, or the Tory Party under pressure from the working class, has made English life so drab and ordinary that they long for the English well-to-do rectory life which is the birthright of every English intellectual and of which they feel they have been deprived. I'd like to take them by their necks and rub their noses in the slums of London in 1912; not that it would make any difference to them. There's nothing like that any more, even in the worst part of the Gorbals in Glasgow. In those days London was just as Engels had described it seventy-five years before.

Paris I hardly remember. Paris has never been a city I liked until recent years. It seemed cold and artificial. Years later I discovered the working class of Paris, with a rich urban folk culture of their own. For a boy Paris is relatively uninteresting. It has a great thrill for a little girl, but it left me with no memories except for the Seine and the Cathedral and the trees and boulevards, and the pictures in the Louvre, especially the Salle Rubens. The Salle Rubens turned out to be a great disappointment when I saw it this year for the first time since. I also remember the Closerie des Lilas, which has always been my favorite café, next to the Deux Garçons of Aix-en-Provence, which it greatly resembles. And I remember as though it were yesterday the Hotel Odéon and the marvelous couple—straight out of a fairy tale—who kept it, and the kitchen and the food in the hotel restaurant.

CHAPTER 8

We came home to America, but not to stay in Elkhart. We came back to my grandmother's for a visit. I went over to see Helen Carpenter and we had an impassioned and tearful parting after a picnic. We went with our parents out to the moraine country along the Michigan border to a pasture by an old mill where the water flowed over colored pebbles, like a stream in the Western mountains. It was very unlike most muddy, Midwestern streams. We went wading and ate roast chicken. We were never to see each other again under such ideal circumstances. Things were to be changed when I came back the last time.

Then we left for Battle Creek, Michigan, where my father was interested in a breakfast-food company called Maple Flake. This was the first whole-wheat flake. It had a maple leaf for a trademark, and the government ruled that it gave the impression that it was flavored with maple sugar and that this was illegal. The trade name was suppressed and the business went bankrupt. I think it went bankrupt for the second or third time, as a matter of fact, and from the time we came there and for the next three or four years there was a continuous onslaught on the company, or speculative operation of it—I was much too young to understand. Unbeknown to my father, this financial attack on the company was already beginning. It reached its climax while we were there but lasted three to five years after we left, a long-drawn-out war of attrition. My father and the initial investors were driven out early. We moved to Battle Creek and he became interested in the business and active in it, and then the whole thing blew up and we left the city, all in a little over a year.

Battle Creek was a charming town in those days. Like most of the small industrial towns of southern Michigan, Kalamazoo and Battle Creek were quiet places then. The automobile business was largely strung out along the New York Central and Lake Shore to the south. Elkhart and South Bend and Fort Wayne were more automobile towns than Flint, if I am not mistaken. I believe that the Michigan

Central about this time gave some sort of preferential to the automobile companies and the industry shifted to the next railroad north. The only big companies that stayed on the Lake Shore Railroad were Willys in Toledo and Studebaker in South Bend. This period just before the depression which preceded the World War was a time, as is always the case with depression eves, of wildcat speculation and all sorts of shady financial operations. Fortunes were made and lost in a matter of weeks. The Indiana automobile companies in which my father had always had a small interest survived only as part of the Lycoming-Auburn Motors empire, which was wrecked in the 1929 crisis. In fact, the speculation in those stocks was one of the things that precipitated the stock-market crash in 1929. A similar thing was going on at this time, and we got caught up in it.

Battle Creek was a mixed small industrial town and farm market. The largest businesses were the breakfast-food companies and Kellogg's Sanatorium, where they gave nature cures and fed the patients vegetarian pork chops and roast beef made out of carrots. My father became friends with the breakfast-food kings, their executives and competitors, and for a short period we were to see a great deal of them.

The first place we lived was much the most elaborate we ever had. The chief breakfast-food king had a home at right angles to our house in what must have been the best neighborhood. Our house was a tall, purple-brown Victorian mansion, like a typical brownstone front, but of wood, with an overhanging cornice, eighteen-foot ceilings, and plasterwork bas-relief, in all the elegance of its period. There was a naked front yard, all sun-scorched, and in the backyard large linden trees. In one of them was a tree house already built by the children of the previous owners. There was a four-horse barn which had been turned into a garage, and here we had, as far as I can remember, our first cars—first a Stanley Steamer, which my father wrecked almost immediately, and then a Locomobile. There were vast crystal chandeliers in the lower halls and a boudoir for my mother that seemed as big as a bowling alley. For my father there was a den on the second floor, on the back of the narrow part of the house. The den had portholes on three sides, brown and dusty like the cabin of a nineteenth-century sea captain, with my father's Félicien Ropses on the walls. I remember that a little girl and I were playing in the tree house when my father, tipsy, in the den, saw us doing something we shouldn't—I don't know what—and put his head out of a porthole and called us to come down. His head stuck and we had to get a carpenter to get him out.

He became a splendid dresser. He carried a cane; in fact, he had quite a collection of canes. We bought a lot of furniture and everything was most grand. My mother took a trip to New York and got herself completely and elegantly garbed. Possibly she had also brought back things from Paris. They had a great fight about furs. He had a business connection with a furrier someplace, but my mother, for humanitarian reasons, refused to wear furs. My father then got a beautiful broad-cloth wolverine-lined coat, I got an astrakhan coat and cap, and my mother compromised and got a tailored sealskin which was as little like fur as possible. We got these toward the very end of our affluent period in the purple wooden mansion.

My father started to drink even more heavily and there were card parties and smokers in the billiard room almost every night—the fast life of the breakfast-food aristocracy. My father had always been a heavy gambler, but he always won, so it wasn't so bad as it might have been. He was an expert poker player, and he won even when very drunk. Sometimes when most drunk he won fantastic things. He won the Stanley Steamer gambling, and once he won a boudoir set in ebony and silver with every conceivable kind of brush and hoe and lance and stabber for fingernails and toenails, both male and female, and all sorts of pomade pots and perfume bottles of cut-crystal with silver and ebony inlay and multiple mirrors of curious construction. All laid out, it filled the boudoir and all the table tops and shelves in my father's dressing room as well. He came home hilariously drunk in a taxi with a trunkful of this stuff at four o'clock one morning. He routed us out of bed and spread it all over the hall floor. At first my mother was a little miffed at being awakened; then she was amused, and as more and more implements kept appearing she was overwhelmed. She took a couple of drinks herself and at last we all romped around brushing and manicuring each other in the lavish hallway under the absurd chande-liers that blazed away on us as the dawn came in at the doors.

Our royal neighbor had a beautiful young daughter. My father had a crush on her so my mother was a little cool to her. We used to go to banquets at the hotel, which was part of her father's empire and at which everyone lived dangerously and brilliantly and noisily. For a while my mother was well and there was no sign of her lung trouble. She seemed to be elated by all the excitement. She used to go riding and dancing with a lecherous-looking young man with a title who was married to one of the local heiresses. His wife was in a sanitarium for alcoholism, so he had lots of leisure and paid continual attention to other women. My father and grandmother and I all hated him, but no-body said anything to my mother.

Various odd, transient characters would turn up to be entertained at dinner and to stay at the house. One night a girl came to town who went up in a balloon, did various tricks on a trapeze suspended from it, and then parachuted to earth. After her act she came over to us and was introduced by this villainous nobleman, and I remember the intense sensation that went through a little boy as he stood close up to her sweaty body in black tights with long silver fringe. She had gypsy-like dusty black hair hanging down her back. My parents invited her home and there was quite a party with the aristocrat and the trapeze performer, which I watched from the staircase.

Famous reformers and Socialists and suffragettes came to call when they lectured in Battle Creek. Here I met one of the most memorable human beings I have ever seen—a dynamic Negro leader who I believe must have been Mrs. Josephine St. Pierre Ruffin, a lawyer in Boston. We knew Mary Church Terrell and Ida Wells Barnett, too, but the stories about them and their visual memory have become vague and distorted. Not Mrs. Ruffin, however—a handsome elderly lady with pince-nez and a pompadour and the personality of a lioness.

Then things began to get rough and my father would come home with a long face and there would be dinners with businessmen and their wives, after which the men would go into another room and there'd be loud arguments. One night the back gate flew open and the daughter of the breakfast-food king ran in half-naked in a torn night-gown, babbling gibberish and screaming. Their house was suddenly all lit up and we ran over, unable to find out from the girl what had happened. The servants were running around like in a movie comedy, half-dressed in livery, the women screaming at the top of their lungs. My mother took the daughter and put her to bed and she passed out instantly. I still didn't know what was the matter. At last the ambulance came, and then I saw her father on the floor of his study. He'd taken a double-barreled shotgun and put it in his mouth and had pulled the triggers of both barrels with his toes and blown his head off.

Shortly after this the sky fell in. The sheriff came, we were dispossessed, and we moved out of the house with no furniture. Fortunately we had not moved our real furniture from Elkhart where it was stored. Apparently all this stuff was bought on credit or rented for our new life.

The only things I missed were the tree house, a little boy who lived next door of whom I don't have a very clear memory, and a little blonde girl named Natalie whom I had met in dancing school. She was the best dancer in the school and I think she later became a ballerina. She had all the hauteur and delicacy of a fairy-story princess, and once more I fell in love. Like all the children of the rich whom I have ever known, she was precocious sexually, and with her I had my first real, rather delicate and haughty, ethereal and precocious sexual experience. We took off all our clothes and I lay down against her and kissed her.

Alas, we were caught by her governess, who gave her a merciless whipping. Somehow I sensed that it was the governess who was the obscene member of this situation and who got most out of it. She came storming over to my mother, dragging poor Natalie, who was crazy with fright. I trailed along behind, very disturbed, and my mother calmed her down and promised her that I would be severely punished. Nothing happened that afternoon and when my father came home I was in a panic of anticipation. He took me to his den and sat me down and started to talk. Almost immediately my mother came in, and together they explained to me that I had been very unwise, that most people, especially parents and more especially servants, had no sense about such things and almost always behaved violently and nastily, and therefore I should not do things like that until I was older. They pointed out that they gave me no real pleasure and that they might get the other child into terrible trouble. So passed a great climacteric of childhood, and from it I learned once again that there was something very odd about most adults. That was the end of my affair with Natalie.

I had not yet gone to school and my mother was still teaching me, but at this time I went to someone who taught me French, and at this French class and in the dancing school was another, solider, and more modest little girl whose name was Carolyn Richter. She had Dutch-bobbed hair and looked like a larger-boned and more stalwart Helen Carpenter. I don't mean she was fat. She was quite slender and very pretty, and I decided that she, and not Natalie, was the prettiest girl of my age in Battle Creek. I used to go over to see her in another part of town and we started reading the Oz books together, and she would come to play in my tree house. When everything fell to pieces and we had no money and we walked out of our house in our fur coats, Carolyn and I remained sweethearts. The other children I never saw again. My mother immediately sold her sealskin and on that, I guess, we lived.

All the magnificence tumbled down in a day and left no trace. It's quite possible that my father was a dummy for someone else. Knowing the way we had always lived, I don't see where we had saved any money for such a venture. We always spent all the money that came in, nor did we have any credit, except ordinary retail credit. Possibly somebody connected with the Herkimer Wine Company was using him as a front, and there may well have been some operation of questionable legality which led them to drop him altogether for a while.

Anyway, the whole thing vanished, and we moved into a real slum. I saw my first cockroaches and rats. We set big rattraps and we put out in the kitchen and bathroom phosphorus-baited slices of potato, which glowed in the dark, to poison the roaches. The bathtub-shaped beds had gray sheets and ragged quilts and smelled of the kerosene with which they had been doused to kill the bedbugs, and my mother went over the bedsprings with a blowtorch the day we moved in. However, the odor, the unforgettable odor, of bedbugs still lingered in the bedroom. The plumbing stank and broke periodically, and ran over the floor and stained the ceiling. The house was bitter cold and drafty, and there we spent Christmas.

I don't understand why we were so penniless. The whole liquid assets of the entire family must have been thrown into this, because otherwise my aunt and grandmother would have come to the rescue, and I don't understand why my father temporarily lost his job at Kinsolving & Granisson, because he had been working in both the drug company and Battle Creek until the catastrophe.

Now occurred the first real quarrel, the only conventional marital battle that I ever witnessed. There had never been any explosions of anger or shouting or abuse or name-calling or recrimination, let alone fisticuffs. I really have to deduce from the turnover of the servant girls that my mother objected to my father's relations with them. They were innocent Mennonite girls from the country living in the house, which could lead to embarrassment with their parents. But my mother had no moral objections; she was more interested in keeping my father out of trouble than out of bed. Never once do I remember any sign of jealousy about anyone else. Complete sexual freedom was the latest advanced theory for marriage relationships in those days. I don't think my parents were shockingly promiscuous, though after my mother's miscarriage and hemorrhage I think they both had occasional affairs, and my father probably even more so when he was in Chicago and on the road. This was the period when people prided themselves on their liberated ways, and made a great point of calm discussion with all the cards on the table. As you know from plays and novels of that period, the favorite first move in a breaking up of a marriage was for the woman and her lover and her husband or the husband and his mistress and his wife to have a solemn meeting and to sit down and discuss everything like "mature adults." Well, nothing like that ever happened in my family, fortunately. Family friction was lubricated with good manners.

My ninth birthday, before this, had been extremely simple, and I remember that my father was not there. He had gone down to Chicago, I think, to straighten things out, and all I had was a little Ward's one-pound packaged cake with nine tiny candles on it. Then when Christmas came we had a roast leg of lamb, roast potatoes and onions, and some out-of-season vegetables. It was a simple but carefully prepared repast. We had a few little presents. I don't even remember what they were, but they were small and cheap, mostly clothing that we needed. We had saved some good wine, and my father got tipsy and said something ambiguous to my mother. She answered him back with something that he didn't understand, and he got up drunkenly and took hold of the tablecloth in a stagger, and as he did his plate fell on the floor. My mother said, "Well, all right, you fat old drunk, if you don't like my dinner, here it is!" She picked up the platter with the roast leg of lamb and the potatoes and hit him across the belly. The meat and potatoes went all over the floor. He burst into tears and ran into the bedroom—there were only three rooms in the place—and had a fit of hysterics. She went out of the house sobbing violently. I suspect that she, as well as he, was drunk. I think it is significant that it was economics that caused the only quarrel I ever witnessed. People put up with all sorts of things in marriage, but sudden poverty will cause more trouble than almost anything else.

When we recuperated we moved out. Our furniture was shipped up from Elkhart and we got an apartment next door to Carolyn Richter. To me this was the best thing that could have happened, much better than the ridiculous and uncomfortable mansion with its noisy life. My mother had been quite ill in the little flat. It was cold and insanitary and impossible to heat. The recuperation was rapid. It took place from Christmas to the beginning of spring, and by Easter we were well established, taking trips to Chicago and New York, Toledo and South Bend. We traveled to Benton Harbor and Holland, Michigan, and I saw the festival in Holland, with all the people dressed up in sabots and lace caps like their Dutch ancestors. We also went to the House of David in Benton Harbor, and watched the team with their long whiskers playing the Boston Bloomers, the first all-lady baseball team. Not many years after I was to know Mick McCann, who was then the captain. We were fat and sassy and well dressed and comfortably housed, and my father was back in Kinsolving & Granisson. It was all as though it had never been, both riches and poverty.

I was in love with Carolyn Richter, and we spent long hours lying in the sun parlor on cretonne cushions reading aloud from the Oz books and fancying ourselves as Dorothy, Ozma, Betsy, the Tin Woodman, and the Scarecrow. We used to play Oz plays, into which we tried to induct other children, but they were unruly under our fantasy. We had strict ideas about following the book and developing it only in certain ways. Modern progressive educators hate and fear the Oz books. Certainly they gave me the sense of the lyrical and adventurous possibilities of life, which made me a bad wage slave, and I hope they had the same effect on Carolyn Richter.

One of the things I have always liked about the Oz books is that they envisage a world run by children. We were almost infants, nine years old, but it was 1914 and we had some sense of the chaos overtaking the world, as children now have an even stronger awareness of the moral horror in which we live today. The Oz books, by contrast, gave us a picture of how idyllic the world would be if we ran it. I don't see anything wrong with that. I think they were perfectly right. I think the world would probably be better off if it was run by children with a simple, direct, and so-called innocent approach to the problems of life than if it was run by aged and evil rascals kept alive by injections of calf embryo.

So Carolyn was Ozma and I was the Wizard and we got married and reformed the world. I hope she's alive somewhere still. Maybe she will read this and realize how important that vision of forty-five years ago was—of how wrong fools have made life, and how good it might be. I look back on that little boy and little girl in a sun parlor playing at Utopia during the days of the first and second battles of the Marne and the long first winter in the trenches, and I suppose that again the pattern set still more firmly in my life in relation to woman, politics, and literature.

After the collapse of the breakfast-food venture my father went back to the wholesale drug and liquor business. While we were still living in Battle Creek I did a great deal of traveling with him, on old-time local Michigan railroads, with swinging lamps and soot and cinders, primitive Pullman accommodations, and smokers full of drummers puffing cigars and gambling. My father must have lost his executive position and gone back as an ordinary drummer. At least our life was much less elegant. Instead of traveling about glad-handing people, I remember him actually doing business. Before, we had gone all over the Middle West; at this time our journeys seemed to be confined largely to the Lower Peninsula of Michigan.

Something was going on in the business because we also made trips to South Bend and had long conferences with Mr. Eliel and his even more aged sister. They lived in a house as dark and gothic and odorous as their ancient drugstore, with columns and red velvet and gold molding—as elegant as the palaces in Little Nemo's dreams. All these conferences never came to anything because my father's role in the business never improved.

At this time, too, we took several trips to New York and it was in these days that I was first taken around Greenwich Village by my father. This was the period of the first Greenwich Village tearoom, the more or less institutionalized bohemia that we know today. I was taken to the Liberal Club, the Dutch Oven, Polly Holliday's, Grace Godwin's

Garrett, the Purple Pup, and met people like Alexander Berkman, the Powys brothers, Emma Goldman, and a considerable number of radical intellectuals, artists, and writers, all bound together by an intransigent resistance to the war. Of all of them the man who made the greatest impression on me was Alexander Berkman. He was a distinguished, rather gaunt man in those days and wore pince-nez. My father told me how he had spent fourteen years in prison and I read *Prison Memoirs of an Anarchist* and thrilled over the abortive escapes and the hair-raising brutality. Years later I was to meet Berkman again. He was then old and fat and bald and dying of cancer, with a mind warped and embittered by his experiences in revolutionary Russia, and shortly after, he killed himself. But in those days he was full of electric dynamism. Besides, he had a fascinating red-haired girl, who was a friend of my family and who later became the muse, administrator, and general work horse as well as psychiatric nurse of the Provincetown Theater.

In contrast to this radical circle there was a high-life bohemia that centered around the studio of Willy Pogany. He was a commercial illustrator and designer who was still doing covers for the *American Weekly* when I had become a grown man. It was at his place that both Stanford White and Harry K. Thaw met Evelyn Nesbitt—"the girl in the red velvet swing." By 1916 the set of Robert W. Chambers, Vance Thompson, Huneker, and White seldom went there, but it still functioned as a gaudy studio, where men about town went to meet models.

I was as unaware of all this lace-slipper sin as I was of the arguments about Strindberg, Nietzsche, and Richard Strauss over the champagne and open kimonos, but I enjoyed playing with the studio props, the lay figures, and the plaster heads and arms while my elders lived their high life around me. It was there possibly that I first saw James Gibbons Huneker. I was unlucky to have encountered this Edwardian high life when I was so young and it was dying out. Still, I can look back and reconstruct my childhood memories and form something of a dim picture and a faint flavor of those days, now more dead and gone than those of the Pharaohs. The Thaw case was a minor climacteric in American life—when the first member of café society murdered the last man about town. It was this type of Edwardian sophisticate that I think my father tried to be. He greatly admired people like Stanford White and Stuart Merrill and Huneker, but I feel that as a provincial and a man of modest means and eventually a man who did not hold his liquor well, he was not successful at it. Still, everyone seemed to like him. And his popularity has given me the chance to look back on an old New York life, far beyond my years.

Years later I met one of the last of these people. I was hitchhiking

across the desert east of San Diego. In those days the road was made
of great planks strung about four inches apart on two cables. The sand
would drift across the planks and they'd lift them up and put them
back on top. Off in the middle of the desert was a crossroad gas station,
restaurant, and store. I went in for a cup of coffee and a rest from the
wind and a haggard, careworn, elderly woman stared at me as she
served me. She said, "Aren't you Charlie Rexroth's boy?" She was Grace
Godwin, one of the more spectacular Village beauties and proprietress
of Grace's Garrett. She got tuberculosis and married a man with the
same disease and had come out here to recuperate in the desert. We
sat around in her woebegone, ramshackle shop, drinking boiled coffee
with canned milk, out of the tearing wind and the baking heat, and
recalled the glories of a bygone bohemia that I had known only as a
little boy in short pants.

On these trips to New York my mother was usually along and we
stayed either in the Brevoort or the Lafayette. The Brevoort is long
gone. I was in New York the night the Lafayette died, but I didn't go
because I thought the people celebrating the wake would either be
senile or have no conception of what it was they were mourning. At
the tables should have been Fitzie, Polly Holliday, the Powys brothers,
Jack Kearny, Berkeley Tobey, Hippolyte Havel, Sadakichi Hartman,
Jim Larkin, Moishe Nadir Ba'sudeb, Tarik Nath Das, Sen Katayama,
and a whole lot of other people whom I can no longer identify, busily
engaged in liquidating the British Empire. Sadakichi came to visit us
once, and greatly scandalized Battle Creek. Of Emma Goldman I have
only the slightest memory. To me, she was just a dowdy woman who
did not know how to get along with children. She loved them and
wanted to make friends, but like people who spook horses she had the
wrong sort of aura.

CHAPTER 9

In my tenth year we packed up suddenly and left Battle Creek and went to Chicago to live. First to my Uncle John's apartment on Lincoln Park West and then for a while we moved in with my aunt. In those days her husband still worked in the stockyards and they lived Back of the Yards in a large run-down house on Emerald Avenue. The street was paved with wooden blocks, like large round pegs driven into the mud, and was full of deep holes and permanent puddles. There were stables nearby. Rats used to run marauding through the streets in gangs. My aunt carried on an endless war against bedbugs with kerosene and blowtorch; against cockroaches with slices of raw potatoes smeared with phosphorus paste, which we used to put out every night in the bathroom and kitchen and which glowed in the dark like great rotten eyes, staring at me all around the floor when I got up in the night for a drink or to go to the toilet.

To the amazement of all the family, my aunt, who had been so proud, so fashionably dressed, and such a militant suffragette, took care of this large house, which was reeking with built-in dirt, four stepchildren, and her husband. She did all the baking, laundry, and sewing. Before she was married she couldn't cook at all and never touched a needle. My uncle was a morose, almost completely silent man. He had been greatly in love with his first wife and it took him years to recover from her death. To me, who was used to noise and activity and conversation about the house, not just the Emerald Street house itself, but the family, the very children, seemed haunted. Meals were eaten in complete silence, something I had never witnessed before. On Saturday night my uncle's friends, all Irishmen, and their wives came over for a family poker party that usually lasted until 2 A.M. There was a lot of conviviality then and my aunt got quite gay, but my uncle sat silently sipping his beer and playing cards and confined his remarks to monosyllables: "Pass," "Raise," "Call." I had never seen anything like this and was dumfounded. My aunt, with no preparation in life whatsoever, kept the squalor of Upton Sinclair's Jungle at bay, single-handed.

My father's first attack of delirium tremens occurred when we were living in the old brown wooden mansion in Battle Creek. He went away to the Keely-Cure Sanatorium and came back half-dead with the cure and started immediately to drink again. About the time we got back to Chicago there occurred one of those incidents which are supposed to permanently warp the mind of their infant witnesses. Near the drug house there was a shoddy, sporty hotel in which my father had some money. For all I know, he might have been half owner. Since it was only a few doors away from the business, he always stayed there when he was alone in Chicago, and sometimes against my mother's objections we would all put up in the bridal suite. It may have been a good place once, but it had become a hangout for carnival people, card hustlers, pimps, and grifters. In the evenings, there were always two or three quiet but impressively dressed girls sitting unoccupied in the lobby.

One morning, just before noon, my mother got a telephone call from the manager of the hotel that my father was dying. She took me and hurried down town. He was not dying, but he was in a state of acute alcoholic shock. He was lying on the bed, nude, his flesh gray and his lips blue and caked, his eyes rolled back in his head, snoring with a horrible roar. Just as my mother arrived a doctor friend of the family also showed up and they started to work on him to restore some measure of consciousness. It proved impossible to bring him fully to, so they called the ambulance and took him off to the hospital.

While this was going on, the door opened and a young woman walked in. She looked rather fast, with dyed hair, narrow waist, wide hips, and big breasts, but she wasn't painted or overdressed and she didn't look at all vulgar. In fact, she looked terrified. She introduced herself in a frightened, almost inaudible voice. "I am So-and-so. I didn't know you were here. The hotel called me and I came as soon as I could leave my children." There was the slightest momentary stiffness in my mother's response, but she said, "It's all right. You can help. He looks like it was going to kill him this time." So the two women and the doctor worked on him with black coffee and injections and got him a little way out of his coma, but not very far, and went off with him to the hospital. My grandmother, who had arrived in the meantime, took me home. From then on, this woman was an occasional visitor to my mother. They would have long and private conversations that I was never able to overhear. She was a little older than my mother and I have a feeling that she was an old girl of my father's, from his more splendid days, who had come back to him to help him when he began to go to pieces. She continued to visit us until my mother's death, and once after that, when my father and I had gone to Toledo, she showed up for dinner, quiet, mournful, and abstracted. After that evening, when she and my father just sat and looked at each other and said practically nothing, she never came back.

Shortly after this episode at the hotel my mother and father separated. He may well have gone to a sanatorium for a long session, because, when he left, there was no quarreling nor even any strain, but just a kind of melancholy. He kissed me and said that he would be back soon, that he was going on a trip. He went out to the taxi with his handbag and disappeared for about three months.

My mother got a small furnished apartment in Austin, then a suburb of Chicago. It was in a private home, on a quiet, heavily-shaded street with big maple trees that began to turn color shortly after we moved in. There was a kitchenette, the first one I had ever seen, a toilet and shower, the first bathroom I had seen without a bath, and two very small bedrooms and a large parlor, which must have been a Victorian boudoir. The first afternoon we moved in, we went to the ten-cent store and bought a tea service of bright red Japanese export porcelain and had tea together by the big bay window in the early autumn evening—smoke in the air and the first streaks beginning to appear on the maple leaves. A great sense of relief and a great sorrow came from my mother and communicated itself to me. With the tea we had cracknels, a dry biscuit shaped rather like a small summer squash, very light and brittle. Cracknels have long since gone out of date, but I never see them in some old-fashioned grocery store without buying a few and the exact experience of Proust's madeleine overcomes me. Just the sight or thought of them can call back that old-time suburban world: boys and dogs and bicycles and porch swings, falling leaves and bonfires and my mother's knowledge of death. Nowadays, alas, so few people ever buy cracknels that they are almost always very stale, so I have to throw them away, and can't share with Proust the oral stimulation of which his psychoanalyst critics make so much.

At this time I went to school regularly for the first time. Perhaps my mother was too ill or weak to devote to me as much time as once she had. Also, she spent a lot of her time going to concerts and the theater and the Art Institute with her old girl friends from South Bend and with a doctor who had been her friend for many years and who tried, at this time, to get her to divorce my father and marry him. Still, even though I went to school, my relationship with my mother was closer than it had ever been. We were drawn together by our need for my father and had to find most of our emotional satisfaction in each other.

Then, too, although I was completely unaware of it, I realize now that
my mother knew she was not going to live much longer.

Although I had never liked school before when I visited it, I was far
ahead of my age, so I was advanced about two grades, something no
longer permitted in democratic American schools. Even so, I was still
ahead of my class and I was permitted a lot of time off which I spent
hiking in the nearby Forest Preserve with my mother or going with her
to concerts or museums. We spent many hours carefully studying the
exhibits in the Field Museum and I then, that early, acquired a strong
interest in primitive art. Later in life its inhumaneness and sterile for-
malism have come to bore me. I am afraid I look on it as a childish enthusiasm rather than an adult highbrow fad. Anyway, in those days I
spent a lot of time under my mother's coaching, making crude drawings of New Guinea masks and African figures and Mexican gods. Saturdays I went to the children's classes at the Chicago Art Institute, and
here, that autumn, I was introduced to the art of sculpture in plasticine
and turned out a number of very African-looking figures, large and
ambitious for a child, which baffled the other children and annoyed
the teacher.

Ten years later, when I was dancing in White City to the music of
perhaps the Benson or Goldkette Band, a couple of the musicians
came over during the break and introduced themselves as old friends
from that Austin Grammar School. I am sorry but I don't remember
who they were. Not, I think, Bix Beiderbecke, who I believe was a
year younger than I. It was on this occasion, however, at White City,
that I first met Dave Tough, who I am sure was several years younger
than I, and who was to be a close friend for several years. Anyway,
fame brushed me early. I went to grammar school with a couple of
the oldest members of the Austin High School gang. In those days no
one had the remotest idea that these boys would become historical
figures. Most people looked on them as nuisances.

Chicago children were much more sophisticated than the small-town
children I had known and Chicago itself seemed like Paris, Athens,
and Florence to a little boy being shown its sights and wonders by a
lonely, dying mother. I remember visiting somebody my mother told
me was a famous young writer, married to a famous young painter,
who lived out in the old South Side studio colony, facing Jackson Park.
This, I believe, was Floyd Dell. There was also a slightly seedy bearded
eccentric, an embittered man who drank too much and whose mistress
was a little milliner my mother had known. Years later I discovered
that he was Chicago's leading artist in any medium—Louis Sullivan.
Certainly it was a different atmosphere from New York. Full of girls

with peasant blouses and sandals and bobbed hair, batik curtains, homemade pottery, and the first tremors of Chicago abstract art.

As always, it didn't take me long to get a girl and fall in love. This was the first colored girl I had ever known closely. Her mother and father were both musicians, but except for jobs in Negro churches, unable to make any money out of it. They worked as domestics for a rich doctor in Oak Park and it was there while visiting their employers that my mother met them. During the time that we lived in Austin they seemed to have been our closest friends, and often we went to their home to dinner or to parties at which there would be one or two white people and a lot of rather stuffy middle-class Negroes and a lot of very nice children. They themselves were anything but stuffy and middle-class but I imagine in those days a young cultivated Negro couple could not be too choosy. Their daughter was slender, very dark, and I thought she was enormously brainy. She used to come to the house and play difficult duets with my mother although she couldn't have been more than eleven years old. She came along on many of the expeditions that I went on with my mother. We were devoted to each other and used to talk about how we were going to get married when we grew up, but at the same time she had me thoroughly intimidated. Shortly after we left Austin, her family moved to New York with their employers, and I never heard of her again. Unless some disaster overtook her, she should have become famous. I can still see my mother's white face and chestnut hair and her round head of unstraightened hair and long thin black aquiline face, eleven years old and immeasurably solemn, as the two of them sat side by side at the piano playing Mozart and Debussy.

That Christmas my mother and father came back together. We went out to my aunt's for Christmas Eve. They had a new apartment near Forty-third Street, on Indiana Avenue, and my uncle had a new job as a letter carrier, a decided step up from Back of the Yards. There were lots of presents, a huge tree, still lit in those days with candles, and a sumptuous feast. Even my uncle came to life. He was quite jolly. At midnight he went out on the back porch, shook a string of sleigh bells, and came bounding in dressed as Santa Claus, while the children ran and hid under the bed. Just as this was going on, my father showed up. In a little while he was slightly tipsy. He made a maudlin speech about how good everybody had been to him and how undeserving he had been. My aunt burst into tears and shut herself in the bathroom.

That night we didn't go home to Austin but went to my father's Christmas present and surprise. Unbeknown to my mother he had rented an apartment on South Park Avenue, near my aunt, and got our furniture from Elkhart and fixed it all up. For a week or two my parents had a second honeymoon. Then, one day while they were skating in Washington Park across the street from our apartment, my mother had a severe hemorrhage and had to be carried home. She didn't recover at all, and in a few days they took her to a sanatorium.

My mother was taken to the Oak Forest Tuberculosis Sanatorium. This was a charity hospital run by the city. One reason we went there was that the director, Dr. White, was a close friend, but I am sure the main reason was that we no longer had any money. Then began a long diagnostic conflict. Some specialists said my mother had tuberculosis. Some said she did not. She had severe pain and a large shadow in the X ray and frequent hemorrhages and no cough, but it was never possible to find an appreciable number of Koch's bacilli in her sputum. One of the saddest things about the case is that now she would have been diagnosed correctly at the outset, operated on and cured, and might well be alive today. That short a time ago lung surgery was almost unheard of and modern diagnostic methods had yet to be invented.

She stayed in Oak Forest the better part of the winter. Early in the spring Dr. White called us in and had a conference first with my aunt, then with my father, and then with me. He told me that my mother would die within a few months. There was nothing they could do for her and they weren't even sure what was wrong with her. She had not improved with bed rest and rich diet, the way most TB patients do. She looked like a dying woman.

She borrowed money and left the hospital and took me to Elkhart. She rented a house on Second Street, about two blocks from where we had lived before. There was a great mulberry tree in the front yard and cherry trees in the back. My aunt came down and stayed with us part of the time and my grandmother all the time. To me this meant a wonderful opportunity to renew my acquaintance with Helen Carpenter. Helen's mother as well as a number of other old friends came over often to visit and help out as best they could. And Mrs. Carpenter, my mother, Helen, and I, as long as my mother was ambulatory, spent a great deal of time walking and driving in the spring countryside.

My mother had a lot of dress goods of all sorts—fine duvetines, taffetas, broadcloth, tweeds—and she had them all made up. They had accumulated over the years with plans for using them always postponed. One of these dresses, which she herself designed, was particularly beautiful. It had a long, slender, tailored line; what I believe was called a walking dress in those days, with the skirt above the ankles, made of gray-pink duvetine. This dress was to be important a little later. About this time she put on her best clothes and carefully made herself up and took me to a photographer for a batch of pictures, small pocket photographs to carry in my wallet when I grew up. I still have one, but it is the last, so it's not in my wallet but in the family Bible. In the picture she is wearing a black velvet coat and a velvet turban with a taffeta, featherlike appendage, a humanitarian's substitute for sealskin and ostrich plumes.

This burning farewell to life, although it was constantly running on a diminishing supply of fuel, became every week more fierce and desperate. Pretty soon the walks and then the drives in the country stopped. The last excursion was a canoe trip. We went from our house to the still water above the dam in the St. Joe River and an old man paddled us about among the swans and ducks under the flowering trees. That night she was very tired and after that she seldom got out of bed. I didn't go back to school. She spent long hours reading me stories, history and elementary science, and the biographies of great writers and artists.

In those days someone decided that, of all things, creosote was a specific for tuberculosis and she began taking enormous chocolate-covered pills, about thirty grains each. Of course they made her ill; they would have sickened a horse, but she went on desperately taking them, till finally my father arrived. He took one look at them and said, "My God, Delia, those things would kill you even if you were perfectly healthy." After she had told him about her newly developed stomach pain, he took her to have an X ray. There was a large ulcer on the left upper surface, directly below the shadow in the lung. As it turned out in the autopsy, the picture had been inaccurately read. What was actually happening was the beginning of a psoas abcess.

She was now in constant severe pain, hardly able to eat, unable to get out of bed, and very gaunt. In spite of constant brushing, her hair had become snarled and matted, so one day she bobbed it. She said that although she was too sick to vote and didn't believe in it anyway, at least she could keep up with things and bob her hair.

Just before she became totally bedridden she did a most hysterical thing. Presumably it should have had a terrible effect on me, but I looked on it, as I came to look on everything that happened in those years, as perfectly normal behavior under the circumstances. She found a bolt of satin which exactly matched the duvetine dress and she took it to the undertaker and got a coffin with burnished silver handles and covered with some flocked substance matched to the satin lining and the dress. The undertaker called it "ashes of roses." She took me along and consulted me about which design I preferred. I can still remember the collapsing framework, like a folding bed, on which the coffins were displayed. We spent a whole evening selecting the most handsome and weatherproof one and arguing about the price.

She apparently had quite a bit of insurance, because although we had almost no money, she bought the most expensive coffin in the place—custom-upholstered to boot—and in addition a lead-lined concrete underground vault. Quite possibly she is there beside the St. Joe River, relatively unchanged to this day.

This may all sound morbid to an adult, but it is amazing what shocking things a child can accept. I am inclined to think that what are called traumatic experiences in modern couch slang do permanent damage only to children who are already vulnerable—usually because they feel unloved and unwanted. The painful experiences of my childhood seem only to have given me a cast-iron psychological constitution.

Things got much worse. She didn't sleep or eat, was in constant, violent pain, and moaned almost inaudibly with every breath. Then suddenly the pain stopped. She looked almost well again. Although I doubt if she could digest anything, she even started to eat. That night the moon was full and she lay awake all night, sometimes singing very softly to herself. In the morning she said, "Send for Charlie. Last night I saw the sun and the planets hanging in the cherry tree like a great diamond surrounded with a turquoise, a sapphire, an emerald, a ruby, and two topazes. I am going to die in a week." My father showed up late that afternoon from Toledo, Ohio, and my aunt from Chicago.

The last six days were a period of quiet, secure happiness. She had no pain and although every day she seemed more transparent she didn't look sick, but rather as though she were turning into a slightly different species of humanity. She had long conferences with me in which she gave me advice about all the contingencies of life she could foresee. Somewhere in the back of my mind I suppose I remember it all and have even acted on it down the years. Over and over again she stressed the importance of never allowing anyone to deter me from becoming an artist and a writer. She explained that my father would probably never make much money again, but that there was some educational insurance for me and that the two families would help me. Of course, she said, if I discovered I didn't want such a life, that was fine, too, and she hoped that I would become a doctor or a scientist, but that above all things I should never allow other people to determine my life for me.

My mother was received into the Roman Catholic Church—an act no one was expecting. She had, without our knowledge, been in continuous correspondence with her Poor Clare friend and the day after my mother's vision, this girl appeared on special leave from her convent with a priest and the materials for baptism, communion, and extreme unction.

Various financial arrangements were made. I was supposed to go live with my father in Toledo, where his mother would help take care of me. He was supposed to have stopped drinking, and as far as anybody knew, my grandmother was a kind woman and certainly the best educated in the family.

Although it had been far beyond her capacity for weeks, my father picked my mother up and put her in a wheel chair.

With death so imminent, it made little difference what she did. They took long walks in the park and beside the rivers. He even lifted her into a buggy and took her out to Silver Lake and to the old mill beside the brook in the Bristol moraine. One morning I went to the library to get some books. One was *The Boys' Parkman*. One was a *Life of Rembrandt*. One was Andrew Lang's *Blue Poetry Book*, which had not come down with our books from Chicago. One was a book about Boy Scouts called *The Buck's Hill Troop*. On the spine under the title were five white dots like the dots on a die on the brown cloth. I sat on the front porch, watching the orioles in the mulberry tree, looking at my books, and basking in the late spring sun. My aunt came out and said quietly, "Your mother has just died." I turned the book over and stared for a long time at the five white spots and a great sense of peace and well-being came over me as though I, too, had died and gone to a heaven which was all one calm, limitless vision.

CHAPTER 10

My mother was buried in her ashes-of-roses dress and coffin, looking as beautiful as I had ever seen her, so transparent as to seem cut from glass.

The day after the funeral my father took me to Toledo, Ohio. America was already in the war and he had built up a chain of drugstores that had belonged to men who had entered the Army, and which he operated in their absence. There were five or six of them and I believe he made a fair amount of money. What happened to it I don't know, because there was little in evidence. We lived with my grandmother —my grandfather was dead by then—in her run-down, overcrowded house. She was quite senile and the house was full of two lifetimes' accumulation of everything imaginable. The staircases were stacked with back numbers of the *Century*, *Scribner's*, *Harper's*, *National Geographic*, *The North American Review*, and *The Saturday Evening Post*. The bedrooms were piled with unironed but washed linens. The closets were full of dresses years out of date and dozens of pairs of worn-out shoes. The drawers were full of dress-good yardage. Books were stacked all over the place. There were three sets of Dickens piled on chairs and the ninth edition of the Encyclopaedia Britannica piled up on the floor. In all the years since her children had moved away and since my grandfather had died and she was all alone, she had gone right on "putting up." The basement, which was very large, was packed solid to the ceiling with grayed jars of tomatoes and browned jars of sweet corn and glasses of crystallized jelly that tasted like wine. Not only were there such semipermanent preserves, but there was crock after crock of sauerkraut that had molded away and pickled pigs' feet that had turned into a mysterious brown paste; also what we used to call mangoes—green peppers stuffed with cabbage— which had turned to shriveled dark objects like Jivaro heads.

To an outside observer, my grandmother's appearance would have been horrifying and the conditions under which she lived worse. But I was used to her and I just thought everybody's father's mother lived that way. By this time her goiter was quite as large as her head and its weight had pulled the skin over her bones and given her face the look of a polished brown skull. Her hair, which was once luxuriant, was very thin, but it was kept covered indoors and out by a battered bonnet— pronounced "bunnet." She always wore the same black watered silk-taffeta dress. The bust and sleeves were ornamented with elaborate ruching and jet beads. Around the house she wore pince-nez glasses attached to a locket pinned to her dress. Outside she carried a lorgnette with an inlaid tortoise-shell handle half the size of a ball bat. Always, indoors and out, she carried a cane.

None of this surprised me. My mother acting out her own tragedy had prepared me for the life of an orphan. If I had been chained to a fence post out in the pigsty and fed on slops, I wouldn't have been in the least bit surprised. As a matter of fact, I looked on myself as rather lucky. Certainly the house was full of stuff to fascinate a little boy. There was a yard with a grape arbor and two chickens almost as old as my grandmother and a rabbit so old he was grizzled all over the face and blind. She even continued to care for a small vegetable patch and there were several abandoned buildings in which I could play. They, too, were full of junk, warped and moldy—stereopticon slides of the Holy Land or John L. Sullivan's fights, half-melted cylinder phono-graph records, a broken battery telephone, and rusted dress forms.

Then, too, there were my girl cousins who lived nearby. I was in love with Marcella, the youngest, all the time I stayed in Toledo. My father and aunt used to talk about our getting married. Just behind us, on the next street, lived a remarkable boy. He was in his late teens, but he had built himself a glider in which we used to fly short distances. It was so good that he later put an engine in it. In this contraption, which looked as though it had come straight from Kitty Hawk, I had my first airplane ride, sitting on a motorcycle seat, hanging on to a couple of wires, and looking down at the Willard-Dempsey fight at Bayview Park, while the plane bucked and reared like a kite as it moved over ploughed fields, water, and grassland. This boy not only built an airplane but was an expert at taking apart and putting to-gether cars, and he taught all of us little kids to make wireless sets. We wrapped wires around oatmeal boxes and tickled crystals with cat's whiskers to signal each other in Morse code all over the neighborhood until the government put a stop to it for the duration of the war.

I joined the Boy Scouts. The Boy Scout handbook says, "A Scout is truthful." I was only eleven, but I told them I was thirteen and got in. This was a peculiar Boy Scout outfit. The man who ran it was a left-wing Socialist, one of the "Ohio Group," which later formed the first leadership of the Communist Party. He had little use for the patrioteering reactionary policies, which, just at this time, were being forced on the Boy Scouts, and which led to the resignation of all the founders, men like Dan Beard and Ernest Thompson Seton. In our troop the emphasis was entirely upon woodcraft, outdoor sports, and various skills. Also our scoutmaster collected from around the city, I realize now as a matter of policy, Japanese, Negro, Chinese, and American Indian boys, so that it was quite an interracial organization. Shortly after I joined they decided to turn themselves into the first all-Eagle troop in the country. A high-pressure campaign to accumulate merit badges got under way. Weekend after weekend I was taken in hand by assistant scoutmasters and pushed through test after test. At the end of the summer I got my eagle. We went off to Buffalo, where we defeated the first Canadian Eagle Scout troop in practically all the events. I was such a fast semaphore signaler that only one Chinese boy in the troop could read what I sent. The next year I took up fire-by-friction and went to the Chicago Coliseum, where I spun a bow drill and made a great smoke while thousands cheered. I'm not sure but I think I was champion fire-by-frictioner of the United States. I almost immediately lost the gold medal which I won.

My father was liberal in providing me with excuses for staying out of school and since I was way beyond my class and probably a dreadful pest to my teacher, nobody seemed to mind. I spent most of my time in the woods. I became a passionate bird watcher. My father gave me a full-sized, brass-bound microscope and a microtome. I sliced and dissected everything imaginable. At last I could see real bacteria and I was overjoyed. I built a reflector telescope with which at first it was difficult to see anything. Eventually I got it just right and spent hours staring at the Andromeda Nebula, the Beehive, and the Hercules cluster. Mostly, though, I just idled in the woods. In those days Ten-Mile Creek was on the outskirts of the city. Its bottom land was covered with a jungle of marsh trees and undergrowth. The water was still clear. There was a swimming hole with a high dive up in a tree and a rope to swing out over the water. I spent days swimming and lying on the bank plastered with mud. I still remember with the greatest immediacy the first rose-breasted grosbeak I ever saw, the first indigo bunting, the first dickcissel, my first sight of the Milky Way in Sagittarius through my homemade telescope, the first carnivorous plant and lady's slipper, and, especially, the unbelievable sight of a small flock of European robins which appeared out of Lake Erie, moved across northern Ohio, and vanished, causing great excitement in all the newspapers.

In the bottom land of Ten-Mile Creek, under the high banks, on top of which there was a graveyard for old streetcars, we had a special hideout. There was a small clearing in which generations of kids had built several shacks of packing boxes and flattened oilcans. It was possible to get there with a great deal of trouble by crawling through the thorny underbrush, but our customary means of approach was by a trapeze strung to the top of a tall tulip tree which took off from a secret spot back of the carbarn and swung the cliff. Since few kids played hooky most of the time the way I did, I usually had the place to myself. I took over one of the cabins and there I kept bird books, nature guides, microscope, and magnifying glasses. Although all the kids were tireless thieves, nobody ever bothered my cabin, even though sometimes I left a rather valuable camera or my telescope there. I used to fill a rucksack with potatoes and canned goods and stay there sometimes two or three nights. There was another place farther out called Hubbard's Woods, the wood lot of a farm on the bank of a small river, where I used to go for even longer periods.

I was never short of money. My father bought me the largest Butter-Kist popcorn machine. It looked like a modern glass-top railroad car, it was so big. It popped, salted, buttered, and sacked the popcorn, all by machinery, and roasted and sacked peanuts as well while a robot clown turned somersaults above the machinery. We put it outside the best of my father's drugstores on Collingwood Avenue, then the city's best street, and I ran it all year, except in the coldest of winter. At first I did it all myself, but later, whenever I wanted to go out to the woods, I'd hire some other boy to take care of it for me. The intake was simply fabulous. I made more money than I was ever to make again in my life, until the post-War II inflation made all income figures meaningless. I sometimes suspect that my actual cash income was as high as my father's, whose financial operations with all these rented drugstores were much too complicated. There was only one trouble with it: I ate too much popcorn, which gave me piles, a disagreeable affliction from which I have never suffered before or since. Still, I met a lot of nice girls, which made up for this minor occupational hazard.

After a considerable row with my grandmother, my father managed to get an area in the basement cleared out, a little room with a gas plate and sink, and here he set up a comprehensive chemical laboratory for me. There were ground-glass bottles of every conceivable chemical, glass retorts, mortars, batteries of test tubes, Florence flasks, all of the best quartz glass. We not only had every chemical apparatus I could use, but built a lot of the simple machines, electrical and otherwise, that they use to teach physics in high schools. I could outstink and outbang any other kid in the neighborhood and the place became a favorite hangout.

Although most of the boys I played with seem to me now to have been bright and precocious, we didn't spend all our time as baby scientists, performing chemical experiments and building airplanes. Most of our time was spent doing things we hadn't ought to do, and especially hadn't ought to do to little girls. I have never been able to figure out if most adults lie about their childhood or if we were exceptionally precocious. I have talked to other people who have grown up in Toledo and whose childhood has been spent elsewhere as well. They all agree that there was something peculiar about the kids in Toledo, especially some of the kids in this, the best neighborhood. Certainly the level of sexual activity was not that kind of childish play that you read about in books on the subject. When I look back, it seems to have been perversely adult. Later, in Chicago, I was never to find anything like it. Nowadays, with the threat of imminent extermination, kids have taken to going steady from the first blush of puberty. No draft card or atom bomb hung over the heads of the children in Toledo, so I have no way of accounting for their early sexual maturity.

The development of childhood sexuality is supposed to be of great importance. So it probably behooves me to talk about all this at some length. As a matter of fact, I do not look back on it as a period of crisis and I can't point to any specific experiences or relationships that now seem to me to have been determinative. It all seems to have been gradual and easy and relaxed. In my memory at least, this group of children, ranging in age from eleven to fourteen, were one year very actively engaged in exercising their scientific curiosity. I think these activities had grown out of imitation of their older brothers. The boy who built the first airplane was a powerful influence on the whole community of kids. It was the girls who introduced the erotic element and in a little while everybody had paired off and was going steady. From then on the little cluster of shacks in the woods, which by the way we called "Greenwich Village," became what the newspapers call a teen-age love nest, though we were mostly about twelve years old. There was a considerable amount of juvenile homosexuality. I attended some of these activities, but they bored me. I was restless and ill at ease at a thought of what a waste of more than willing little girls these purely male capers were. Certainly I look back on none of this as having left any kind of indelible scars on me.

One of the things that gave Toledo, Ohio, its special character in those days was that it was a sanctuary, like the monastic properties in London in the Middle Ages. Extradition was extremely difficult. You could commit a crime somewhere else and run to Toledo and as long as you behaved yourself, it took all hell to get you out. This meant that the crooks policed the town. It was no place to stick up a grocery store or prowl houses. You might find yourself full of holes in the gutter. This meant also that the town was wide open. There were whorehouses all

over the place. On the best corner in town, above the drugstore where
I ran my popcorn machine, was a whorehouse that ran as wide open
as the Farmers' Market. I was a great favorite of the girls and ran intimate errands and sold them lots of popcorn. Gambling was wide open
and I often called for my father at cardrooms with no thought that I
was doing anything unusual.

There were several burlesque shows and nobody ever stopped me
from attending them. It is true that I was already very tall and was
beginning to acquire that look of misleading maturity which was possibly to keep me alive through my adolescence. In a dim light I might
have been mistaken for a smooth-faced, very young man—but I didn't
look all that old, even though I did wear long pants, something few
little boys did in those days.

I am sure that in no other city in America could I have come and
gone into brothels, cardrooms, and burlesque shows without question.
I did better than run errands for the biggest burlesque show; I sold
them, each evening before we both began business, all the popcorn
and roasted peanuts left over from the night before—at a tremendous
discount, of course, but still we both made money and I always had
fresh popcorn and peanuts at no loss.

Possibly it was this connection with the adult world of hustlers that
led me to change my friends among the children. The street we lived
in was a dividing line between rich and poor neighborhoods. The kids
I have been describing all lived in the rich neighborhood, on a group
of streets whose names ended in "wood"—Collingwood, Cherrywood,
Oakwood, and so forth. In the other direction the streets ran downhill
to the Libby-Owens Glass plant, a number of foundries and small factories, and then to the creek bottoms and off to the right, to the Willys-
Overland plant. Here the poor kids lived.

The first one I met in the Boy Scout troop. He was a dwarf, or rather
a red-haired midget with a large head, and around the Boy Scouts he
conducted himself with grave, impeccable decorum. His name was
Meade Somers. Why Meade belonged to the Boy Scouts, I have no
idea. Possibly because his other life was not enough to satisfy his extraordinary intelligence. Although we were only little boys, I look back
on him as one of the most intelligent people I have ever known. His
other life certainly provided plenty of satisfactions. He was the leader
of a gang of perhaps fifteen kids ranging in age from ten to eighteen.
Although he was younger than the majority of boys in the gang and a
midget, his leadership was never questioned. He was by far the brain-
iest and the toughest and incomparably the most cool. Nothing fazed
him.

We used to go on our bicycles on pilfering expeditions in drugstores and groceries all over town. We did a regular business in hot bicycles and automobile accessories. Meade had discovered that during the busy times of the day the most unattended cash registers were to be found in small garages, for everybody would be busy underneath a car. He used to take another boy whom he could leave outside riding up and down, ringing his bicycle bell continuously, and yelling, "Bang, bang, bang, here come the cops!" at the top of his lungs. Meade would coolly walk in, punch the key of the largest denomination on the cash register, clean it out into a paper sack, get on his bicycle, and ride coolly and slowly away.

The gang had one inflexible rule: if you got caught, you got kicked out. So it, too, was a sort of Eagle Scout troop. By definition, as they say, it consisted of kids who didn't get caught. Whenever anybody started doing anything really dangerous, Meade put his foot down. Some of the older boys were expelled one day for rolling drunks, which Meade considered tempting fate. Everybody in the gang had his girl and the sexual relations were much like those that prevailed among the rich kids, except that they were much tougher and never promiscuous. Every new member, male or female, was "initiated," but after that, you paired off and stayed with your partner or you got kicked out. There was no homosexuality whatever, nor were there any public orgies of the sort the rich kids went in for.

I suppose I was a sort of traitor to my class, because I became assistant brain and under my guidance we drove the rich kids out of almost all their activities around town and along the creek and confined them to their own neighborhood. We took over the Village and spent our time drinking homemade beer we had stolen from our parents' cellars, roasting potatoes and wienies, stewing up oilcans full of slum gullion, spooning with our girls, and plotting devilment. We also took over the swimming hole.

At this time I acquired a nickname which I was never to lose among hustlers. To this day many people in the San Francisco Tenderloin and the Fillmore district call me Duke. I never told anybody that back home in Toledo or Chicago or wherever I came from last that people called me Duke. It always reappeared spontaneously; just as certain people in the underworld are always called Blackie or Whitey or Kid, some are called Duke. It's no great compliment. The most affected girl in a whorehouse is usually called Duchess. There is a slightly different type who, in the words of Engels, has also cut himself loose from the upper classes, who is invariably called Professor. A few people, down the years, have called me Professor. Possibly I occupy that ambiguous category between Duke and Professor for which there is no name.

At the swimming hole there was a pest whom we had inherited from the rich kids—the first adult male homosexual I had ever seen. He had been more than welcome among the rich kids, to whom he used to give dimes. Dimes didn't mean anything to us, and Meade decided that he should be charged a dollar. After he had thought it over for a few days, he raised the price to five dollars and finally decided to chase the homosexual away altogether. So he delegated the four biggest kids in the gang to get rid of him. Meade and I didn't go swimming that afternoon. He was a strong disbeliever in violence and taught me never to be around when it took place.

We also terrorized the rich kids who worked as caddies at the golf course in Ottawa Park. Within a short time we all became bored with caddying, so we sold the jobs back to the rich kids and confined ourselves, whenever we came and went through Ottawa Park, to using the holes in the golf course as privies. I realize now that the boys of this gang were strongly affected by their fathers' ideas. They were reflecting the general radicalization of the working class at the end of the First War. Their universal term of contempt and abuse was "bushwa," which we believed was French for bullshit. Meade seemed to operate on the principle that anyone who didn't work hard in a factory for a living was a rascal, and that the children of the middle class were idiots. Curiously enough, the boys in the gang never made any attempt to take away the rich kids' girls; in fact, they had even more contempt for them than they did for the boys. My girl, whom I had brought along with me, was known as Duchess and was just barely tolerated. Meade used to say that she was immoral. He never explained what he meant, but I think he had an infallible nose for what was really a budding fashionable country-club sexuality.

The gang took up a lot of time and consumed a lot of mental energy. So Meade and I, and Duchess, and Meade's girl Red used to relax just like Al Capone, by going fishing. Just like Al Capone we had our own private fishing preserve that no one else ever touched. On the outskirts of the city there was a large cemetery. It was beautifully landscaped around two small lakes. At some time or other these lakes had been stocked with pan fish, perch, blue gills, sunfish, bullheads, carp, yellow catfish, and even a few pike. The place was patrolled during the day, but the nightwatchman was terrified of the dead and never went out of his little house. So we used to go in at night, shine a couple of flashlights on the water, and carry away a gunnysack full of fish. My father and grandmother were greatly pleased with the fish dinners, but though my father begged me to take him with me, I never told him where we went.

One of the finest adventures that my association with this gang involved me in was the Willys-Overland strike. This took place shortly before the Armistice and was one of the most bitterly fought strikes of the time. Who led it, I don't know. Possibly the IWW. It had all the characteristics of a strike under revolutionary leadership—a big rank-and-file strike committee, soup kitchens, a mass picket line, dozens of soapboxers. The kids of the strikers got jobs as runners. This was a necessity because the plant covered a good many acres and the mass picket lines were concentrated at several gates, considerable distances apart. We went on our bicycles carrying messages from one picket captain to another, general orders from the strike committee, bundles of bulletins, and big sacks of sandwiches. The National Guard was called out and set up machine guns inside the plant and sentries with bayonets at the gates. I became quite a hero, but I can't remember exactly what I did. I can remember bicycling furiously past the administration building, convinced that I was going to be blown off my bicycle by a hail of machine-gun bullets, but what it was all about, I do not know. That night I was introduced at the mass meeting and everybody cheered and clapped.

A few days later the strike came to its climax in the most spectacular battle I was ever to see in my years in the labor movement. Tear gas had just come in and I believe the Army loaned a supply of canisters to the city police. The mayor ordered the mass picketing stopped, and the strikers, of course, ignored the order.

The next day the street in front of the main gate was a solid mass of cops, stretched for more than a block past the next factory, the De Vilbis Atomizer plant. First were a couple of platoons of mounted police, armed with long sticks like the lathis that the British used on the Indians. Behind them were foot police and amongst them a detail of tear-gas hurlers. The mounted police rode very slowly toward the gate, pushing the strikers back a foot at a time with the breasts of their horses, but not using their sticks. The strike committee was prepared for them. They had gone up to the carbarns across the street and taken the junked poles—whole pine trees rotted out at the base and presumably stacked up with the rest of the junk to be sold as firewood. Each pole was manned by about eight heavyweight Slav and Hungarian strikers, and they were planted behind the picket line, just in front of the bridge across Ten-Mile Creek, invisible to the cops, who were a couple of blocks higher up the street.

Now, as the street (Cherry Street, I believe it was) went down the hills to the bridge it passed between cut banks about thirty feet high, so there was a narrow canyon rising straight out of the sidewalks. When the strikers had been pushed away from the main gates, a mounted police officer fired a shot in the air and shouted a proclamation ordering them to disperse. Instead, the picket line surged back against the horses and the mounted police charged, swinging their lathis. The picket line ran back toward the bridge and the cops were drawn down into the canyon, between the masses of strikers on the sidewalks. The picket line opened up and the boys with the poles came through. When this happened the tear-gas detail hurled the canisters over the heads of the mounted police into the front ranks of the strikers. Unfortunately, scientific warfare had not reached the point it was to achieve in World War II. There was a gas detail, but there were no meteorologists in the police force, and a couple of hundred cops had not noticed that the wind was blowing in their faces.

The pandemonium was indescribable. The horses were enveloped in clouds of tear gas, which made them scream with the bloodcurdling scream of horses in a fire and they took off up the steep banks, spilling their riders, as the boys with the poles, with wet handkerchiefs wrapped round their faces, charged.

Considerable time passed before order was restored. The cops were shooting in all directions but lucky for us they didn't shoot one another or anybody else. I think a few strikers got flesh wounds, but they were hauled away to safety and the only serious damage was done to the horses, some of whom broke their legs on the cut bank and had to be shot. When the battle was at its height, out the gate came the U. S. Army on the run with fixed bayonets and the strikers vanished like snowflakes or Sitting Bull's Indians after the Battle of the Little Big Horn. A few strikers who had been thrown into the muck of the creek were fished out and locked up. The press exploded and demanded that everybody in the union be tried for attempted murder, but a few days later the strike was settled.

This was my first strike and, except for the poor horses, that I can still hear screaming, certainly my most enjoyable. When I look back on it one of the most significant things, it seems to me, is that at the age of twelve or thirteen, like all of Engels' "Members of the upper class who cut themselves loose from their own class and go over to the workers," I got on the payroll. I started off in the labor movement as a pie-card artist.

At the time of the strike I was no longer living with my grandmother. During the first year in Toledo it turned out that she had become quite senile and had a secret horrible temper. She used to beat me unmercifully with the cane she always carried. I suppose it was a typical sexual derangement of the aged, but although I was a budding gangster at the age of twelve and some of the girls were a little odd and rough, especially my Duchess, such refinements of pathology were beyond me. My grandmother's attacks were utterly incomprehensible to me. I had a kind of perverse loyalty to my father's love of his mother, so

I never told him anything about it. I did tell my aunt, who flew into a rage as bad as my grandmother's and told me I was a liar. These beatings, of course, took place in secret during the day, and on my part in grim silence.

Fortunately for me, one day my grandmother left the window open and the shade up and the next-door neighbor saw the whole procedure. This woman, a broad-shouldered, broad-behinded, red-faced Irish Catholic woman, one of those inconspicuous saints, the rocks on which the Church is reared, suddenly burst into the bedroom and got in a boxing and wrestling match with my grandmother. The police and social-service agencies were notified and my father was told he would have to take me out of there or I would be put in a home or sent to my mother's family in Chicago.

I believe that my father was terribly shocked by all this. He insisted that my grandmother had never punished him corporally in all his childhood and he had run away from home because my grandfather had beaten him. Until his death he never went back to visit his mother, although she lived just two blocks away. Looking back and putting the time sequence together, I suppose that my brief spasms of delinquency, as they are called nowadays, however much I enjoyed them, were the direct result of my grandmother's treatment. I must say that even at the time I bore her no malice. These beatings were so irrational and unmotivated that I knew she was crazy and couldn't help it, but as for myself, since my aunt refused to believe me, I saw no way out. It was a pretty frightening situation.

The social workers and my Aunt Minnie, who came from Chicago, set my father and me up in a new establishment. We rented the upper floor of an old Victorian house from a family named Nims. They were wonderful people, straight out of an early Wells novel. There were bicycles in the bathtub and lethal roller skates on the staircase. The rugs were always wrinkled and the dishes were never washed. Mrs. Nims tried to keep house, but she handled a broom exactly like a Pullman porter wielding a whisk broom. At first we were supposed to board, but the cooking was inedible. So we did our own, which meant that in a short time I did it all. The Nims family were full of the highest ideals. In England they would have been Fabian Socialists, or disciples of William Morris, and they would have been immortalized in dozens of novels. Unfortunately, in America most novelists have come from narrow, bigoted, small-town families. They have been so busy revolting against Gopher Prairie that people like the Nimses have been passed by. From the Forties of the last century on, they were probably more common in America then they were in England. The toilets broke down practically every week, but there were fascinating discussions of Nietzsche, Herbert Spencer, free love, and deep breathing. The Nims boys were the only truly progressively raised kids I ever encountered in my childhood. I found them considerably more interesting than even Meade, and I suppose, just like it says in John Dewey, it was they who redeemed me from my delinquency.

My father's draftee drugstore empire had blown up: the principle draftee's wife took up with somebody else and pulled the rug out from under him. For a while he worked as a common laborer in the Libby-Owens Glass factory and at the time of the strike he was working at the Willys-Overland plant and went out. Very possibly these were the only two proletarian jobs he ever had in his life and I don't think he liked them very much. Other boys told me that the workers on the job, even worse class snobs than they are nowadays, resented his intrusion and persecuted him constantly.

While he was out on strike he got a job as the manager of a nearby drugstore. He was always home at noon and we did the cooking and housekeeping together. He was certainly an epicure and from him I learned to be a pretty good cook, so good that a little later in life I was able to get a job at it without any further preparation. I didn't realize it but his life was narrowing down. He became a great devotee of the one-dish meal. I would cook a big pot of *Hasenpfeffer,* German spaghetti (which is hamburger, whole tomatoes, green peppers, chopped celery, and onions all cooked up together) chili con carne, *coq au vin,* curried mutton—you could still buy mutton in those days—or some other inflammatory mixture. At dinner my father would have little appetite, but then he would go to bed with a pot of food beside him and a quart of port wine and a stack of pulp magazines and read, eat, and drink himself into oblivion. At one time he had been a serious and alert reader, always up on the latest things in science, politics, or philosophy. Now he read only *Argosy, Cavalier, Allstory,* and *Blue Book.* Slowly, the quart of Harvey's port changed to two quarts.

A girl showed up. She helped me cook and take care of the house and in the course of time it began to be necessary for her to take care of my father. I remember her with the greatest affection. She went on hikes with me in the country and the three of us took a long excursion to Put-in-Bay and came back in a terrific storm. She stayed several nights with my father and he talked vaguely about getting married, which in spite of my mother's Grimm brothers' theories about stepmothers and orphans struck me as just dandy.

I got flu and scarlet fever together in the second and more deadly year of the great flu epidemic. The onset of both diseases, the fever, hit me in the form of a vision. I was lying on the couch in the early evening with the sunset coming through a beveled plate glass somewhere and making a brilliant spectrum on the wall. I lay and watched a long time and then called my father. "Look, Charlie," I said. "The whole room is filled with silver lines like thousands of spider webs of light. They all come together over there where there is a spot so bright you can't stand to look at it. That is the other me on the other side of the universe." I can still remember the look of terror on my father's face. I guess it was altogether too much like my mother's solar system in the tree. He took my temperature, which was about as high as it could be, and called a doctor. I was in a coma for several days and then a long time recuperating. This was the last appearance of my father's girl, who nursed me through this sickness and disappeared before I was quite out of bed.

Like everybody who had the flu in those days, I was pretty run-down and pekid. One day my father called a doctor to give me a general checkup. He went over me thoroughly and said that I was recovering better than he expected but that we had to realize that such things took time. I remember so clearly: he was a little fellow and cocked his eye and looked up quizzically at my father and said, "Charlie, do you mind if I give you a going over?" When he got through he called a taxi and took my father to the hospital. Three mornings later my Aunt Grace woke me up where I was sleeping alone in our little apartment and asked, "Do you know your father is dead?"

He had a pretty fearful death, the result of years of dissipation and self-abuse and in those few days it seemed to me he coughed up most of his lungs and stomach. He died in a Catholic hospital. At the end of his ward was a chapel where the Sisters said their offices every couple of hours. Just before he died he was received into the Roman Catholic Church. When I visited him the last night, he gave me a little self-conscious and half-conscious speech about the evils of overindulgence in food, alcohol, games of chance, and commercial sex. One of the last things he said was the old gag that he was dying of fast women, slow horses, crooked cards, and straight whiskey. I have never been a heavy drinker and I have never had the slightest interest in any form of gambling. Sex and food I have managed to cope with.

CHAPTER 11

After my father's death I had to grow up or at least give a convincing imitation of it. What do I seem like at this time of my life, now, to myself? Fortunately I was quite tall and, although my face was youthful enough, I was able to pass for older. Also I had spent an unusual amount of time with much older people. My character was, it seems to me, to undergo little change from my thirteenth or fourteenth year to the present day. All my characteristic tastes and activities had already developed. I spent as much time as I could outdoors, in as wild country as I could find. I loved skiing, swimming, hiking, and riding—bicycles or horses. I was completely uninterested in competitive or spectator sports. I have been to five baseball games and three football games in all my life. I already looked on myself as a writer and artist. I had no intention of ever becoming anything else, but, again, there was abiding temptation—looking back like Lot's wife to the sciences and especially to medicine. I still wish I had become a doctor as well as an artist and writer, and I seem to get along better with doctors than with any other kind of people.

Extended families like the Rexroths and Reeds had hundreds of remote kin, collaterals, and ancient family friends who were known as aunts and uncles, scattered all over Ohio, Michigan, and Indiana. From early childhood I used to be sent off alone on visits, turned over to the conductor, who was often a friend of the family, and to amuse me rather than for any practical purpose a baggage tag was strung through my lapel: "PLEASE LET KENNETH OFF AT WHITE PIGEON. HE IS GOING TO VISIT HIS AUNT VONEY." I spent a great deal of time in the company of the very aged, some of them old enough to have been first settlers on the outer fringes of the old Northwest. They loved nothing better than to tell a little boy stories of ghosts, sea serpents, or monstrous births, and bucolic jokes, to teach him songs from the medieval Scotch border, the Black Forest, and nineteenth-century American music halls, while stuffing him with chicken and homemade ice cream.

My grandmother had a fascinating old crony named Mrs. Kelly, an

Irish widow much older than she. This lady's life was operated entirely and exclusively by superstition. She always put her shoes left on left and right on right, side by side at the foot of the bed. If she put on a garment wrong side out, she left it that way for the rest of the day and sprinkled a little salt on it. Everything had a significance: not just dropped forks and tea leaves, but birds in the air and the behavior of dogs in the street. She was always sure of herself in the present and in the future. Life was saturated with her doctrine of signatures. She was provided with more explanations than a Roman augur. She was, in fact, a haruspice and always inspected the fresh liver and gizzard of the chicken before she started Sunday dinner. The best things about Mrs. Kelly were her neighbors who lived upstairs. Either they were very noisy or the floor was very thin. The husband stomped up the stairs at night and planked himself down in a spring rocker, smoked his pipe, knocked his ashes out on the arm of the chair while his wife cooked supper, trotting about the kitchen in her high heels. You could hear her beat eggs and put bread in the oven. At night you could hear them undress and drop their shoes beside the bed, and then, later in the night, they'd make the bedsprings squeak. They led a rich, active life. The only trouble was, there wasn't any upstairs to the house. It had been a two-story flat, but the upper floor had been destroyed in a fire and the shell had been remodeled into a cottage. The young couple who lived upstairs, some thirty years before, had been burned to death in their sleep. Mrs. Kelly not only had ghostly neighbors; she had brought over from Ireland most of the Fenian cycle. She had an inexhaustible repertory of fables, legends, and broad humorous tales. She was only one of dozens of such old people whom I knew as a child.

Then there was the lucky, probably quite accidental richness of contact with Indians and my own rather remote Indian ancestry. It was a little as though an Athenian boy in the days of Plato had had a chance to play with real, if somewhat run-down nymphs and satyrs and heroes. So many Americans have complained of their lack of contact with the soil. I have never felt that way, but rather like a little French boy of the Dordogne who numbered among his acquaintances several Cro-Magnon artists.

Again, for so many Americans, even of very old families, the revolutionary tradition was lost in the post-Civil War period—the age of the robber barons. This was very far from being the case with me. It was not just that I was aware of a living physical continuity going back to Thomas Paine; I wasn't aware of anything else. Here, again, I was the fortunate victim of a long string of coincidences. All my life, in fact, radicals of the old American type have turned up for me in the most unlikely places. Either I attract them, like female moths attract males or pederasts attract each other, or there are a lot more of them around than you would judge from the records of mass culture.

For instance, during my father's draftee financial operations he acquired a mortgage, which was unpaid and foreclosable, on a farm near Milan, Michigan, which is now, I suppose, in the suburbs of Detroit. It belonged to three wonderful old women—two old maids in their late sixties and their massive, granite mother, who was ninety-two and who, mother or no, had all the characteristics of an intransigent nineteenth-century old maid. They ran the farm like a small state agricultural station and grew everything from mountain rice to loofah squashes. For all I know, they were the first people in Michigan to grow soy beans. They had bees and goats and sheep and cows and a tame raccoon and fishponds in the creek and a dovecote and two old donkeys and three old horses and a blind, ancient, tame Cooper's hawk, so old that he could no longer fly, that dated back to the days when they read William Morris and took up falconry. They had been, mother and daughters, among the first suffragettes and they were extreme left-wing Socialists, who didn't believe in voting or in the Socialist Party. Looking back on the things they told me, I imagine they had been members of Daniel De Leon's Socialist Labor Party, but they also seem to me to have been very much survivals of the wild revolutionary movements of backwoods America of the 1840s. This is not so outlandish as it sounds today. The mother, ninety-two in 1918, had been born in 1826.

I spent the better part of two summers on this farm, purportedly working for my board. I learned to milk, take care of stock and ride, and even make a stab at cold-shoeing horses, very old horses anyway. The old ladies gave me all sorts of books to read, quaint and rather embarrassing "children's books" out of bygone radical movements, British Labor Party propaganda pamphlets, Upton Sinclair's *The Jungle,* the scientific romances of H. G. Wells, which I had already read, and a book which, more than any other, has influenced my life—Wells's *The Research Magnificent.* There were speeches by Debs, tracts by Charles Kingsley, Read's *Martyrdom of Man,* Ward's *Ancient Lowly,* and various classics from the Charles Kerr Socialist Library. The first year I left, the ladies gave me as a present for my very own a book I have never been without since: Upton Sinclair's anthology of the literature of social protest from the Egyptians to Max Eastman, *The Cry for Justice.*

On the next farm lived a family descended from pre-Civil War Negro freedmen. They had several children near my own age with whom I spent the happiest hours of those Toledo years. There was a picture of Harriet Tubman on the parlor wall and works by Frederick

Douglass and John Langston on the shelves, along with the first poets of the Negro renaissance and W. E. B. Du Bois's *The Souls of Black Folk*, and a thrilling book, *The Ethiopian Cicero*: a collection of speeches of Negro Senators, Congressmen, legislators, and governors from Reconstruction days, ending with their final speeches—"Some day we'll return." Here, however, I was not indoctrinated. I can't remember the father's name, but it was some purely Jewish name like Levy or Cohen and the original ancestor in the North was a manumitted slave of one of the old Charleston Jewish families for whom he had worked as a clerk and bookkeeper. He had been hustled out of the South by his employer during one of the worst pre-Civil War Negro riots when the community in which he lived had revoked the free status of all Negroes. The father was an agricultural official and teacher in Ypsilanti, the county town. I asked various polite questions and was answered simply and informatively, but most of my information about the family came from the old sisters and their mother, who had been friends of the second generation of the Negro family and had come to that farm because of them. The children were the happiest and best raised—"most secure," as we say nowadays—youngsters I have ever encountered. No one could be further from Uncle Toms, but the whole family was perfectly adjusted to a good world that they knew they had made themselves. There was none of the sex obsession of the rich kids in Toledo. I would hate to give the impression that I looked on them as "natives," but I look back on those days spent playing and working with them in the orchards and pastures—and swimming with them, boys and girls together in the fishpond, the baby fish nibbling at our toes—much as romantic painters and writers from Melville to the present have remembered their days in Tahiti.

My father did not foreclose the mortgage, and shortly before his death he gave it to the old ladies before somebody got it out of his hands. For all I know, he may have won it gambling, because it seems to me to have been quite beyond our means. It was agreed that I would go there every summer until I was grown, but after my father died I never went back, and some years later one of the Negro boys with whom I continued to correspond wrote me that the three old ladies were killed with their old horse and buggy at a railroad crossing.

The second summer there appeared at their farm another summer visitor, who was to introduce a new and from then on recurrent theme into my life. The first day he asked what I thought of the Catholic Church and what my religion was. I told him that I was an atheist and gave him the standard Socialist line on the evils of Rome, just as I had been taught. "Ah," said he, "you're talking about Roman Catholics, but there are other Catholics called Anglo-Catholics of which those things are not true." Thus began my introduction to that splendid and slightly crazy sect in which you can believe anything with considerable elegance. So, along with my already out-of-date Socialism and the Abolitionist tradition seen from the point of view of an educated Negro, my head was stuffed full of exciting information about the significance of the colors of medieval chasubles, the Sarum rite, and the proper place to take the ablutions. When I got back to Toledo, one of the first things I did was to attend a Solemn High Mass, sung to Tudor music, in a dense cloud of incense.

Before I leave Toledo I would like to say something more about my discovery of H. G. Wells. I remember with great vividness taking home from the branch public library *The Time Machine* and *The War of the Worlds*, which had been recommended to me by Meade. I read all the scientific romances in rapid succession. Not only was I captivated by the subject matter, but I had at last encountered somebody with whom I agreed completely. Science fiction was not common reading for little boys in those days and there wasn't much of it. When I had exhausted the scientific romances, the librarian gave me other books in the same genre. Jules Verne I found deadly boring. The vulgar writers like Edgar Rice Burroughs and Roy Cummings I was already familiar with from pulp magazines. They struck me as entertaining enough, but very much in the class of something to read while drinking yourself into oblivion. So I went on to read Wells's novels and read all of them to *Mr. Britling Sees It Through*, which of course marks the end of Wells. I don't know that these books formed my mind, but they certainly crystallized attitudes that were to endure for the rest of my life. Because Wells cohabited openly with young women who were his social equals, he was boycotted by British literary society and a sort of Reform Club myth of what he was all about was invented to put him down. None of his novels is about the things the critics say they are about: progress, human betterment, social optimism. *Tono-Bungay* is no more about the evils of patent medicine than Henry James's *Golden Bowl* is about a piece of bric-a-brac. Wells was the major influence on D. H. Lawrence, but since he had become unfashionable, D. H. Lawrence kept this quiet. All of Wells's novels are concerned with the social responsibility of the artist, the enlightened man, the determinative man. All of them are concerned with the quest for and the usually tragic failure to find what Christians call sacramental marriage. Wells is not to be found in Herbert Spencer or Ramsay MacDonald. He is to be found in Plato's *Republic* and in an etherealized heterosexual interpretation of the *Symposium*. Or perhaps it is more accurate to think of him as a kind of secularization of the two basic principles of Judaism: the "genius," as prophet, *nabi*, or *vates*, and the source and the final end of creative action in marriage. Two generations have been so busy abusing Wells that nobody has noticed that, but at the age of twelve I noticed it.

When I had finished with Wells, librarians started lending me writers like Bennett, Shaw, Martin Andersen Nexo, and other writers of the Naturalist and Socialist traditions of the 1890s and 1900s. In the library of the old ladies' farm, along with books by Frederick Douglass and the Abolitionists, were Havelock Ellis, Ellen Key, Edward Carpenter's *Love's Coming of Age*, and Robey's *Art of Love*. I can't really think my way back into the mind of a small boy encountering this stuff, but it seemed to have put an effective end to whatever juvenile tendency I might have developed from my association with the peculiar children of Toledo, and embarked me on a career of tireless sexual idealism.

Since I was so precocious, I did not get a great deal out of my friendship with any other boys except Meade. With boys my own age, however close friends, I tended to be given so dominant a role that there was nothing very fruitful in it for me. I suppose it is an illusion, but this did not seem to be the case with a couple of little girls. This has remained the pattern of my life. Very few masculine friendships have ever seemed male enough to me, have ever offered adequate resistance. One thing that I did learn from running with quite antagonistic sets of kids was the manners and lingo of maximum social negotiability. As soon as my father was dead I had to learn fast how to get along with almost anybody. Probably the most remarkable thing about the whole Toledo episode was the way in which, once the pressure of my dying mother's hope was withdrawn, I effervesced all over the place. I acquired hundreds of new interests, not the least of which was an intense interest in other people. I became socialized and liked it very much.

After my father's death I stayed for a week or so with his sister. I had a fine time with my cousin Marcella, but my uncle, Charles Carsten, rifled my luggage and took out my manuscript book of poems and several watercolor pads of painting. He called me into his den and I was horrified to see them on his desk. He gave me a long lecture about how bad and foolish I was and about how, now that I was an orphan, it was essential for me to forget all this nonsense, acquire the business virtues, and start working up from the bottom. This was my first encounter with the type of personality who is, alas, to judge from their novels anyway, the father of most modern intellectuals. It wasn't just the evil and the hypocrisy, although I recognized everything he was saying as completely false. There was a kind of obscene undertone, as though he was seducing me sexually. I was reminded of nothing so much as the man with a pocketful of dimes who used to hang around the swimming hole. Fortunately, I had met him in the novels of H. G. Wells. Still, the experience made me physically sick. I recognized only too well the enemy with whom I would have to deal, off and on, for the rest of my life. I resolved to avoid him wherever possible, at any expense. It's remarkable how easy it has been to do, but at thirteen, when I was sitting in his den, the future looked pretty grim. Meanwhile, just as in H. G. Wells, he was busy pilfering my inheritance.

At this time I went to Sunday school with my girl cousins. This experience was at one with my uncle's lectures. I sat among children whom I had known on both sides of town, absolutely appalled at the total irrelevance of the "progressively" told Bible stories—it was a liberal Protestant church—and the sly obscenity of the Sunday-school teacher. I had already read the Bible, which I found a shocking book, and had been briefed on its anthropology and archeology by my mother. I didn't need any briefing on its morals. I remember so well asking her why Jehovah didn't put "Thou shalt not lie" in the Ten Commandments. She said, "Why do you think? Think hard." After I had thought hard for a while I said very timidly, "Is it because He was always telling lies Himself?" She gave me a dollar spending money. My Uncle Charles's nickels for Sunday school I spent for ice cream.

The experience of my uncle's family, coupled with the propaganda of the young Anglo-Catholic I had met at the farm, gave me the typical American intellectual's dislike of Protestantism and mild admiration for Catholicism, which, I suppose, I would have come by anyway. For years, though, I always thought the horrendous pictures of life in the typical Midwestern Protestant family that you read in books were overdrawn and were the result of embittered childhoods or were deliberate atheistic or Catholic misrepresentations. During the Second World War, working with various pacifist groups, I came in considerable contact with the liberal Protestant clergy and their more devout laymen, laywomen, and what they call "young people." I must say that I felt like I was right back, if not in my uncle's den, at least in his Sunday school.

This ordeal was of short duration. My Aunt Minnie came from Chicago to get me. There was a frightful row. My father's brother, my Uncle Will, had come up from Columbus to the funeral and had stolen most of my father's most valuable portable property, including his watch and jewelry and toilet articles, and the Carstens had taken all the stuff we had in our little flat, which by the time my father died had become completely furnished by us. Even some of my own clothing was missing and my father's bank account had vanished and the funeral bills and other expenses had been loaded and charged against his insurance. As a matter of fact, the funeral cost nothing. He was buried by the city as a pauper in the potter's field, where he is today. My Aunt Minnie was an expert hell-raiser. She tore up the house and found a considerable amount of property. She called up the district attorney on my Aunt Grace's phone and reduced her to hysterics and recovered the whole burial policy.

So I went off to Chicago. On the train I read that fantastically sentimental perversion of history, *John Inglesant*, loaned me by my Anglo-Catholic friend, and Carl Sandburg's *Cornhuskers*, which had just come out. We took a Pullman late at night in Toledo and came through Gary early in a winter morning. It must have been mid-December, because I know my father survived the Armistice by only a few days. I woke up and looked out of the train window. The train had stopped and was backing onto a siding. The great steel furnaces were blowing off long purple and red flames into the sky. The train was not to move for several hours. There had been a wreck of the passenger train just before us. Crumpled and burning cars were flung like dominoes, wrecking cars with great cranes were moving back and forth, and laid out along the snowy bank beside the right-of-way were a dozen or more charred, black, and bleeding corpses. I suppose this is the dramatic place to say I had come to the end of my childhood.

CHAPTER 12

I was made welcome at my aunt's home in Chicago. It was different
from the Toledo family, where I had felt not only unwanted but actively disliked, as though I was a member of an outlandish, inferior
race. My father's sister's family were typical middle-class people, superficially like my own. My mother's sister's family were pure proletarian
Irish, but this did not prevent them from making me feel wanted and
actively loved. There was some insurance money and a little later my
father's mother died and, ironically, left me enough for a small income
throughout my adolescence. Also, my mother's mother had sold out all
her property in Elkhart and was living with the Monahans and she contributed something to my support. Nevertheless the burden on my
Uncle Paul must have been considerable, but nobody ever reminded
me that I was an orphan and owed them gratitude, as the Carstens
had never ceased doing in the few weeks I had stayed with them.

I was familiar enough with my aunt's way of life through long visits.
Before, however, my mother had imposed her own pattern of living.
Now I was completely a part of their world, and it was a strange one
to me. They were passionate baseball fans. They went to Mass and
confession. The children went to Corpus Christi School. The pattern of
life was exactly that of young Studs Lonigan, so much so in fact that I
find it very difficult to believe that my cousin Jim was not a model for
James Farrell's hero. After I had left Chicago he got drunk one night
at the Golden Lily one New Year's Eve and passed out in the sub-
zero street. He almost died of pneumonia, suffered from "weak lungs"
for a few years, went swimming, almost drowned, got another attack
of pneumonia, and died. Farrell says Lonigan, to whom exactly the
same things happened, is somebody else. I don't doubt it was a common end for young Irish kids on the South Side. At least I do know
that I was the Kenny who helps them steal the bananas and works for
Vause's Drug Store in the opening pages of the book. As is well known,
probably to avoid suit, Farrell moved Studs Lonigan three blocks south
in space, from Fifty-fifth to Fifty-eighth Street and three or four years

back in time. This whole world has been so exhaustively documented by Farrell's fiction that I feel like an intruder with my own real biography.

Like the milieu of Céline's childhood, the neighborhood of Fifty-fifth and the El wasn't all that bad. The Monahans had a fine Irish social life. Saturday night poker and rummy parties, wakes and weddings and First Communions, baseball games and picnics. I didn't feel in the least like James Joyce about it. I enjoyed it. The peculiar toughness, singularly empty of content, which characterized the Irish Catholic boys of the neighborhood and which is so well portrayed by Farrell was another matter. With this I could not come to terms, for the simple reason that there didn't seem to be anything to come to terms with. The gang Meade and I had in Toledo had been constantly active, our lives had been full of events. We entertained ourselves thinking up all sorts of ingenious capers. These Chicago kids didn't seem to do much of anything except what nowadays they would call goof off. My uncle was the manager of the champion boys' baseball team in nearby Washington Park, on which Farrell played, I believe, but my cousins didn't play on it, nor did any of their friends. They were just too inert. They were too busy hanging around street corners smoking cigarettes and spitting. For this reason my friends were Jewish (the neighborhood was about fifty-fifty Jewish and Irish Catholic). So I suppose Jim Farrell and I missed a great juvenile literary friendship, although the Jewish boy who married Studs's sister was my closest friend for a while. The girl he calls Helen Shires was another extremely close friend. Some years later I stopped in a gas station up in the Forties on Michigan Boulevard, and the attendant, a most impressive Irish youth, reluctantly put down a volume of Proust, which was just then coming out, and filled the tank. For a long time afterward I thought of him and wished I had spoken to him and wondered who he was. When I read about Danny O'Neill's career in that same gas station I realized that it had been Farrell. I am talking about this at such length not to show off my early contact with the great, but for exactly the opposite reason. I think it extremely significant that we two boys could grow up within a few hundred feet of each other, both, I suppose, lonely and amazed in a world we never made, needing friends of our own kind and never meeting until we were middle-aged men.

My uncle had long since quit the stockyards. For several years he had been a letter carrier in an office building where the Wrigley Gum headquarters were located—before the Wrigley Building was built. Wrigley had taken an interest in him because of his baseball team, which Wrigley endowed with equipment and uniforms, and eventually he loaned my uncle enough money to start a package-delivery service. It is a tribute to my uncle's lack of business sense and the ethics of success or, perhaps, to his refusal to cooperate with the gangsters who run such things in Chicago that he never made any money and after several years of managing the business and driving a truck himself, went broke. This was one of the first, if not the first, businesses of its kind in America. Everybody else who went into package delivering became fabulously rich. My uncle died a nightwatchman.

In those days the business was earning a comfortable amount of money and we lived in a nine-room apartment on Michigan Boulevard, just above Fifty-fifth. It was quite a good neighborhood, very far from the slum that critics of Farrell's books call it. Today it is entirely a Negro neighborhood and one of the better ones in America. For example, we paid $125 a month rent, a stupendous sum in those days. Maybe I have a false and euphoric memory but it seems to me to have been a most pleasant place to live. Michigan Boulevard was not so crowded with cars and Fifty-fifth Street was a boulevard with a parkway down the middle, which ended just a few blocks away in Washington Park. Across the park was the University and the Midway, and about half a mile out on the Midway, Jackson Park and the beaches. This was a good many miles of open space and I spent as much time in it as I could, bicycling or afoot.

I went back to the Art Institute, where my mother had started me as a little child, and I went somewhere else, possibly to Bush Conservatory, and took some elementary classes in piano, harmony, counterpoint, and musical theory—for children, of course. I never learned to play the piano, but I did learn to read and understand music. Wherever this was, there was a local modern composer, who gave a course in the appreciation of modern music. So I heard a lot of Schoenberg, Debussy, Satie, Stravinsky, Bartók, and even the new Les Six. Some of the stuff was not to be recorded for many years, but he rattled it all off on the piano, lecturing as he played. There was a lot of other stuff, better forgotten—Scriabin, Reger, Richard Strauss—but I did hear the great music of cette belle époque when it was brand-new. This man may have been Leo Sowerby, because I believe he was an organist in a church and no other Chicago modernist composer in those days was. He knew a great deal about early English music and the revival led by Vaughan Williams and Peter Warlock. This was music I had never even heard of and I immediately took to it. William Byrd, Orlando Gibbons, Purcell, and the great Tudor composers remain my favorite musicians to this day. I don't want to give the impression that this rarefied taste and knowledge smote me all at once in my fourteenth year. I attended these classes, off and on, until I was about eighteen, but I can't for the life of me remember where they were.

I went the last half year to the nearby Edmund Burke Grammar School and then to Englewood High School, but, as usual, I attended school as little as possible. By this time I had become a consummate master in the art of plausible hooky. I did bicycle across the park and go to lectures and concerts at Mandel Hall at the University. I remember hearing Chekovna lecture in French, the winter the Moscow Art Theater played in Chicago. I didn't understand ten words of it but I was absolutely enraptured. I had ridden on the top of a bus on the same seat with her all the way from the Loop and carried on a pidgin-English sight-seeing conversation. I would have been quite willing to ride bus tops with her to the end of the earth. I must have had a special fondness for fascinating Russian women, because I have almost as excited a memory of Madame Kollontai, who was still I guess in her late thirties and still the Great Lover of the Revolution. She certainly looked it and troubled my dreams for months.

One night, at the Fifty-fourth elevated station, I encountered a great pink balloon of a man, completely enveloped in an immense three-layered macintosh. It was Gilbert Keith Chesterton, on his way to a lecture at the University, who had got off at the wrong station. I gave him directions and suggested he get back on the El, but he insisted on walking across the park, in the night, in what had suddenly become a terrific storm. So I went along, like a pilot fish with a spouting whale in tow. I don't remember what we talked about, but it was as violently oratorical as the storm, which was turning on sky-long bolts of lightning and earth-shaking claps of thunder. It was all like one of his books. The lecture was rather tedious, a farrago of paradoxes. Afterward he took me along with a couple of professors to the old Stoney Island Avenue studio colony, where he drank home-brew and continued to spout. He spent the next week in Chicago and made me a sort of mascot. I think his theory must have been that he would make a lifelong disciple out of me in one overwhelming week. I can't really account for an elderly famous man taking up with a precocious child, because I didn't even like him very much. Pound may have compared his cheeks to a cake of soap, but to me he seemed covertly unwholesome. His system of paradox, even then, struck me as a vulgar gimmick. Worse still, he was the first anti-Semite I had ever encountered or even heard of. If my cousin's Irish friends were anti-Semitic, they kept it from me; probably they thought that I—Rexroth—was Jewish. He was considerably more anti-Semitic in conversation than in writing, and this itself struck me as dishonest. Still, he had a lot of violently opinionated information on all sorts of things I was interested in and knew little about. In those days I think he had yet to swim the Tiber and was still an Anglo-Catholic. He did get me to read—in fact, he gave me a copy—a book which made an indelible impression on me, Hilaire Belloc's *The Servile State*. He was full of all kinds of gossip, especially the most fascinating gossip about my idol, Wells, whose sex life, I was greatly pleased to discover, differed little from my own in the woods by Ten-Mile Creek. What impressed me most of all was the discovery that Chesterton's famous controversies with Wells and Shaw were really just an act. I suppose he was sincere enough about the issues. He certainly made a profession of ostentatious sincerity, but I was surprised to discover a camaraderie and even loyalty and dependence, like that of Mutt and Jeff or the Marx Brothers. It was my initiation into the secret that ideas are a business. The nicest thing about Chesterton was the gusto with which he related Wells's public flaunting of British sexual hypocrisy and the envious hilarity with which he described Wells's capers with overintellectualized adolescent girls.

In those days the Field Museum was still out in Jackson Park in a crumbling plaster reproduction of all the buildings on the Acropolis at once, set in the midst of a chain of weed-choked lagoons. I used to bicycle over there and spend whole days wandering through the collections and eavesdropping on the lectures. A little later the place was deserted, the skylights were shattered, and the columns and the frieze of horsemen and the maidens of the Erectheum began to topple over into the lake. I used to wander there in the evening, my head full of the sadness of empires. Somebody had told me about Spengler and I felt just like Gibbon listening to the friars singing their superstitious chants amid the shattered glories of Rome, or De Volney meditating on Palmyra in the desert.

More than any of the official education and cultural institutions my favorite school was the Washington Park Bug Club. This was a spontaneously evolved public forum which met every night except in the dead of winter in a shallow grassy amphitheater beside a lagoon off in the middle of the park. Years later it was to be moved to another part of the park and equipped with a concrete floor, benches, a podium, and an all-powerful Party faction. In those days it looked like something in ancient Greece, very sylvan and peripatetic, and I suppose, if the truth be known, it really was like ancient Greece, of which possibly the cynical Jewish doctor St. Luke was a better judge than Plato or Pater. Here, every night until midnight could be heard passionate exponents of every variety of human lunacy. There were Anarchist-Single-Taxers, British-Israelites, self-anointed archbishops of the American Catholic Church, Druids, Anthroposophists, mad geologists who had proven the world was flat or that the surface of the earth was the inside of a hollow sphere, and people who were in communication with the inhabitants of Mars, Atlantis, and Tibet, severally and some-

times simultaneously. Besides, struggling for a hearing was the whole
body of orthodox heterodoxy—Socialists, communists (still with a small
"c"), IWWs, De Leonites, Anarchists, Single Taxers (separately, not in
contradictory combination), Catholic Guild Socialists, Schopenhau-
erians, Nietzscheans—of whom there were quite a few—Stirnerites, and
what later were to be called Fascists. There were even leftover apostles
of Free Silver and unemployed organizers of the Knights of Labor. It
was better than Hyde Park. In fact, the only place I have ever seen
anything as good is Glasgow.

At the Bug Club I met a man who I suppose was then a small determinative influence in my life. His name was Walter Freeman Cooling. He had once been a police magistrate and was always referred
to as Judge. He was about sixty-five years old, moderately and rather
loosely plump, with fine white hair which always needed trimming,
and one of those rare but specially Welsh, infinitely wise moonfaces
that you see in Wales on men just like the Judge—profoundly learned,
unbelievably intelligent, and totally wrongheaded. A. E. Waite and
Arthur Machen looked something like the Judge, and with proper
make-up he could have been played by Orson Welles or Peter Lorre.
He had created singlehanded an all-encompassing system of dissent.
With the intelligence of an Aristotle or an Aquinas, he disagreed all
along the line with all organized thought.

He had elaborated a system of total eccentricity which encompassed
practically every department of thought known to man from ontology
to mechanics to cookery. Philosophically he called himself an Aris-
totelian, but his interpretation of Aristotle was as odd as a cabalist's
interpretation of Genesis. The core of his system was a fantastic cosmology. This involved his own special physics, astronomy, and geology
and led to a religion which was outlandish beyond belief. Even in economics he had worked out a doctrine which he called a development
of Henry George's Single Tax and which was, if I remember rightly, a
kind of combination of Social Credit and Mutualism, Single Tax and
the systematic inflationary theory which was just then being evolved
by J. M. Keynes. He wasn't just a crackpot who thought these things
up out of thin air. For most of his life he had been writing a great book
of many volumes—a complete exposition of his system, organized with
the rigor of the *Summa Theologica*. He kept this in about a hundred
old-fashioned letter cases and several steel files. They were chock-full
of photographs, diagrams, mathematical equations, thousands of quotations in all the civilized languages past and present, most of which
he read fluently. It was wonderful to hear him in the twilight, under
the trees in the park, get up and attack a Catholic or a Socialist or a
Darwinian. He would rattle off a series of hair-raisingly incongruous

ideas, all tied together in a sorites of irrefutable syllogisms and end with a long quotation from Homer, the *Rig-Veda,* or the *Zend-Avesta* in the original language and in the sonorous tones of a Welsh revivalist or labor leader. I might mention that he had special dissident theories on the correct pronunciation of Greek, Sanskrit, and ancient Persian, and I must admit that he always sounded better than the professors at the University. One night, to make a point, he quoted a long passage that sounded vaguely like *Hiawatha* in Japanese. "What is that, Judge?" I asked. "Why," he said, "I am surprised you didn't recognize it. That's the *Kalevala,* the great Finnish epic." I have known a lot of polymaths in my life, but I don't believe even Carl Jung, who was always talking about the *Kalevala,* ever bothered to learn Finnish to read it. It occurs to me now that he was a natural for Jung. He had read everything on alchemy in all the scholarly libraries in Chicago and in this instance, curiously enough, he had hit on the correct interpretation —that it is a kind of elaborate physical code, based on magical psychophysical parallelism, for what we would call sexual Yoga. Not only could he quote the Talmud or the *Pirke Aboth,* but he knew most of the *Zohar* by heart and great chunks of Rabbi Nachman, Luria, or Avicebron. He could not only quote anything from Aquinas, but most everything else in Migne's *Patrologia Latinae* and *Graecae.* He introduced me to Duns Scotus, who, once I had acquired the Latin, fascinated me for years, and also to the incomparably beautiful poems of Abelard. After he got through with his evening dispute at the Bug Club, where he was always attended by throngs of fascinated listeners, he and I would sit on a bench by the dark lagoon and he would expound his system to me till midnight.

Now, for the system. He believed that the galactic universe was an immense organism and that the heavenly bodies were its cellular parts. The solar system was a kind of ovary of which the earth was the just fertilized ovum. The comets were rejected spermatozoa. At the beginning of historical time the earth had been enclosed in an ectoplasm, a living film which completely covered it above the atmosphere and reflected the sun's light more or less evenly over the entire surface of the earth. Hence, the subtropical coal measures found near the poles. This ectoplasm descended as a kind of funnel through the North Pole and into the fecund nucleus within the earth. Out of it came all life, thus accounting for the puzzling arctic radiation of species past and present. Within this funnel was an island, the Garden of Paradise, a trial hothouse for all new species. Through the living film of this funnel they passed out over the earth. "This," said the Judge, "accounts for the peculiar grain of the hair on the head and arms of the human species, which so interested Darwin. Adam and Eve used to put their arms over their heads as they came and went through the film." He believed that all species past and present had flourished as contemporaries prior to what has come down in legend as the Deluge. The reason for this sudden proliferation of life on the earth was due to its fertilization by a comet. Within the earth in what has survived in myths as the Heavenly City, were Christ and the Twelve Apostles, the polar centrosome and the twelve chromosomes, who could assume the forms of living men. Below the Heavenly City, arranged in its sewers in layers, each damned soul feeding on the feces of the other, were the rejects of creation who had been tried and who had failed on the earth. Coiled against the antarctic pole was the Kraken, the great serpent of the Edda, the worm Ourabourous, Satan biding his time until the fulfillment of the process of creation, the antipolar centrosome. This process was in its final stages, marked first by the Deluge when the ectoplasm of the earth had broken and fallen to the surface. Following some mystic law of its own of like seeking like, it had enveloped the various species arranged by paleontology in evolutionary sequence and laid them down in the geological strata we know all in a period of forty days and forty nights. This detail, I might say, was the only thing in the Judge's system which he could not prevent from being hopelessly implausible. After the Flood, there occurred a diffusion of culture over the earth from what the Judge called the Aryan Commune of Mesopotamia, where the survivors of the Ark, a whole city of men and animals, had settled after the Flood. The Ark had indeed landed on Ararat, but it was an electrically controlled airship larger than the largest ocean liner, powered by atomic energy. Obviously the cultural diffusion which took place was comparable to the survival of culture passed on to savages by men who had landed in a jungle from a strange planet; that is, for thousands of years before the appearance of Cro-Magnon man it had been continually declining and only with the late Paleolithic did it turn to start up the long road toward civilization again. To announce the coming of the end of the earth—Christ had appeared on earth to preach the coming of the Kingdom. Here the Judge quoted in Coptic from the apocryphal gospel of Thomas: "Those who are close to me are close to the fire. Those who are far from me are far from the Kingdom." All this was substantiated with photographs of the spiral nebula of Canes Venatici (obviously a budding amoeboid cell); the cast of a machine-sewn boot welt in the Jurassic of Arizona imprinted by someone fleeing from the Flood; fossilized tree trunks in the Nova Scotia coal measures which go right on up through two or three layers of sandstone and mudstone of widely separated orthodox dates. He must have had a couple of thousand photographs and drawings. He was a master of the late nineteenth-century fashion for comparative mythology. He could bring to bear on every question a battery of quotations from *The Sacred Books of the East* and the observations of travelers, missionaries, and anthropologists which would have made Max Müller and *The Golden Bough* look like Guffey's *First Reader.* The history of the world, past and future, was dated by the constellations, which had been arranged by the wise men of the Aryan Commune of Mesopotamia as a historical clock, timed by the precession of the equinoxes.

This all sounds like Ignatius Donnelly or Eliott Smith, but the Judge's learning and his enormous mass of relevant information so far surpassed theirs that there is really no comparison. The system of Charles Fort, whom the Judge knew (it happens that Fort was a friend of my father, too), was absorbed and explained in the Judge's system, where it was only a minor detail. Like Fort, the Judge had gathered from the newspapers of the world thousands of items of inexplicable meteorological and similar occurrences.

All this was delivered in the speech and written down in the style of an Elizabethan bishop. His prose resembled nothing so much as the sermons of Donne or the writings of Sir Thomas Browne shorn of their flowers of rhetoric, or perhaps a more excited Richard Hooker. There was nothing wrong with the Judge's system, except one thing. Elaborate as it seems, it never violated Occam's razor—entities were never multiplied without necessity. More than conventional thought, it recognized in the universe the rule of the same laws of reason to be found in the human mind. Its mass of evidence was stupefying, but it violated the principle of sufficient reason and, like all other totally organized paranoias, it was impossible for the nonparanoiac to accept. It just didn't seem likely. But it was sure beautiful. The Judge taught me that all knowledge has its unreal system. St. Thomas Aquinas has all the answers but he ignores most of the questions. So, to a lesser degree, does Lyell or Einstein. Back in those days, incidentally, the Judge was one of the few men who understood Einstein and he had worked out a different set of equations which did not take the speed of light as a constant, but assumed that it slowed up as it passed through vast spaces, a theory not unlike Eddington and Whitehead's "light reddens and grows old as it travels through space." Now the Doppler Shift and the exploding universe have always worried me and here I think he well may have been right. He anticipated the modern Cambridge school and believed that hydrogen atoms were continuously appearing out of nowhere (according to him, out of another space-time continuum). Before most orthodox astronomers he believed that the galactic nebulae were separate universes, which extended on forever, an endless herd of animals of light. Speaking of light, he knew all about light metaphysics from the ancient Persians through the Shingon Buddhists, the Gnostics, the Manichaeans and Cathari, the Hasidim, and St. Bonaventura to the German romantic philosophers. One of his favorite thinkers was Jacob Boehme, of whom I had heard from Mennonite distant relatives.

The Judge taught me to sit lightly, not just to human opinions but to philosophy and science, and to appreciate it all as a great work of art —man's construct over and against the ultimately unfathomable universe. As I grew older I introduced him first to Rabbis Hirsch and Gonzales and then, later, to Sam Putnam and Ben Hecht. We persuaded Pascal Covici to publish a large selection from his immense masterwork with an introduction by Sam Putnam. But the Judge got the idea that he was being brought out as a literary curiosity, and refused. Several years went by. I left Chicago and returned for a visit about 1929. I met Putnam and asked him how the Judge was and if he didn't think it might be possible to revive this project. Sam told me that the Judge had died the year before. "Well," said I, "that's a terrible shock. I certainly loved him. But at least his pride will no longer stand in his way. His widow should be able to live on the royalties of the book for a long time. Look at how amateurs like Charles Fort and Ignatius Donnelly sell."

Now the Judge had a wife who was a perfect submissive handmaiden. She went to all his lectures and typed all his manuscripts and kept his immense files in order and went childless and kept his house spotless and fed him good French cooking—he was quite an epicure, with special theories about food—and attended him every night at the Bug Club and lit his pipe, which was always going out, and picked up after him and for all I know bathed his feet every night and dried them with her hair like Mary Magdalene. She was a little gray wisp of a woman, so inconspicuous that many of his close friends never noticed her and were unaware of her existence, although she was always present. Sam said, "You're due for a still nastier shock. Before the sun had set on his dead body, she took everything he had ever written and all his cases and files and burned them up."

From the Judge I learned a great deal about the nature of human thought. From his wife I learned even more about life.

CHAPTER 13

From the beginning in Chicago I worked after school as a pharmacy apprentice, delivery boy, and soda jerk for Vause's Drug Store at Fifty-fifth and the El. During the summer I worked at my father's old wholesale house, Kinsolving & Granisson. My father had a devoted friend whose presence around the family goes back as far as I can remember, but who dropped out during the years we were in Toledo. His name was Mr. Braun and he was what was euphemistically known in those days as a bachelor. This doesn't mean there was anything effeminate about him, quite the opposite. He was one of the ultramasculine Edwardian type, like one of the beloved apostles who gathered about the deathbed of Oscar Wilde. I think he was just a drummer, but he looked for all the world like an art dealer from pre-Hitler Munich. He had reddish-brown hair, worn in a stiff pompadour; an immense red-brown pre-War I mustache; great yellow teeth, which matched the one on his watch chain; and round, devoted, doglike eyes. My mother used to say that all he needed was a keg of brandy tied under his neck. He also had a thin, vast lambent nose, which looked as if it were carved out of a narrow slab of alabaster. He was the family's good fairy. He always showed up when there was any trouble to help straighten things out. He was usually there at Christmas and birthdays and he spent long hours giving my mother sage and calm counsel. It was he who had introduced my father to the man who wrote that first, long-forgotten "vulgarization," in the French sense, of psychoanalysis and he was the only man I ever knew in my childhood who had ever been analyzed himself. He was also the only Jew whom I remember as such from my very early childhood. He used to tell me Jewish fairy stories, which were an odd combination of the anecdotes of the Talmud or the Hasidim and the fairy stories of Oscar Wilde. In fact, I think he wrote a book of them. On my first birthday back in Chicago he sent me a present. It was a little cap for a child much younger than I. I wrote him a letter and thanked him, explaining that he had not noticed how the years were slipping away. He came to call and took me down to

Kinsolving & Granisson and introduced me to the last baggy-eyed Kinsolving and set me up for a job for the summer.

We then went down to visit Mr. Eliel in South Bend for a conference. Mr. Eliel offered to buy me into the business as I grew older and make sure I would become one of the top executives. He pointed out that the other families connected with the business were disintegrating and that the block of stock which belonged to him and his sister was the only stable thing in it. This he promised to leave me in his will or to give me outright when I came of age. This meant that I would almost certainly become principal owner of what had been, before the war, the largest wholesale drug house in the Chicago area, no mean legacy. I said I didn't want to be a merchant prince, but an artist and writer and that my father on his deathbed had implored me not to go into the business. Mr. Braun and Mr. Eliel together persuaded me at least to try at it for a few summers. After all, I had to make a living, and they guaranteed to see me through medical school and, in addition, get me a Ph.D. in organic chemistry. So, come summer, I went to work, first as a messenger boy for a week or so, dodging traffic through the west side of the Loop and carrying pharmaceuticals from Lilly, Parke-Davis, Squibb, and all the rest. I became quite a pet around the various drug houses. Looking back, I often wonder why I never got robbed because I sometimes carried thousands of dollars' worth of narcotics. Then I worked for a while as an order picker under a warehouse boss who had an immense and utterly cynical knowledge of patent medicines and who as I used to bring the stuff up to the shipping tables would give me pithy lectures on the fraudulent contents of the merchandise. Then I went to the "wet room" as a pharmacy apprentice. There I stayed two summers. The wet room was exactly what it says. There liquid drugs were put up in retail lots: tinctures, essences, oils, and ethers. In the "dry room," powders, salts, and such were packaged. We also handled, out of a big walk-in safe in the wet room, all narcotics, barbiturates, and biologicals. This sounds very scientific, but it was quite a wet room. In the first place, it was Prohibition and most of my mornings were spent putting up "Beef, Iron & Wine," a legal alcoholic mess from which, I suspect, came most of the profits of the business. In a little while I didn't only bottle it, I mixed it.

The boss was an aged doctor of medicine and chemistry who had been in the business for over thirty years. He came in in the morning, sat in the sun in an old creaking oak swivel chair with his feet in his roll-top desk, read the Chicago *Tribune*, and fell asleep. The assistant was a chubby, red-eyed, foul-breathed little man who always arrived an hour late with a pronounced tremor. He took a pint graduate and mixed up essence of orange, ether, grain alcohol, a few drops of tincture of cannabis indica, and distilled water and drained it off, stretched out on a long zinc table at the back of the room, and went to sleep. Usually he slept all day.

I took the orders off the spike and filled them and sent them out to the shipping room. This meant not just two gross of four-ounce bottles of sweet spirits of nitre, for which I had first to mix the alcohol and nitrous ether, but in addition prescriptions for customers all over the Middle West who were old and experienced pharmacists and had sent them in for us to fill because they found them too complicated and beyond their knowledge. I used to wake up the Doc and read him the prescription, note his mumbled instructions, and go ahead and fill it.

The place was so run-down that it didn't even have city water, but was still served, like many ancient Chicago office buildings, by its own well, the water of which was nonpotable. One day I discovered we didn't have large cans of nitrous ether and we did have a rush order for sweet spirits of nitre. I phoned around and just at that moment there wasn't any nitrous ether obtainable. I woke up the Doc. He said: "Oh, hell, we've got a lot of 100-c.c. ampoules. I don't know what they're for. We never sold them. Take a large funnel, put a platinum sieve in the bottom of it, put some loose cotton on top of that, and put a larger sieve on top of that. Take a glass rod and break the ampoules and let the ether run down into a five-gallon carboy of alcohol. That'll do it." Then he went back to sleep. Naturally, snapping those ampoules and standing over the funnel, I soon passed out. When I fell down I made quite a clatter. Mack, the assistant, rolled off the table and held me up. "Give him water," yelled the Doc. "There ain't no water," said Mack. The Doc said, "Stick the syphon tube from the distilled water in his mouth." Mack grabbed the nearest syphon tube emanating from a carboy of clear fluid. Thank God it wasn't hydrochloric acid, but it was grain alcohol. I choked back into consciousness and they sent me home in a taxicab, ready for the Keely cure.

Another time, I reached up to get a half-gallon bottle of copaiba balsam and discovered too late that over in that corner of the top shelf a whole bunch of essential oils and balsams had been piled on top of one another. Down onto my head came a pint of oil of anise. Dogs followed me for months. Shortly after, Mr. Eliel died and the firm went out of business.

During the winter, running errands in the early evening for Vause's Drug Store, I had long debates with myself. Should I become a successful wholesale druggist and a gentleman writer and artist, or should I become a real writer and artist? My father's old friend Chatfield Chatfield-Taylor had been held up to me as an example by Mr. Braun and Mr. Eliel. He was all right but I had no desire to be like him when I grew up. I decided against it. This was really no easy choice. There was a lot of money lying there for me to pick up. I was already well provided with a powerful father image, which I could easily inflate into the picture of myself as an overcivilized, high-life millionaire, rolling in the hay with Ida Rubinstein in a permanent suite in the Lafayette Hotel, lined with obscene classics bound in polished levant. It would have been nice, but after great struggles in the frosty night, carrying cod-liver oil and Old Overholt along South Park Avenue, I gave it up.

I decided to be an artist and writer. I did not seek refuge in the arts because I had acne, fell on my face when I tried a broad jump, or was unable to get little girls to go in the bushes. Nor, on the other hand, did I take to abstract art and free verse because my parents were small-town, middle-class puritans who washed my mouth out with American Family Soap when they caught me using four-letter words.

All my young days, it seems to me now, I took myself more seriously as an artist than as a writer. It seems to me that I started off practically in infancy as an abstract artist because the first pictures had made an impression on me, and that I tried to imitate, looked pretty abstract to me even if they weren't.

The Armory Show came to Chicago. It is difficult to convey the furor that it created in my parents' circle of friends. Even the most spectacular scandals of the Ballet Russe never came up to it. We went again and again in company with practically everybody I've mentioned so far—Mr. Braun, Mr. Eliel and his sister, as well as all my mother's fascinating feminist and actress companions.

My father had a friend, Arthur Jerome Eddy, one of the circle of rich fellow travelers of the first Chicago Renaissance. He bought the heart and guts of the collection. Back in those days before the First War the pictures were fantastically cheap, and he paid less for all of them than one second-rate Kandinsky brings today. It seems to me that he didn't long survive the First War. His daughter became a movie actress, Helen Jerome Eddy, and was out of Chicago most of the time. The pictures were in semistorage, and all during my adolescence I used to pay them periodic visits to be shown them by a servant. Shortly after he bought the collection, Eddy published a book, *Cubists and Post-Impressionists*. This was the first book of its size on the subject and almost certainly the first in color. It must have been contemporary with the first books by Apollinaire and Gleizes and Metzinger, which were much lesser productions and were only about Cubism. I still remember the book, fresh off the press, its thick expensive paper, the smell of the ink, the really expert and accurate color reproductions dibbed onto heavy brown stock. Although I have seen them countless times since,

Kandinsky's "Improvisation" with toppling buildings and cannons, Villon's "Young Girl," Duchamp's "Chess Players," and Picabia's "*Sacre du Printemps*" return to my memory as reproductions in Eddy's book rather than as paintings. All through my later childhood and youth the book was one of my most prized possessions and I feel that I could make a reasonable copy of any one of its pictures, sight unseen, today.

Another book that was of tremendous importance to me was an early work by Jay Hambidge, probably *Dynamic Symmetry: the Greek Vase.* It made me a compass and ruler constructivist or suprematist painter when I was still in short pants and completely unaware that there was anybody else like that in the world. Some of the paintings weren't too bad. One, done when I was sixteen, a kind of Moholy-Nagy treatment of the Annunciation, hangs in my daughters' bedroom today. Another book that I took with utmost seriousness for a while was a pamphlet, published by the Chicago Art Institute, called "Futurist Color Schemes." This took the six so-called primaries and secondaries and graded them across the spectrum in terms of hue and value. Each one of these color chords, of which there were twelve basic ones, was supposed to have an emotional significance. For instance, a small, brilliant area of yellow-green balanced by a large dull area of gray-violet with the other colors graded across from one so-called complementary to the other was supposed to represent sorrow. I have often wondered if Marc Chagall ever got hold of this little pamphlet, because for years his color schemes exemplified its theories, and he is the only artist I have ever seen of whom that could be said, except myself. I followed the pamphlet devotedly for a while.

I did not, I assure you, become an artist by reading books of bad theory and looking at reproductions. I spent a great deal of time in the Field Museum and the Chicago Art Institute. I took all the courses I could take, and soon learned to lie about my age to get into the more advanced classes. I also tried to follow conscientiously the advice of every real artist I met. I spent hours in the Field Museum making bad copies of New Guinea masks, which were then exhibited sideways, stacked up in fly-speckled glass cages far off in a very dim corridor and rated considerably below the stuffed ducks. I took sculpture because it was supposed to put bones in your painting. I can still draw all the drapery on the reclining ladies from the pediment of the Parthenon from memory. I persuaded the bosses of the Art Institute to let me draw in charcoal bona-fide naked ladies when I was very immature. I even took anatomy. In fact, somebody told me that the best thing to do was to audit the course in medical anatomy at Loyola, where the Jesuits "demonstrated" the subject in Renaissance fashion. So I went up and contributed my share to a cadaver, and got my fingers calloused with embalming fluid. I sometimes wonder if there are any artists left alive who have done this, outside of the Socialist Realists inside the Iron Curtain.

What good all this did me I don't know, because I doubt if I have painted what nowadays they call figurative pictures a hundred times in my life. This didn't all take place, naturally, when I was a grammar-school boy, but it started then and lasted until about my eighteenth year. I did a great deal of copying, too, because somebody else told me that that was how the old masters learned to paint. I copied the El Greco "Assumption"—not, however, life size. I also copied several of the Eddy collection's Picabias and all of its Analytical Cubist paintings; and I also have the clearest memory of the excitement with which I copied the first Cézanne which the Art Institute ever got, a rather mediocre "L'Estaque" all hung on the chimney, smack in the center. Then, too, I copied Odilon Redon and Cazin, Pissarro and even Inness, painters I like better now than I did then, as well as lots of old masters. Most of the Art Institute's old masters in those days were Dutch. I have never cared very much for Dutch painting since.

People like Judge Cooling may not have sold me their eccentric ideas, but they did provide me with some very eccentric reading lists. Every time someone like the Judge would mention a book, I'd make a note of it and get it out of the library and try to read it. He was by far the best-read man I knew, and therefore provided me with the most books. Since one of the foundations of his philosophy was the then still-fashionable subject of comparative mythology, I read everything of that sort that I could find. Not just The Golden Bough or the speculations of Max Müller and Andrew Lang, but since the Judge was always quoting from The Sacred Books of the East, I dutifully read them all.

It might seem odd that a schoolboy should subject himself to such unending dreary wastes of human folly, but somewhere around my twelfth year I acquired the questionable accomplishment of being able to read absolutely anything. Perhaps this is a vice or neurosis, the symptom of some serious lack in real life. Maybe, but I still have it. I can still sit down and read a lengthy report on the uninteresting archeology of some about-to-be flooded Western American river basin from cover to cover, and really enjoy it. So I read the Laws of Manu and the Vinaya Texts without blenching. The Judge was always talking about Egyptology, so I tried to learn Egyptian. I didn't get very far with this, even though I used to play hooky from high school and sneak in and audit Breasted's courses at the University. However, I can still write my name in phonetic hieroglyphics. I did read everything that had been translated in the Royal Egyptological Reports and such like. This was dreary stuff, too, believe me, except for the Tell el-Amarna letters. They fascinated me and produced my first extended literary effort, a play about the heretic king Ikhnaton. This was a romantic production— I had been reading not just Shakespeare, but dreadful gibberish like Schiller in English (fortunately the English of Coleridge.) So the play, which was in two sets of five acts and many scenes in Egypt, Ethiopia, and Syria, was full of long messengers' speeches, philosophical mono- logue, political observations in the style of Shakespeare's Wolsey, and talkative love suicides. It was elaborately documented. Even the names of the dogs were authentic. It lay around Chicago in a trunk for many years, but was lost with the dispersal of my aunt's papers. Just recently I got a letter from the boy who had helped me type it, and whose aunt and mother went over it with me line by line and gave me critical advice. I hadn't heard from him in forty years, but one of the things he asked was if I had ever done anything with my Egyptian play.

I read a good deal of science, too, in those days, of an already some- what outdated sort. There is an old library of nineteenth-century classics: Tyndall, Haeckel, Clerk Maxwell, Herbert Spencer, Lyell, Darwin, Mendel, Faraday—I read them all. My father had known either Soddy or Rutherford, or possibly both, at I believe McGill, and so I read the first books on radioactivity and relativity theory. As I men- tioned, we knew the first American bowdlerizer of Freud, and I read the early popular works on psychoanalysis by Brill and Beatrice Hinkle and others whom I've forgotten. I don't know how much good all this stuff did me, but at least I got it all read.

This omnivorous appetite for reading things in sets and subjects stood me in good stead, because it meant that I got most of the world's im- portant fiction out of the way in adolescence where it belongs. I would take the Constance Garnett Chekhov, Turgenev, or Dostoyevsky, the Archer Ibsen (a dreadful translation), the New York edition of Henry James, or the mail-order sets of Joseph Conrad and Jack London, start with Volume I, and read straight through. I'm not proud of this. It seems to me now to be more or less a substitute for nail-biting. How- ever, it purged me of a taste for nondescript fiction and indiscriminate light reading. I have read very little fiction except detective stories and science fiction since. A few years later, when I began to frequent bohemia, I discovered that I was marvelously well equipped for im- pressive name-dropping and deep critical analysis of the Russian masters in perfect studio-party style. Sets of bad translations of French writers, even Flaubert, Stendhal, and the Goncourts, existed in those days, as well as immense sets of Balzac and Sainte-Beuve. I read all this, too. And even behind the foulness of the translations I could sense that there was something radically different about French and Russian literature.

Young as I was, and reading this stuff as kids read Henty or the Rover boys, I still could feel the total rejection of middle-class civilization, and I never could find anything like this in any of the American major novelists except Mark Twain. When I meet friends today who teach American literature and who are capable of long articles in *PMLA*, or even whole courses, on the moral problems of James Fenimore Cooper, I always feel like I'm being kidded. American fiction, even Hawthorne, even Melville, to this day seems to me to be absolute trash.

This custom of blindly plowing through whole subjects had rather ridiculous results, because I would simply sit down and, just as though I were boning up on biology, read straight through the Aldine poets. So I am probably one of the few actual practicing poets who has ever read all of Mark Akenside or Kirk White or Beattie or Parnell and Tickell. This did mean, though, that I read Skelton, Wyatt, Crabbe, and other stuff that I otherwise would not have got around to for many years. I suppose this is one way to form a taste, if you don't destroy it first, because Skelton and Wyatt sure looked awful good after reading through Kirk White. Those were the days of *The Little Review* in Chicago and the heyday of *Poetry Magazine* and *Others*. I heard them talked about excitedly by my elders, but I am afraid that I read them uncritically and preferred the poorer stuff they published—the Voices of Revolt.

CHAPTER 14

I don't want to give the impression that I had become a self-educated antiorthodox precocity, because I had not. I spent my time reading history and the sciences and philosophy. The lunatic fringe of radical Chicago in those days—the Hobo College, the Bug Club, the Dill Pickle, Bughouse Square—taught me one thing, that the orthodox view of the universe, although acceptable and empirically satisfactory, was probably so only because millions of men had devoted their work and their attention and their consent to seeing the universe in that way. If it were possible for a ragged hobo in a gaslit room off West Madison Street to work out a fairly adequate world picture, it is obvious that if historically men had worked along lines which had in fact diverged from the accepted orthodox path to the understanding of reality, they could have evolved an equally acceptable but radically different scientific universe.

Rather than being converted to the deliquescence of orthodoxy and heterodoxy, so characteristic of our time, I was inoculated against it. The radical disbelief which has been characteristic of all my contemporaries I shared from the beginning, but I was never led by it to embrace any of the extraordinary follies which were to become fashionable in intellectual circles in the next thirty or forty years. I have known Socialist-Realist novelists who religiously consulted the astrology column in the daily newspapers every morning before breakfast. The whole Socialist movement after the First War, led by Frank Harris and Upton Sinclair, embraced the Abrams electronic diagnosis machine. Twenty years later, after the Second War, the reborn Anarchist movement committed suicide in the orgone boxes of Wilhelm Reich. Anyone who had taken a course in high school physics would have known that this stuff was arrant nonsense but the trouble was that these people had lost belief in high school physics along with their belief in capitalism or religion. It was all one fraud to them.

Dr. Abrams had been San Francisco's leading diagnostician. He almost certainly was self-deluded. The same is true of Wilhelm Reich, who before he was persecuted first by Freud, then by the Nazis, then by the Stalinists, was one of the more valuable of the second generation of psychoanalysts. Both Abrams and Reich were taken up by criminal promoters who used their madness to defraud thousands of people and to make hundreds of American radicals ridiculous. Being a skilled public nuisance, I got a job back in those days going around to public meetings addressed by the Abrams-machine apostles and asking embarrassing questions and demonstrating to the assembled innocents that a fourteen-year-old boy whose knowledge was no greater than that of the electrical handy man at the corner could expose the fraud. This was a lot of fun, but it only lasted for a couple of weeks. As soon as everybody in the expensive, high-pressure Abrams organization came to know me, my usefulness was over; but the gullibility of my elders who considered themselves scientific Socialists taught me something about the nature of scientific Socialism.

During this time I still had a basement laboratory and I did a series of experiments on pigments and artists' materials. I subjected everything from hog bristles to ground lapis lazuli to every kind of abuse I could think of. I was still going out bird watching, camping out in the woods and fields around Chicago, lugging around a flower press, collecting specimens for my herbarium, and collecting minerals and rocks and fossils.

Out Western Avenue past the Argo Corn Products Refining Company was a belt of hills, terminal moraines of the last glacier, like those I had known in Bristol, north of Elkhart, with the same clear streams running over colored rocks. The place was a bird and wild-flower sanctuary and there I often spent a week at a time. I met somebody who had been on a Himalayan expedition and was inspired to a season of winter camping. That January and February, every time the temperature dropped below zero or a first-class blizzard blew up, off I went with a one-man tent, a down sleeping bag I myself had made out of a German quilt, and a Primus stove, training myself for the ascent of Everest. It was a great deal of fun and I never lost the taste for camping in the snow. I know of few activities that give more of a sense of mastery over nature, and I have never spent nights more saturated with peace than those in a narrow tent in wind-drifting snow under black winter skies. I discovered hitchhiking. I took trips to the more scenic or wilder parts of the Middle West, up into Wisconsin, over into Michigan, down into the hill country of southern Indiana. I also took a wonderful canoe trip from Momence on the Kankakee River west of Chicago down to the Mississippi in the early autumn. In those days all the old portages and waterways of the French *voyageurs* were still French. Along the Kankakee were villages with no communication with the outside world except the river and a muddy track impassable half the year, where only one or two people spoke English at all. We had a fine time camping in pastures and sitting round campfires in fair weather and around stoves in country stores in the rain, singing French folk songs with the *habitants*. The Kankakee had already been straightened out a little but it still had much of the appearance of the waterways of the lower Mississippi— backwater bayous with drowsy herons and logs lined with immense turtles and marsh trees hung with moss.

In those days the sand dunes at the south end of Lake Michigan had not been built up solid with cottages. I used to go there, but it was already becoming an outdoor suburb of the Near North Side. West of the sand dunes lay a long stretch of marsh and woodland reaching to Calumet Lake straight south of Chicago. This was one of those wild, abandoned tracts that you often find on the edge of a great city. The steel mills were just beginning to encroach on its edges. Wolf Lake, the center of this area, was a bird sanctuary and there I met America's most famous bird watcher, Nathan Leopold, and we spent several weekends bird watching. At one time, only once, I was invited by Dick Loeb to come to his home to meet Eleanora Duse. There were very few people there, the family, Babe Leopold and his girl, and a handful of people from the Chicago Little Theater. I never thought anything of this, but it was to be recalled to me under pathetic circumstances many years later.

My closest friend, the Jewish boy who married Studs Lonigan's sister, was at least as precocious as I was. He was always dressed in the latest thing out of *Vanity Fair*. His father was a tailor on Fifty-fifth Street and he must have been one of the few boys in Chicago ever to show up in high school sophomore class in striped pants, a dickey under his waistcoat, and a flower in his buttonhole. Evenings he sported a black Borsalino and a walking stick and we used to cruise Washington Park, the Midway, and Jackson Park and pick up girls and take them to Merry Gardens, the Trianon, and White City dance halls where we'd dance to the music of bands in which the first white musicians of the Chicago style were learning to play.

Helen Shires, the confidante of Studs Lonigan, was a class friend of mine and one of the circle of Englewood High School intellectuals. It was through her that I met a much faster, more intellectual set of children at Hyde Park, and from then on till I left the South Side most of my friends were over on the other side of the Park. I hardly ever went to classes at Englewood—I had too much work to do, although I would often spend the day in the branch of the public library near the high school reading and writing. Along about 3:30 P.M. every day, in would come a page, a senior from Hyde Park High School. He considered himself a Dadaist poet. Later I was to meet him again on the Near North Side where he had already become a legendary harum-scarum newspaper reporter. His name was F. Fithian Healy. He is still quite a legend amongst old-time newspaper men, but he played a quite different role in my life. Together we explored the current literature of the avant-garde and it was he who showed up one day at the library with the first two issues of *Broom*, to which I immediately subscribed.

Up until this time modern poetry to me meant Sandburg, Masters, the Chicago school, the early Imagists, and, in Europe, my father's favorites—Dehmel, Rilke, Verhaeren, the *fantaisistes*, Jammes. Now I discovered the contributors to Kreymborg's *Others* (what is now the classic generation of American modernists), the new contributors to *Broom* (Hart Crane, Malcolm Cowley, Yvor Winters), and modern French verse, from Mallarmé, LaForgue, Rimbaud, and Apollinaire to the postwar revolution of the Cubist and Dadaist poets. As might be imagined, this produced an indescribable state of excitement. *The Little Review* was part of the Chicago scene and I had met the editor, Margaret Anderson, at Jake Loeb's. The magazine seemed to me a little frivolous, while, on the other hand, the local group of young modernist poets, products of William Vaughn Moody's classes at the University, struck me as being too conventional and too precious. At last I discovered a body of literature with which I could identify myself and which was acceptable to the intolerably strict standards of an adolescent boy.

Every day I'd struggle through a new book by Jean Cocteau or Max Jacob or Louis Aragon with the aid of a pocket French-English dictionary. About this time I read Ezra Pound. *Cathay*, as it has for so many others, introduced me to Chinese literaure. To Pound's own clownish and irascible personality, I formed an antipathy which has lasted to this day. I remember reading about this time, eager for guidance, his essay on modern French poets, and although I was only a schoolboy, I could recognize the opinionated ignorance and violent provincialism. When I look back on those days the thing that stands out in memory is the tremendous pitch of unrelieved intellectual excitement that attended the discovery not just of the poetic explosion that had come after Apollinaire, but the discovery that this was the way I thought—these were the kinds of things I wanted to say.

What people nowadays call the youth of the Twenties was really an infinitesimal minority, but there was such a handful of students at Englewood High School. As is usually the case at this age, most of the school intellectuals were girls, but there were six or seven boys who were even brighter. We seem to have discovered one another all at once, although we were scattered over all four years. At first we dominated the extracurricular serious activities—the English Club, the French Club, the Chess Club, the Ypsls, the Lit—and then suddenly we seemed to come to the conclusion that this was too easy and too conformist and we drew together into a tight little set of our own. We looked on ourselves as extremely sophisticated, extremely revolutionary, and totally emancipated, especially sexually, and we formed alliances with similar children at Hyde Park and another neighboring high school. We must have been insufferable, but from this little circle of South Side precocities came quite a number of successful and intelligent people.

Elmer Simms Campbell and Milton Mayer were both there, and as Mayer reminded me when we met almost forty years later, we all took Latin from Mrs. Manley. She was one of the few perfect pedagogues I've ever met. She taught Latin by the direct method. If you couldn't ask to go to the toilet in Latin, you had to sit and swelter. Her classes were extremely hard and much in advance of the Chicago curriculum requirements. In the second year you were reading Ovid in addition to the required Caesar. But everybody with any pretension to brains in the school studied with her. She didn't only teach Latin but everything else. She was a heavy, gray-haired woman with the face of a benevolent St. Bernard, and she had opinions, all of them absolutely sound, on every subject under the sun. She was a sort of female Sam Johnson and we were her Boswells. We believed everything she said about everything from birth control to arctic exploration, and well we might, because as I look back I can think of no one who ever gave me more useful lessons in life and living. I have known other schoolteachers who were of help to me in a small way, but not many of them. She is the only teacher I ever knew who was a major help and who really aided me to start off in the kind of life I wanted to live. I can still remember her oratorical pronouncements—a compound of Johnson, Chesterton, Belloc, and Clarence Darrow—on manners and morals and the understanding and use of life. Perhaps Milton Mayer and E. Simms Campbell and I owe the intransigence which we notoriously share to the example of Mrs. Manley—the one thing we have in common.

There were two girls to whom I was equally devoted: a delicate little redhead whose mother was one of the city's leading dress designers, and Naomi Fitzgerald, who was the exact image of Rossetti's Beata Beatrix in the Art Institute, except that she was a dusty brown-purple in color. She was a violinist and painter and her twin brother played the flute. The four of us organized a class in art history and got one of the more widely traveled, cultivated women in the school to conduct it. Since it didn't require any work, it became popular with child bohemians and juvenile delinquents, but a few of us and the teacher carried on a wonderful seminar with lantern slides and visits to galleries and museums and passionate, esthetic discussions, all with a strong Cubist bent, except for a couple of fairies who held up the standards of Aubrey Beardsley and the *Yellow Book*.

I was very much in love with Naomi and her brother was my most intimate friend. I have never been able to find out what became of them. There are not many Negroes named Fitzgerald and when I met Ella I asked her if she was related to the girl I had known in school. She was not. I have always felt that they were the children I met in my childhood most likely not just to succeed but to become extremely famous. I think it is significant that these two brilliant young Negroes vanished utterly within five years. Before I left Chicago I was unable to find them and although I later knew many Negro musicians I never met anyone who ever heard of them. They were the first people I ever met who were not only absorbed in serious music but whose taste was the antiromantic taste which was just then becoming popular. After I left my aunt's, but before I moved to the North Side, I used to spend a great deal of time in their house. Their mother would play the piano, the father the oboe or cello, and the boy and girl the violin and flute. They played Bach, Mozart, Haydn, and the mother played a great deal of Renaissance English and Italian organ and harpsichord music on the piano. Although I had known plenty of people with the ordinary cultivated musical tastes of the time and my mother had even heard of Bartók and Satie, this was my first contact with the exclusive classicism which was to be the fashion for the next twenty years. Its analogies with my own architectural tastes in painting and poetry were obvious. We went to concerts together and read stories together and took courses in harmony and counterpoint from that man I can't remember.

One day there walked into the study hall where I was working a boy with a very pretty and extremely wise face. He was Jewish but he looked more like a Japanese. That noon he came to our table in the cafeteria. I had known other homosexuals but he was the first real fairy I ever met. He became a member of our group and we became fast friends. He was a great deal more sophisticated than any of the rest of us, but probably the least brainy and the poorest educated. He was the mistress of a male nurse, the supervisor of an old men's home, and he introduced us to the art and literature and sentiment of decadence.

We had all been busy discovering Strindberg and Apollinaire, Picasso and Kandinsky. He came up with Oscar Wilde and Aubrey Beardsley. We were all atheists. He was a Catholic convert and devoutly churchy. Since then, of course, I've met hundreds like him but he was certainly an anomaly in a circle of passionate fifteen-year-old revolutionaries. None of us quite knew what to do about him.

He became one of the country's most successful female impersonators. He in turn introduced into the group a ravishingly beautiful high school boy with an Apollonian profile and golden curls who became the most highly paid show-girl impersonator of his day. This boy, however, was considerably more civilized. He reached the top as a drag queen and was paid fabulous sums of money to make a brief appearance all decked out in sequins and glass egret feathers in front of a chorus line of real women at national Kiwanis or American Legion conventions. Before he left high school he gave it up and became in due course a successful artist, which I guess he still is.

One of the people from whom I learned a great deal in my fourteenth, fifteenth, and sixteenth years was Rabbi Hirsch—the rabbi of Sinai Temple in what was then Chicago's fashionable Hyde Park district. Sinai Temple was run like an extremely liberal Protestant church, with all sorts of miscellaneous cultural activities. I don't know who first brought me there, but I think it was Robert Conney, or Harold Wolf, or one of the Mayer brothers. Anyway, I soon got deeply involved in activities from life classes to Ibsen. My first bit in a play outside of school was a little boy's part in one of Strindberg's dramas—possibly *The Spook Sonata*—except for one night when I played Trouble in the Bucklin Theater in Elkhart, pressed against the heaving bosom of an Italian Cio-Cio-San.

Rabbi Hirsch took a personal interest in me—possibly because I was an orphan and obviously doomed to make a career for myself in the arts. He spent long hours talking to me in his study and on walks in Jackson Park—about literature, philosophy, and especially history. It was my first encounter with a man to whom the philosophy of history was a passion, except for poor Judge Cooling, and Rabbi Hirsch wasn't crazy and it was possible to believe what he said as well as enjoy it. He introduced me to another man, older than he—Rabbi Gonzales—also a Reformed rabbi full of information about the strange byways of Sephardic Judaism and Hasidism, both Polish and Levantine. Probably he wasn't so learned as he seemed to me, but he remains in my memory as a combination of the older Gaster and Martin Buber. I must have had fetching ways as a listener and a disciple, because it's extraordinary how much time these men, as busy as any Protestant minister with a huge social-service plant, managed to give me without any asking on my part.

Another person from somewhat the same milieu who took a great interest in me was Esther Czerny. She was one of four sisters who were intellectual beauties and much about the highbrow world of the first quarter of the century. She was originally from Peoria, Illinois. Her home in Chicago was a quiet salon for radical and intellectual leaders. There I listened to long arguments by William Foster, Jim Larkin, Charlie Ashleigh, William Bross Lloyd, Caleb Harrison, Mary Marcy, Bill Haywood, Vincent St. John, Irving St. John Tucker, and especially to the finespun dialectic of "Pepper," the Hungarian revolutionary who in those days was what was later called the CI Rep—the representative of the Comintern in America. He vanished from the earth into Russia long ago. He was the first contact I ever had with the typical Bolshevik: completely competent for any problem, absolutely unscrupulous, totally military—fundamentally unlike the Western European humanist revolutionary.

About this time I was sitting one afternoon on the grass at the Bug Club in Washington Park and a boy about my own age came up to me, looked furtively around him as though he were carrying morphine or the Hope diamond in the heel of his shoe, and slipped me a small book, wrapped up and tied with string.

"Don't open it now," he said. "Take it home and read it."

Until this time no book-length work by any of the leaders of the Russian revolution had appeared in English, although I think there were a couple of books by Trotsky in Yiddish. The only things available were pamphlets by Lenin, Trotsky, Bukarin, Zinovieff, explaining, just like today, the twists and turns of Russian politics, internal and external. As a boy raised on the Charles H. Kerr library of Socialist and revolutionary classics, what I wanted to see was a real book—what the Bolsheviks themselves would call a "theoretical contribution."

"It's Lenin's *Materialism and Empirico-Criticism*," said Sigmund. "Just out!"

I carried it home as though it were radium and unwrapped it in my room. I can still remember the cover—a dull green, mealy paper like pre-Raphaelite wallpaper with a blood-red scrawl of script for a title. I sat up all night reading it.

"This is not my revolution," I said.

It is hard to convey to a generation casehardened to such behavior the effect of Lenin's abuse, lies, and paranoid accusations on a young boy saturated with the lofty moral optimism of the pre-Bolshevik revolutionary movement. I could see the same moral characteristics in Pepper more cautiously expressed, but I really believe he was a smarter man than Lenin. It was amusing to watch him twist a bufflehead like Bill Foster around his little finger. His unscrupulousness was so much more polite and civilized than Lenin's ignorant vituperation. Of course, Pepper was a Hungarian, and half in, half out of the Western revolutionary movement—only partly a Bolshevik. And then, after all, he was performing in public—being entertained at the home of a bourgeois sympathizer. I've always wondered about men like this—how they must feel when they wake up all alone in bed in the middle of the night—and I recently thought of Pepper, who was probably shot after some hideous forced confession, when I read his friend George Lukacz's pathetic apology to Western European intellectuals for his life spent as a Vishinsky of literary criticism in the service of Stalin.

It may seem a little farfetched that a boy just out of short pants should be capable of such judgments, but children are like dogs and horses—they have keen noses for moral qualities, or immoral ones, and it is probably due to the fact that I was still really a child and had not yet entered the confusions and obscurities of adolescence that I was enabled to make such sound judgments.

Alexander Berkman's reports from Russia had begun to circulate amongst the Anarchists and IWWs in Chicago—reports that later appeared in the book *The Bolshevik Myth*. It was easy to believe them after having met Pepper and read Lenin.

Up until this time the actual Left of the revolutionary movement had collaborated with the Bolsheviks in Russia, in the U.S., as a matter of fact, all over the world, although they considered the Bolsheviks just perverted and unscrupulous social democrats. These were the years of the first great Right Turn, of the New Economic Policy, the collapse of the German revolution, and the murder of Kronstadt. The Budapest and Munich revolutions had gone past so quickly that nobody had noticed they had been "betrayed," except the unfortunate participants. It was a time of countless all-night arguments, meetings that never adjourned or that recessed never to meet again, of bitter personal quarrels that made lifelong enemies, and of disruption in the literal sense of the word.

Until this time, except for the cantankerousness of Daniel De Leon and his followers of the Socialist Labor Party, everybody in the American radical movement got along pretty well together. Socialists, Anarchists and Syndicalists shared platforms for general causes in which they all believed (an activity later to be dirtied by the term "United Front"), came to one another's defense when in trouble with the law, and all piled in and worked like demons in big mass strikes and spontaneous movements of the working class—which they had sense to recognize were bigger than their own sectarian groups. The internal factional snake pit and the erratically shifting foreign policies of the Bolsheviks exploded this coherent foundation of radical activity like a series of land mines. While the American labor movement was recovering from the Palmer raids, its leaders discovered that they were being swept away in a maelstrom flowing from a world with which

they were little concerned. The remarkable thing is that, with almost
no exceptions, all of them continued for many years to defend Russia
and what they called "the gains of the Revolution."

It was not until fifteen or twenty years later—after the Bolsheviks
had recruited the ragtag and bobtail world of unemployed social workers, neurotic physicists, foundation experts, corporation lawyers, dis-
contented capitalist politicians—that the ex-Communist breast-beater
and stool pigeon became a popular figure in American life. The only
people I ever met in my early youth who were willing to invoke the
aid of "the class enemy" against the Bolsheviks were emigrated Russian revolutionaries. To us in those days their vindictiveness was incomprehensible.

Today most non-Bolshevik radicals under about fifty years of age
have come to their opinions by an intellectual evolution which developed specifically in opposition to Bolshevism. In fact, Bolshevism has
been the dominating factor just as nineteenth-century capitalism was
the dominant factor in the minds of Marx or Engels or the czarist secret
police in the mind of Lenin. Many thousands have turned to reaction,
religion, or plain folly because to them Socialist revolution meant Bolshevism. This was not at all the case in my youth. The social revolution
was our revolution. It was just an accident that capitalism, in the words
of Lenin, "had snapped at its weakest link." That we had captured
one of the enemy's outlying regiments was a fluke of battle. The fact
that this position we had gained was a marsh into which everybody
would tumble nobody believed. It was a tactical accident which could
not seriously change the development of general strategy in the class
war in Western Europe. Soon the center of the revolution would move
to Germany and the Bolsheviks would be just the accidental victors of
the first victorious skirmish, like Senagalese troops which by chance
had gained a vast bog out on the enemy flank. The Bolsheviks were
heroes in spite of their bloodthirsty terror against other Russian revolutionaries, because all Russians were looked on as not quite civilized.

For the first fifteen years after the Russian October, the Bolsheviks
enticed into their ranks, one after the other with each change of line,
all the groups in the West which represented the old Western European revolutionary humanism, and systematically destroyed them until there was no one left who was not completely centered on the
Kremlin, either as a mindless Stalinist hatchet man or a psychopathic
anti-Bolshevik. It's hard to say whether this was a deliberate matter
of policy.

I remember so clearly a writer from Milwaukee named Sam Perlman, who was then a member of the Milwaukee Central Committee
and who later quit and edited the magazine *Milwaukee Arts*—one of

the last manifestations of the Midwest Renaissance. The Workers' Party had, at that time, a considerable following in heavy industry in Wisconsin, and Perlman had been ordered to put through a change of line which he knew would alienate a large number of his workers. He had come down to Chicago to see Pepper. Doubtless they had long private meetings, but it is characteristic of the time that they were still arguing in public about the issue in the salon of a bourgeois radical—not even a sympathizer, in their sense of the word.

Perlman, in making a point, said, "When we have made Socialism in Wisconsin . . ."

Pepper, with a smile of gentle contempt, said, "My dear Schmelke, neither you nor the Wisconsin Ukranian Federation nor the workers at Allis-Chalmers are going to have anything to do with bringing Socialism to Wisconsin. The Soviet Republic will be established in Milwaukee on the bayonets of the Red Army."

A chill went over everybody present. I doubt whether anyone interpreted the remark as anything but sarcasm at the expense of the weakness and confusion of the American radical movement. None of us realized that what Pepper meant was that we were all nothing but rubbish to be swept out of the way.

A few weeks later Pepper called a meeting of the "underground" Central Committee in a woods in Michigan. The police arrested everyone present except Comrade Pepper, who watched with his benign, quizzical smile as his colleagues were led away.

As I remember, this conversation did not take place at Esther Czerny's but at the great Chicago salon of those days—the incredible house of Jake Loeb, a more important Middle Western cultural institution in 1923 than the University of Chicago, the Art Institute, the Symphony, and the Chicago *Tribune* put together.

Jake Loeb was an outstanding example of what a civilized man can do with comparatively little money. Although he was a member of the Loeb family, which include some of the richest men in the world and is intermarried with almost all the other older rich Jewish families of America, England, Switzerland, France, and Germany, he himself was an insurance broker of modest circumstances. The bohemians of Chicago who came to his home doubtless thought him a billionaire. He had a Chicago Romanesque house, possibly built by Richardson, on Goethe Street on the Near North Side. There were five in the family —Jake; his wife Claire; two daughters, Esther and Sara-Jo; and a son, Myndiert. Still, there seemed to be plenty of room in the place to put up all sorts of visiting notables, impoverished friends, and just plain bums. On Thursdays the Loebs kept open house, but there wasn't much difference between Thursday and any other day—the place was always full of people. It was usual to have twenty people helping themselves to a big pot of stew or spaghetti at dinnertime.

I was taken there by Esther Czerny toward the end of Jake's life and I knew the place only in its last couple of years. There I met everybody who was anybody in the Chicago of the Twenties and everybody who was anybody who was passing through town—D. H. Lawrence, Mme. Kollontai, G. K. Chesterton, Harold Bauer, Prokovief, Bertrand Russell, the Loeb who founded the Loeb Library, Sen Katayama, Micho Ito, Isadora Duncan, Eleanora Duse, and various European painters I can no longer keep straight in my memory. Besides the famous transients, many of whom stayed in the place, the house was full every night of the cream of Chicago's intellectuals in the brief postwar period of Chicago's second renaissance. It seems rather pointless even to list them—any of them—because they were all there: Clarence Darrow, Eugene Debs, Ben Hecht, Sherwood Anderson, Carl Sandburg, Vachel Lindsay, Harriet Monroe, Margaret Anderson, Mary Garden, Rosa Raisa, Adolph Bohm, Sam Putnam, John Alden Carpenter, Leo Sowerby, Frederick Stock, Eric Delamater, Rudolph Weisenborn, Edgar Miller, Emil Armin, Fred Ellis, Bert Eliot, Stanislas Szulkawlski, Frank Lloyd Wright—the list could go on for pages. Every few days the neighboring florist sent over a boy with flowers to decorate the house and a suitcase full of the best cognac and Scotch whisky. The florist's name was Dion O'Banion. There were young people—Ruth Page, Lawrence Lipton, Oscar Williams and his wife, Gene Derwood, and two boys of my own age, Nathan Leopold and Dick Loeb. Present, too, were all the leaders of the labor and radical movement of America—Bill Haywood, Bill Foster, Carlo Tresca, Morris Hillquit, Bill Dunne, Abe Cahan, Fitzpatrick (who organized the great steel strike), John L. Lewis. Charlie Ashleigh, the Wobbly poet, lived there. Even Morris Fishbein, the head of the American Medical Association, and Dr. Lindlhar, the country's leading naturopath, were there.

I remember them as arguing in every room in the house about all the most important problems the human race has ever concerned itself with. At the time of the famous murder, the gutter press tried to make out that this intellectual commotion had a deleterious effect on Jake's nephew and his friend. It certainly had a wonderful effect on me.

Once introduced, I went there night after night and sat quietly in the corner and left long after midnight to travel back to the South Side in the cold empty rattling elevated trains, my head full of fireworks. Every time I heard a book mentioned I wrote it down and went to the library and got it out and read it. Every time I heard a subject discussed that I didn't understand I did my best to bone up on it. I've never understood how Jake managed to let in the door everybody who rang the bell and yet kept the bums and bohemians under control. If you attempted something like that now in any of the major cities of the world, the place would soon break down in a shambles and be raided by the police. Yet at Jake's the conversation was always dominated by the mature, the successful, the intelligent. If psychopaths and drunks interrupted Clarence Darrow, Bertrand Russell, or Harold Bauer when he was in the midst of an argument, I have no memory of it. I suppose a great deal of the credit goes to Claire Loeb, who was a hostess of consummate skill, inconspicuous in the way she managed people. It is not that I met famous people—it is that I learned by listening to impassioned discussion among mature people, all of whom were out in the world putting their ideas into effect. None was an academician whose ideas had never encountered any more severe tests of reality than his students' acquiescence.

Loeb's salon flourished while I was in high school. By the time I had moved up to the Near North Side and was living on my own, Jake was dead. However, he established a tradition which lasted all through the Twenties and which, even today, hopeful Chicago rich try to revive without success. The "at homes" of the two competing doctors Fishbein and Lindlhar were very popular, though always a little more inchoate than the Loebs'. Their respective wives never acquired Claire's skill in handling brokers with pocket flasks of bathtub gin or bohemians who came for the canapés.

There were two sisters whose names I have forgotten who had a large old-fashioned apartment house on the Near North Side equidistant from the universities. They made a practice of Having Youth In. This wasn't so bad as it sounds. The Red youth of the Thirties is largely a myth, but in the early Twenties, at least in Chicago, there was tremendous ferment in the colleges, and at this place I met dozens of youngsters who were later to become famous.

I also met a considerable number of young colonial revolutionaries —among them Krishna Akbar, who was Ghandi's first American representative and who introduced me to Ghandi's movement when it was still in its infancy in India. He had been expelled from graduate school for some article he had written. There was another fellow who had been expelled as an undergraduate from college. After I was expelled from high school we started a magazine of, for, and by expellees, called *The New Student* (a name later used by a Communist publication.) We got an office and a letterhead, and Krishna produced a harem of perfectly fascinating and utterly devoted stenographers and editorial assistants, but to the best of my memory we never got out an issue, though we gave some lovely parties to raise funds and we entertained visiting students from Germany, India, China, Africa, and Russia.

One who accompanied Mme. Kollontai as a secretary and looked like a young Alla Nazimova quit her employer in Chicago and after what I guess they call whirlwind affairs with the editors of *The New Student* vanished into American life to emerge first as a literary flapper. She vanished again and reappeared as a movie writer. On the side she was, as they say, "the Representative of the Center" in the organization of the "Swimming Pool Soviets," but she never lost the look of the Princess Alexandrovna, a dueling pistol in either hand, shooting wolves from the back of a racing droshky.

Another visitor to *The New Student* and to the sisters' salon was a young man from the University of Washington who was reputed to be a secret Russian representative of the Comsomol (the Young Communist League was then organized in an International of its own). He was a prize student in philosophy, under the very bourgeois head of the philosophy department in Seattle, a man who was to have a long history of developing mediocre baby Santayanas and having them turn Red in his hands. This youth had a girl whom he later married, who was rumored to be the daughter of an ex-prime minister of Russia. Years later, in a secret trial, he was expelled from the American Communist Party as a right-wing deviationist, without his name ever being mentioned. Later he was accused of being a police agent. Still later he was reputed to have become Harry Hopkins' personal one-man brain trust, and commonly slept in the White House. After the Great Patriotic War, the FBI and the Immigration Bureau spent years trying to lock him up or kick him out of the country, but if he was any of the things he was reputed to be he had covered his tracks, and he died recently in peaceful retirement on a government pension. I met him only once or twice, but even as a very young man he was one of the most arrogant and disagreeable people I have ever met, and deserved a worse fate.

Wen I-to, the finest of China's revolutionary poets, I met at this place and his friends, the twins Barbara and Robert Ng. They were the children of a wealthy merchant in Chungking and had been raised in that world of Swiss progressive schools and Versailles *lycées* frequented by the young of the Shah of Persia and the Aga Khan and the children of American billionaires, and had done graduate work at all the world's best universities. I was devoted to Robert, in love with Barbara, and, after they went back to China, corresponded with them frequently for several years. The last letter I ever received was from Hong Kong. They were on the committee from the Canton Commune, which went to Hong Kong to deliver an ultimatum to the British. When they went back to Canton they were executed in the street.

There were others as extraordinary, one an African prince who called himself an Anarchist, got drunk, and recited Rimbaud in the Sunset Café. He had quite an effect on the members of the King Oliver Band and other New Orleans musicians who had just come to Chicago. He was always greeted with a fanfare of brass when he came into a joint. He was later assassinated in Africa by a rival claimant to the throne of his Gold Coast kingdom. On the Chicago Gold Coast the neighborhood boycotted the laundry they discovered doing his wash.

At this same place I met the bohemian Anarchist nuisance Louis Kramer, who claimed to have been Alexander Berkman's cellmate in Atlanta prison, although he must have been a boy of fifteen at the time, and who for thirty years was a social problem not unlike a noisy Maxwell Bodenheim in American highbrow circles. I was always able to forgive him all his embarrassing faults because one night an insufferable Main Line Quaker youth in a dickey and mirror-polished shoes, who had been a conscientious objector in the war, appeared. He sat down in a roomful of people busy enjoying themselves, put the tips of his fingers together, cleared his throat, and started out, "The subject of my talk tonight will be . . ." Everybody stood around in embarrassed silence until his hour-long speech was finished. Louis Kramer, then a handsome, redheaded, red-bearded Jewish youth in white silk sport shirt, lurched up from the corner of the floor. "You filthy pretentious swine. You're the dirty Christian who broke the strike at Leavenworth . . ." and went on with a tirade of unrelieved, obscene abuse until the poor guy burst into tears and ran out of the place. Years later, when this man had become one of America's more insufferable celebrities, I always looked back with amusement on Louis Kramer's driving him from the temple.

I can't remember any others of the sisters' youth salon very clearly. They all struck me as what we then called scissorbills and were later to call squares—very innocent, dreadfully earnest, and too well dressed, and they were always quoting textbooks at one another—things that nobody except students ever read. In an argument about the Irish Republic, or free love, or the New Economic Policy, they would fix you with a bold defiant eye and say, "Oh, but you haven't read Liebovitz and Murphy," and leave you speechless. Pretty and eager though the girls were, it was not my world.

Out of this circle of students came a magazine called *The Circle*, published at the University of Chicago. One night at this place where set speeches were never given, the editor, just back from a summer in Germany, gave a speech which held everybody spellbound for a couple of hours. He described the student Germany that he had just seen —a country that we thought of in terms of the Munich Soviet Republic and the revolution in the Ruhr. He described how the old dueling clubs had come back, the pounding of steins in the beer cellars, the persecution of Jewish students, and the heckling of Jewish professors. He prophesied that what we thought was the rising tide of revolution was ebbing all over the world, and that the first country to slip back into black reaction would be the country which we considered the most civilized and Socialist. I remember that night as though it were last week. It was before Mussolini's march on Rome early in 1922. The talk was detailed, backed up by documentation and economic statistics. I can even remember the ribbons of the dueling clubs that he showed us. Like any rash juvenile, he made a step-by-step prophecy of what would happen in Germany—and, almost as an afterthought, in Italy, a country nobody took very seriously. Every bit of it came true. Somehow, listening to his young voice that night, we knew it would.

CHAPTER 15

Chicago in the first quarter of this century was characterized by a rash of "at homes." They were not all radical or bohemian. The grand rich had evenings of the conventional type, where you met only the very famous, but even these were surprisingly tolerant. But the best place of all was Jake Loeb's, and it gave the tone to a whole decade of Chicago's intellectual life. Actually, a place like Jake's took the place of the café *terrasse* in France, rather than of the salon. By the time of his death an open house like his was already beginning to get out of hand, and just about this time this sort of thing took a public and commercial form.

It was early Prohibition. Bars in Chicago were grim and the liquor was bad. Furthermore, women wished to take part in public intellectual conviviality, as they had not much in the days of Rector's or the Herkimer Wine Company Bar. There arose in Chicago and New York, and then in all the principal cities of the country, that now utterly vanished and never successfully revived institution, the bohemian tearoom. I don't remember the first one in Chicago, but the first one to attract much attention was The Wind Blew Inn, run by a young girl circus performer. It started about the time I went to high school, and provided me with a place to meet people, to sit and listen and try to look sophisticated. All my young days I was a marvelous listener, something I find it almost impossible to believe of myself today.

There had already been in existence for a number of years a most important part of the mythology of the Chicago of the Twenties—the Dill Pickle Club. Originally this had been a bona fide club of radical bohemians, founded by Elizabeth Gurley Flynn, the people around the Charles Kerr Socialist Publishing Company, the Chicago leaders of the IWW and a few artists and writers. In the course of time it became a private enterprise in the hands of Elizabeth Gurley Flynn's ex-husband, Jack Jones. These were remarkable hands in themselves, because they lacked several fingers. Like the McNamarra brothers, Jack had been a sabotage expert, employed by various unions. He was an Anarchist and did not belong to any union himself, even the IWW, but whenever things got hot and the boys wanted to make some trouble for the bosses, they used to send for Jack. He was an expert at dosing gasoline with sugar, putting sulphuric acid in the lubricating oil and emery powder in the bearings, crossing wires, and turning off and on the wrong valves. In a strike in the northern Michigan mines he'd blown off two or three fingers on each hand souping nitroglycerine out of blasting powder in a frying pan on the kitchen stove. He was the author of a pamphlet on sabotage often attributed to Elizabeth Gurley Flynn, whose untimely publication helped break one of the great Eastern strikes.

To accompany his clawlike hands he had pale blue, crossed eyes, like quarreling oysters, in a huge, bushy-haired head; very long arms; a very long waist; short bowlegs and turned-out toes, so he looked rather like a duck, happy and angry at the same time. He would have made a wonderful beatnik, because his conversation consisted entirely of nonsensical interjections and obscenity. Talking with the grocery man or the letter carrier, Jack sounded like Tristan Tzara and Gregory Corso both talking at once. In the Pickle he had a coffee bar, a Little Theater, a lecture and dance hall. In addition, he was mad about machinery and was always manufacturing inventions, one of which was a toy duck which looked exactly like him and waddled with precisely his gait. He planned to make several millions with this duck, and put the Revolution on Easy Street, but it never sold, and for years he collected lathes, milling machines, drill presses, like a pack rat, or I suppose, considering their size, like a pack dinosaur. His machine shop, which slowly encroached on the other departments, could have turned out respectable small tanks or cannons, and the Dill Pickle duck was just a little bitty thing, about eight inches long.

On Sunday nights Jack ran a lecture, followed by an open forum. He had only one principle of publicity. He would bill a lecture on relativity theory—and he had amazing talent for getting really important scholars to talk for him—under a lewd title, such as "Should the Brownian Movement Best Be Approached from the Rear?" Saturdays the chairs were cleared away and the Chicago jazzmen of the early Twenties played for a dance which lasted all night. Wednesdays, Thursdays, and Fridays the Little Theater put on Strindberg, Ibsen, Shaw, Lord Dunsany, Synge, and the early plays of Eugene O'Neill. Jack was a fair actor and fitted the early seagoing plays of O'Neill as though they had been written for him. The rest of the company had trouble learning their lines and finding their way on and off the stage. On the walls there was always an art exhibit of the leaders of early Chicago modernism. As the years went on, Jack got old and pretty crazy, the Dill Pickle grew more and more vulgar, was finally taken over by the Organization and turned into a rough and fraudulent operation. Jones had lost his last wife out of a small boat in a terrific storm one night on Lake Michigan, and on the anniversary of her death he always went quite mad. Finally, on the night of the twentieth anniversary of her death, he killed himself. The Pickle had long since become a dangerous tourist trap.

In its heyday, in spite of all Jack's veneer of foolishness, the Pickle was an exciting place. Every important scholar who came through the town, and all those who were attached to the universities, Jack asked to lecture for him, and most of them did—for free. The admission was little or nothing. Although the actors in the Little Theater were often dreadful amateurs and the sets were painted by Jack himself, in a kind of house painter's amateur Expressionism, and the lighting was dim and artistic, the plays were the very best. He put on not only all the classics of early twentieth-century revolt from Shaw to Wedekind, but ethereal things like the dance plays of Yeats and Ezra Pound's translations of Japanese *noh* plays and any even passable play by local talent. Unfortunately, there wasn't any local playwriting talent except Ben Hecht and Max Bodenheim. The Pickle's star exhibit of the Chicago Renaissance was a dreadful thing by Hecht and Bodenheim called *The Master Poisoner*. They managed to invent a new shudder of bad taste.

The Dill Pickle occupied a row of remodeled barns in Tooker Alley. Out the alley and around the corner was Bughouse Square, where every variety of radical sect, lunatic religion, and crackpot health panacea was preached from a row of soapboxes every night in the week when it wasn't storming. The soapboxers, or at least the political radicals among them, hung out in the Dill Pickle and constituted the inner core of club membership. Then there was a group of girls who were almost all prostitutes who had drifted in off North Clark Street, lonely for coffee and company, as whores always are. In the course of time they became the mistresses of various newspapermen, IWW, Anarchist, and Socialist leaders who hung around the place. One was the girl of Lionel Moise, pronounced Mo-ees, the man who is supposed to have taught Ernest Hemingway how to write. At least she was one of what whores call his wives-in-law, and shared him with a newspaperwoman, a sculptress, and the daughter of a millionaire judge. Saturday nights, when the girls got drunk on Bugs Moran's gin, the battles over the beautiful, beloved body of Lionel Moise were epical—deserving, as they say, the pen of a Creasy. None of these people was a fool or a hoodlum. All of the girls were beautiful; even the one who went by the name of Sloppy Liz was fairly good-looking, and they all made devoted mistresses, wives, and nurses for husbands who were always being put in jail or beaten up for alcoholism or the Revolution, or both.

Lionel Moise had sound ideas about good writing; ideas of which Hemingway's Marquis of Queensbury esthetics are only a caricature. Another habitué was the famous confidence man Yellow Kid Weil, the first and original Yellow Kid, who looked like a prime minister of some small, busted nation and was similarly soft-spoken, flashily dressed, and reputed to be shockingly depraved. There were even a number of intellectual gangsters, white-collar hoodlums, lawyers, fixers, accountants for the Organization in white shirts, black ties, and blue serge suits, none of whom ever raised his voice. This leaven of the underworld and of the toughest operators for the labor movement gave the Dill Pickle society a worldly character of a sort never found in bohemia, and from the Pickle, types like these spread all through Chicago's highbrow circles in the Twenties. A world less like Greenwich Village or Saint-Germain would be hard to imagine. Curiously enough, in Paris, on Montmartre, now that the intellectuals are coming back and mixing with the hustlers in the cafés, and always back of the Boulevard Montparnasse on the Gaîté and the Boulevard Edgar Quinet, there is a kind of ragamuffin bohemia of petty crooks, carnival performers, models and prostitutes, and bad, penniless artists and unprinted poets, which greatly resembles Chicago in the Twenties. As the twentieth century slowly overtakes Paris, every year there is less of it.

Like Gaîté Montparnasse, North Clark, Dearborn, and LaSalle Streets were lined with cheap hotels, the winter quarters of carnival and cheap circus people, burlesque queens and comics, stars of the Chautauqua circuit and pitch artists and grifters. They hung around the Pickle and some of them, who had not only acting ambitions but a surprising amount of dramatic education, used to act on its stage. Strippers, like Angela d'Amore and "Lucrezia Borgia" played *Miss Julie* and *Hedda Gabler,* and there is nothing whores like better than to play a whore on a Little Theater stage. I suppose these lumpen entertainers are the loveliest people Western civilization has produced. Today they have vanished from America—radio and TV performers are appalling scissorbills—and there are few of them left even in France. In the early Twenties they gave the Near North Side bohemia both solidity and fantasy of a sort that artists and writers will never be privileged to encounter socially again.

Best of all, as far as I was concerned, was the iron core of Anarchist and IWW free-lance soapboxers. Although most of these men had once been Wobblies and some of them had even been members of the Socialist or the Socialist Labor Party, and others had been members of organized Anarchist circles, by the time I knew them they were all free-lancers, completely disillusioned with the organized radical movement. However, whenever there was a hot strike or a free-speech fight they would volunteer their services—as agitators but never as orga-nizers. The most contemptuous term in their vocabulary was "pie-card artist." They were men of total cynicism, absolute courage, and com-pletely irreconcilable intransigence.

In those days the soapbox was still a most important working class—or at least migratory working class—educational institution. If you were any good, it was possible to make quite a decent living. There was a regular city circuit—two corners on West Madison Street, the Hay-market, a wide area down where the Municipal Pier is now, the Bug Club in Washington Park, and Bughouse Square on North Clark Street in front of the Newberry Library. I never became one of the stars, but if I made all of these points over a weekend I could always pick up a minimum of fifty dollars—a lot of money in those days for two days' work for an adolescent boy.

There was Whitey Miller, who looked like all the Whiteys I have ever known amongst grifters and hustlers. He was the theoretician and quite as well grounded as Rosa Luxemburg or Nicolai Bukharin and a good deal more interesting. He could talk quietly for an hour with the Census Report or the *World Almanac* or a Brookings Institute Report or a copy of *The Analyst* in his hands and hold the crowd, and even draw them away from the Salvation Army.

Rickey Lewis was a most inflammatory spellbinder. He was the boss printer for the Wobbly press and the loudest if far from the best folk singer I have known.

Eddie Gilbert was the most fantastic of all, with a powerful body and the voice of a bull, a head like the Rock of Gibraltar and a lion's mane of iron-gray, wiry hair. He was a structural steel worker and during the First War had led the strike of all the workers, American and French, who were rebuilding the French ports. This was one of the first sit-down strikes, and Eddie sat on the end of a steel beam in Le Havre and threw rivets and obscenities at Jack Pershing until they had to lead the old man away. He never used a personal pronoun: "I," "you," "he" and "she," and their permutations were all "fellow worker." He had been one of the early leaders in the Northwest and in the OBU of Canada and had left behind him a legend of courage and violence. He had been an expert on sabotage but, not like Jack Jones, of the covert kind. Eddie Gilbert went in for defiant, open sabotage, openly arrived at. During a strike meeting with the president of the largest lumber company in the Northwest he had got up and said, "Come on, fellow workers. We'll be seeing *you*, fellow worker, in August, and it's awful dry, fellow worker, along the Columbia in August." He then took a box of old-fashioned safety matches out of his pocket, set fire to it, and threw it into the wastebasket. He caused such a panic that although the fire could easily have been extinguished, it burned down half the office before they got it out.

There were countless stories of this sort about Eddie—of mine shafts dynamited in the Coeur d'Alene, and haystacks, barns, and combines burned up in the wheat country. In a strike in a small factory in Denver he once calmly shot every window out of the building with two pistols. He once saved my life by walking the full length of the barroom under the Wobbly Hall and taking a pistol away from a "Rowanite," crazy with canned heat, who was going to shoot me. He broke the pistol, threw the bullets in the man's face, slapped him to the ground, picked him up, and kicked him out the door. The Rowanites were an expelled IWW faction who got an injunction and came to take over Wobbly Hall. Eddie stood at the head of the stairs with a ball bat and held them off for three hours, knocking them down the stairs like clay pigeons, one after another, until help arrived. He'd been sleeping off a drunk on the floor of the office and was all alone in the place when they woke him up at seven o'clock in the morning. He was the man with the lion, which has since wandered into novels, movies, and plays. When he was drunk he was accompanied everywhere by a young and foolish lion. The lion ate only in Chinese restaurants, and all the waiters in Chinatown were used to Eddie ordering, "Charlie, fellow worker, bring in three raw T-bone steaks on a platter and put them on the floor." He used to go into whorehouses and order one girl for himself and two for the lion. This was too much for the lion, and he got clap, so Eddie took him to Ben Reitman and bought him a course of injections. Various hack writers heard about this lion from Ben Hecht or Sam Putnam or me and he has become part of America's commercial mythology. The original was better in every way than his imitators, for Eddie's lion's name was Georges Sorel.

Reitman had a mascot, a little man with tousled yellow curls who looked like a debauched cupid with a broken nose. I never saw him when he was not quite drunk and I never saw him without a large quid of snuff tucked up against his upper gum. He used to drink a pint of moonshine at one gulp, straight down past the Copenhagen. This resulted in the worst breath ever to emanate from the oral cavity of a human being, no matter how moribund or what he was moribund with. He had been a famous war resister, but by the time I knew him he had only one subject on the soapbox. He would talk to the stiffs in Bughouse Square or on West Madison Street until chased off by the next speaker, all night if nobody showed up, or at least until he fell down, on the pleasures of oral sex, and its answers to the problems of Malthus and Marx. The stiffs threw money in the hat out of loyalty to his past. The Kinsey Report would indicate he never converted any of them.

There was a massive Norwegian with great walrus mustaches, a voice like the rumble of a glacier, and a fist that pounded up and down steadily, rhythmically, all the time he talked. He was known as Trip-hammer Johnson. He had been a patternmaker and a tool-and-die man, and his speeches were full of recherché metaphors from machine-shop practice. He used to recite entire plays by Strindberg, Ibsen, and Björnson, taking all the parts in a voice like that of Thor himself. He could hold a big audience of gandy dancers, harvest stiffs, and smoke hounds spellbound through an autumn night with a lecture on the metaphysical significance of the later plays of Ibsen or on Strindberg as the blind alley at the end of Descartes' *Cogito, ergo sum.* Once he gave three weeks of lectures from the soapbox on West Madison Street on Kierkegaard and Nietzsche. I do not believe that the editors of the *Partisan Review* were aware that Kierkegaard was a popular topic of conversation for a whole summer so long ago and in such an environment.

The best of them all was a man who passes for a fascinating moment across the pages of *Studs Lonigan.* Studs and his friends go to the Bug Club to heckle the speakers and the kind of Irishman they can understand and fear slaps their chops and chases them away. John Loughman was six foot four and massively built, with a long head, a vulpine face, extremely dark blue eyes, a shock of stiff black hair, and the kind of eyebrows called Mephisophelean. He was not only the king of Chicago soapboxers, he was probably the best the country ever produced, or Hyde Park or Glasgow either. Like many others he used to get up on the box with the daily paper or a news weekly in his hand and comment on the contents. Nobody could compete with him, not the Salvation Army, not the Garveyites, not even the belle of the Proletarian Party, who wore heavy circular swirl skirts and no underwear. The size of his audience was limited only by the reach of his voice, and the only other voice I have ever known as powerful or as controlled was Chaliapin's, a man whom he resembled in more ways than one. He was the spokesman and philosopher for this whole group of completely disaffiliated revolutionaries. I don't suppose his disbelief was profound, it's just that it was powerful. His ideas didn't differ much from those of Mencken, Mr. Dooley, or even Will Rogers, but there was an overwhelming violence about them, not just about their delivery. As the years passed he mellowed and became a favorite monologuist on the Orpheum circuit, a speaker at luncheon clubs, and finally a Democratic state senator. I admired him immensely and became a kind of chairman and straight man for his act. I used to precede him on the box, and later at more commercial appearances, I would usually recite poetry.

Thus began my career as a boy soapboxer, bringing poetry to the masses. I didn't have any theories or principles about it. We all used to recite a certain amount of stuff. I tried a whole pitch of it one night and got a big collection and went on doing it because it was profitable and I enjoyed it. All during the period of Proletarian Art I found the discussion of proletarian poetry rather unreal, because I had actually tried poetry on the proletariat and my experience didn't match the theories at all. I used to recite Patrick Magill, Service's *Songs of a Wage Slave,* Belloc's poem to his little son, Vachel Lindsay's socialist poems, Lola Ridge, James Oppenheim, Arturo Giovanitti, and all the other old chestnuts of revolt that can be found in the anthologies of Marcus Graham and Upton Sinclair. This was all right with the stiffs, but what they liked best was the world-weary poetry of the English Decadence —*The Rubáiyát,* Housman, Ernest Dowson, and best of all, Swinburne's "The Garden of Prosperine." This always made a perfect number to go out with and added substantially to the collection. I've often thought, roaring it out into the windy night under a sputtering arc lamp, that its last verses perfectly reflected the hopes and ambitions of the average hard-rock miner, lumberjack, or harvest hand.

In a few years I took this act on the road, so to speak, and found it very successful. Not only was it easier to peddle Red cards in Fargo or Big Timber or Kellogg or Spokane or Puyallup with a brief recital of the preamble to the Wobbly constitution and a big dose of Fitzgerald, Swinburne, or John Davidson, but I discovered that the nooks and crannies of the Northwest were filling up with old-timers, living the lives of hermits in the midst of society, who knew quite as much about this sort of thing as I did. The only poets in the modern taste who were liked as well were Whitman and Sandburg.

CHAPTER 16

If someone asked me today what had been my most active year intellectually, I would have to say somewhere around fifteen. There never seemed time enough for all the thousands of things that absolutely had to be done or written or painted or seen. It seems as though I met most of the important people in America, by my standards, in a matter of three or four years. It is hard to convey to a person born even ten years later how novel and exciting everything was. It wasn't just the freshness of youth; the century was young, and we were building a new culture and self-educating ourselves—learning by doing.

I am not talking about Orphism or dodecaphonic music or dissociated verse or stream-of-consciousness fiction. For instance, I mentioned before how in my laboratory in the basement I carried on two or three years of tests on all the materials of the artist—pigments, media, supports, bristles, diluents. To the best of my knowledge there was no sound book on this subject in English or in French published until several years later, and there were no courses in any art school. I had to find it out for myself, and it was exciting to do so because although of course it was all already known somewhere, as far as I was concerned each experiment had all the excitement of Kekule's ring or the peak on Darien. Dipping hog bristles in weak muriatic acid would not be very exciting to an adolescent artist today. All he has to do is look in the book. Although I might have been able to deduce it, and in fact had a strong suspicion in advance, I shall never forget how thrilling it was to see before me a complete range of colors—granted of rather limited tonality and saturation—all earth colors and all absolutely permanent. Since then, following Weber's course at the Art Students League, a New York American Scene school has come and gone, based on the somewhat overrefined color chords which this palette produced. What happened to an oil or varnish when it evaporated or oxidized, and the mysterious enzyme action of real lacquer—which I don't understand chemically today—I discovered for myself the components of oxidized linseed oil, something I could have read, as a matter of fact, in the Encyclopaedia Britannica.

Although I read Hambidge's *Dynamic Symmetry,* a rather vulgar writer with conventional tastes, and that book on futurist color schemes, I really evolved for myself, by studying what few Cubist and abstract pictures I could find, an exact aesthetic like Moholy and Van Doesburg. I believed then that the art of the future should be capable of being coded and sent by telegram, that all forms in the painting should be evolved from the sides and diagonal of the frame, all proportions should be incommensurate, and all lines should be circles, segments of circles, or straight, preferably at right angles, and constructed with compass and ruler. For a while I believed that the colors in each picture should include the entire spectrum and black and white, organized in a definite curve of saturation and tone across the spectrum.

Now it is true that all over the world people were getting ideas like this, but there were no art magazines which showed their work except in German, and for a very brief period in Russian, neither of which I read. There were no books in English except the two I mentioned. Knowledge of the activities of the golden section and the Constructivists came to me only through personal contact or correspondence.

I don't want to give the impression that I was a great juvenile artistic innovator. Most of these pictures weren't very good. The point is that nobody taught me to paint that way or even gave me sensible advice after I'd painted them. I had all the glory of really doing them myself. Furthermore, I had then even more exciting faith that I was helping to change the very nature of art.

Eventually rather flimsy books on Cubism were translated from the French and then Kandinsky's *Art of Spiritual Harmony.* How well I remember the vertiginous excitement with which I bought this book, and how well I remember the awful letdown along about midnight after I'd read it. Kandinsky's suety Teutonic metaphysic struck me as dreadful nonsense, although I liked his painting. Once again I was thrown back on my own resources.

Similarly, out in the cow-country universities there were no courses in the seventy-seven and a half types of ambiguity. If you wanted to understand Apollinaire, you just had to read him until you did, and if you wanted to know how he did it, you just had to keep on reading until you'd figured it out. Besides the thrill of discovery and participation, there was another far from minor advantage we had in those days. We had no guides, but neither were we misguided. It so happens that practically all the books on the aesthetics of modern poetry are not actually about modern poetry at all but about reactionary poetry. Fortunately, I was able to recognize John Crowe Ransom and his friends when they showed up because I had already read *John Inglesant*.

Reading translations of German Expressionism and Italian Futurism, it didn't take me long to decide that modern poetry meant French poetry, so I set myself to better my French. In a little while I was bringing home from the library Baudelaire, Laforgue, Rimbaud, Mallarmé, Jammes, and Verhaeren, which was all the library had, and puzzling through them with a dictionary. My father had taken me to see Verhaeren and it is hard to believe today that before the First War he and Francis Jammes were considered the leading poets of the French language. In 1924 the *Anthologie Kra* came out, and the first weeks of reading it over and over remain amongst the most exalted of my life. I still have a copy and it's still one of the best collections of the best days of French verse.

At Jake Loeb's I met Sherwood Anderson, whom I discovered to be a distant relative. He not only took an interest in me, but unlike most older authors who take an interest in young ones he took a helpful and comprehending interest. He loaned me books to read, and he gave me a book by a friend of his—Gertrude Stein's *Tender Buttons*. The explosively liberating effect of *Tender Buttons* on an adolescent modernist at the beginning of the Twenties is quite impossible to convey. Although I had deciphered poets like Pierre Reverdy, this was the first thing which seemed to me to be doing in literature what I was trying to do in painting. Today I realize that I was mistaken. *Tender Buttons* is in reality the poetic analog of Analytical Cubism, especially of the paintings of Juan Gris by a writer with a remarkably commonplace mind. Although I was mistaken about Gertrude Stein's intent, she set me off on a program of "abstract poetry." Some of this has survived, some of it has even been incorporated in poems written years later. It wasn't so abstract as I thought it was, but doing it taught me a lot about writing.

About this time I discovered a source for the kind of books I wanted to read. The Radical Bookshop in the old North Side Turner Hall on North Clark Street started importing the avant-garde poetry of the Twenties from France and Germany and Russia. In a short while they were also getting American and English books, published by the first Paris-Americans. I bought them all, and I only wish I had saved them, because they'd be worth a lot of money today. Nobody else wanted them, and I usually got them at considerable discount.

The Radical Bookshop had a Little Theater with a tiny stage in the back room. Here I acted in Shaw and Wedekind. For some reason I was usually cast as an old man, and while still in high school, heavily and amateurishly made up with Oxford glasses on a ribbon, I made a most flatulent Roebuck Ramsden. The Radical Bookshop was run by a frail, white-haired widow, Mrs. Udell, who was totally blind, and who was always accompanied by a blonde and a brunette daughter at her right and left hand, Geraldine and Phyllis. They had grown up in the Little Theater in the back room and knew by heart all the lines of all the desperate young misses in all the Theater of Revolt. I think they fancied themselves as considerably higher-brow Gish sisters, with a dash of Nazimova, and they were, rather. The mother was a Sibylline and sepulchral character straight out of a Greek oracle. She said almost nothing, and what she did say was ambiguous and intimidating. Phyllis was too nervous, too much on the Ida Rubinstein side for me, but Geraldine was even calmer and more collected than her mother and not at all cryptic. All it ever came to was a kiss or two on the stage in a Wedekind tragedy of youngsters like ourselves.

Gradually artists began to turn up who were of help to me. Picabia and Duchamp were in America during and shortly after the war. They may have come to Chicago, but somewhere I saw Picabia's painting, which impressed me more than Duchamp's. Picabia was then just beginning compass-and-ruler paintings of the kind later to be called nonobjectivist, which culminated in his great Barcelona show and the Picabia number of *The Little Review*. These were the first actual paintings of this kind I had ever seen, and all I would see in the flesh for several years. I have no memory of what Picabia said to me, but I somehow felt invigorated and inspired with confidence in my own destiny by whatever he said, and that sensation (which after all was what was most important) is what I remember today. Duchamp's cabalistic affectations baffled me. He already had the fatal marks of a professional young man embarking on a very successful wasted life.

Somewhere I got hold of the two copies of Wyndham Lewis' *Blast* and Ezra Pound's book on Gaudier. I don't know where I could have seen Lewis' paintings of the Twenties, but somehow I did, and their peculiar forms had a decided influence on me. There is nothing quite like them. They are a sort of intact, half-reassembled Analytical Cubism, with a color organization based on crimson and dark green. For some reason impossible to understand at this distance, Lewis had a greater influence on Chicago painting in those years than did the major Cubists and Expressionists.

American artists in Chicago were beginning to develop in ways that were helpful to me. The best in those days was Buck Eliot. He was a successful commercial artist, a handsome, self-possessed *bon vivant*, and an unassuming ladies' man. He had some of the most beautiful girls ever to enter a Chicago studio. He was a Cubist, and one of the very few American painters who understood what Cubism was actually about. He let me paint with him in his studio, and guided me practically brushstroke by brushstroke for a short time. He was a man of many parts and in one of these parts he was a lepidopterist. He went off to the Bolivian headwaters of the Amazon, hunting butterflies. No one in the expedition was ever heard from again. I doubt if anyone in Chicago remembers he existed. One of the best things about him was that he had what laymen consider great skill and technique. If necessary he could paint likenesses which looked like color photographs, and he had much more work than he could do as a commercial artist. It is not true that this is real painting skill, but it is discipline, and his example taught me for better or worse to know what I was doing and to go about it in an orderly manner.

After Buck's death I started working under the direction of Rudolph Wiesenborn. He is still alive and what today is called the "dean of Chicago painters," and he has remained one of my best friends. In those days he was pretty much a disciple of Wyndham Lewis'—for a while he called himself a Vorticist. Lewis was never a purely abstract painter and was opposed to abstraction. Wiesenborn turned out in those days excessively dynamic vorticist portraits of all of Chicago of the Twenties in conté crayon. He taught me to do likewise, and if I have to I can still do it. Better still, he understood what I was trying to do in my geometrical painting, and gave me careful criticism of my dispositions of squares and circles. Besides this, he and his wife Fritzi gave me something else—familial affection. I was always welcome at their house, and they were always ready to feed me, listen to my troubles, and counsel me on my problems—artistic, philosophical, or erotic. They too had "at homes," and perhaps due to the fact that Rudolph was one of the town's important artists, they got only the cream of the habitués of the other bohemian hangouts.

There was one other nonobjective painter in Chicago in those days, Raymond Johnson. His abstractions were motivated not by plastic considerations but by mystical theories. Rather than organizations of the picture space, they were representational paintings of abstract objects floating around in Renaissance space, rather like color photographs of bottomless abstract sculptures. The colors were gaudy, and there was a lot of mystical blue background and all the forms were sharply modeled as in commercial airbrush technique. The only painter who ever resembled Johnson was Helion, but his paintings were more vulgar than Helion's, and there were many more things in them all engaged in busy work. His pictures at least served two purposes: their existence assured me that I was not alone in the world and the victim of my own crackpot theories, and they taught me how not to paint. I studied their devices, and carefully avoided them.

Whether it was the golden section, Muensell's color sphere, even for a few weeks the Ouspensky-derived, fourth-dimensional geometrical design of Claude Bragdon, I tried them all. I was too naïve and ill informed to understand that any colored plane surface can be analyzed mathematically. Although the aesthetic behind this period in modern painting was mistaken, it provided painting with discipline. It produced interesting paintings, but more important, it was fun to do, and you had the additional satisfaction of feeling that you were more than just an artist, you were the peer of Newton with his apple and Clerk Maxwell with his magnets and Einstein with his orbit of Mercury. The funny thing about it is that the greatest painter produced by this school—Mondrian—didn't paint this way at all. The Pythagorean mathematics of dynamic symmetry were quite beyond him. He moved his spaces around whimsically, following the dictates of his sensibility, and he chose to paint in the three so-called primary colors, which of course are not primary at all, for completely demented mystical reasons derived from Rudolf Steiner. Several years later the Bauhaus published a booklet by him. I laboriously translated it and was appalled. Klee, on the other hand, knew more about this stuff than almost any other painter, and chose not to paint that way ever.

I don't understand why French painting—with the exception of Delaunay—had so little influence in America in those days. Everybody seemed to be anxious to distinguish himself from the Cubists by every means in his power. Partly, I think, this was militant provincialism, defiance of the capital. Partly it was the besetting sin of the American arts—the Poe-esque notion that if you had the right theory the masterpieces would appear automatically. About this time Bloch, the forgotten member of *Der Blauen Ritter*, showed up in Chicago and I for one turned expressionistic. I did a lot of improvisations in the Kandinsky manner, but I had sense enough to know that the best of them all was Klee. The sheer technical mastery of the drawings of the period of the "Suicide on the Bridge," the "Concert on the Twig," the "Tightrope Walker" has never even been approached by anyone else in modern times. I suppose it was the contrast between my own abilities and these things of Klee which first intimated to me that I would never be an artist of top rank. Klee's scratchy crow-quill pen drawings of those days were commonly coupled with George Grosz and there were many arguments as to who was better. I feel very pleased with myself today to remember that I knew.

Grosz was exciting just the same. Ben Hecht brought back from the Munich Commune, in which he liked to say he had been a participant (and maybe he had), a portfolio of drawings by George Grosz. They were printed in a little booklet by the Danish Anarchist or Left Com-

munist, Steen Heindriksen. Heindriksen was a friend of Herman
Gorter and Pannekoek, and was then working in Chicago as a printer.
These names mean nothing now, but Herman Gorter was the leader
of the brief Rotterdam Soviet and one of Holland's leading poets and
Pannekoek was a great astronomer who remained a Left Marxist
theoretician to his death in his late nineties, after the Second War. I
worked as a printer's devil for Steen and pulled the proofs on the first
book on George Grosz printed in the States. Another production of
the press was Yvor Winters' *The Magpie's Shadow*, a collection of one-
line, intensely imagistic poems, each poem in the center of a vast white
square of hand-laid paper. The title poem went: "Hunter. Run in the
magpie's shadow." In those days they seemed to me the poetic ana-
logues of Malevitch and Rodchenko. Steen Heindriksen also published
a magazine, *The Wave*, meaning by the title what the French nowadays call *la nouvelle vague*. Unfortunately there were few ripples of
the future available in Chicago in the Twenties, so he had to be content with studio sweepings and the unsalable manuscripts of Ben
Hecht, Vincent Starrett, and Sarah Teasdale. Here I first published a
poem. I no longer remember what it was, or even if it appeared under
my own name. For a while I used pseudonyms—the only one which
I remember was "J. Rand Talbot." There is no reason in the world why
I did this except that I was fifteen years old and thought writers should
have pen names.

Steen Heindriksen and a Dutch bookdealer by the name of Grenzenbach, who had actually taken part in the Rotterdam Soviet, introduced
me to the rigorously irreconcilable economic theories of Left Communism. I can see why Lenin wrote his book *Left Communism, an
Infantile Disorder;* such ideas are not of much use if you are trying to
run a revolution in a benighted country like Russia, but I for one was
overwhelmed by their soundness then in the first years of backwash
of world counterrevolution.

Heindriksen and Grenzenbach were the first men I had ever met
who were at home in European modernist culture. From them I first
heard about Maiakofsky, Benn, Marinetti, or Tzara not just as writers
but as living men whom they had known personally. They read me a
lot of modern poetry in the minor European languages. I no longer
have any idea of what it was, but the knowledge that someone was
trying to do in Danish or Hungarian or Flemish what I was trying to
do in American was encouraging.

All this activity reinforced in my mind the idea that I belonged to a
special elite whose mission it was to change the world. In a sense my
parents and my family tradition had fostered this and H. G. Wells's
The Research Magnificent had made it explicit, and now abstract

painting, "pure" Marxism, Cubist poetry—all, as far as I could see, of the activities of a tiny minority which was right while all the rest of the world was wrong—enormously reinforced this attitude. I looked on myself as one of Plato's Guardians. I became a passionate Platonist. I bought the Vaughan and Davies translations of the *Republic*, then considered the best, in the cheap Macmillan Golden Treasury Series. It was the cheapest available edition, but my copy was bound in three-quarters crimson levant. I carried it with me everywhere for years, on freight trains and in jail, and I still have it. I went up to Grenzenbach's bookshop and bought a library of philosophic classics, including both the Jowett and the Bohn Library Platos. I still have both of them.

There were all sorts of other things—Leibnitz, Lotze, Taylor's *Plotinus*, and Jacob Boehme's *Signature of All Things* in the Everyman's Library—but it was Plato who meant most to me for years. Today, although his Greek, which then I couldn't read, still seems to me the most beautiful prose ever written by man, his ideas are extremely offensive. I wouldn't go so far as to say that the Athenian democratic party was right in their disposal of the Socrates case, but I realize they were right in calling him an arrant reactionary and the leader of a vicious circle of *jeunesse dorée*. For all its beauty the *Republic* is, *hélas*, an open conspiracy of gentlemen pederasts. Young and innocent, I didn't realize this at the time. I suppose Platonism of a sort is what really lies behind the intellectual world that I was moving into —geometrical painting, poetry like Pierre Reverdy's, the music of Satie.

Although I read dutifully my newly purchased library (Kant and Hegel, for instance, in cheap school editions), I was unable to work up any enthusiasm for German philosophy, except for Leibnitz, who has classical elegance, beauty, and irrelevance. Descartes I have never really been able to understand. The problems that bothered him, like the problems that bothered the British empiricists, have simply never had meaning for me.

I had read about the Anarchist philosopher Max Stirner in Huneker, and I bought his *The Ego and His Own* and a whole set of Nietzsche, cheap, in a battered and water-stained condition. I found Stirner pretty crude, but for a while I was entranced with Nietzsche, and then the realization of his dreadful vulgarity began to grow on me. At first I thought it was the English translation and at last I realized that the vulgarity was built into the very foundations of his thought. My father once said, in an argument with a famous critic, "Nietzsche was a boor who peeped at gentlemen, and told." Those were the days before the Nazis had drawn the correct conclusions from Nietzsche. Lots of Anarchosyndicalists, IWWs and even Communists called themselves Nietzscheans. I'm glad I read Nietzsche then, because he taught me

the meaning of spiritual vulgarity. In recent years his popularity with
the existentialists has baffled me. I suppose the French are so totally
ethnocentric that they can't even see the page of Nietzsche in front of
them, and their fondness for him is at one with their fondness for the
equally dreadful Poe.

In that same purchase I also bought Rickaby's *Of God and His
Creatures*. This is a folio volume, beautifully printed; a free translation, considerably abridged, of Aquinas' *Summa Contra Gentiles*, the
first and for many years the only Aquinas in English. I had no idea that
there could exist a philosophically respectable justification for Christianity. Then, too, Aquinas was so pretty, like Leibnitz. He gave the
illusion of the same kind of mathematical elegance that makes Euclid
beautiful and convincing.

I bought Augustine's *The City of God* and his *Confessions*. Later I
was to come to enjoy Augustine's Latin, particularly his passionate,
mystical erotic dithyrambs. But reading these two books in the wooden
English of bad translations, I was horrified. I still remember him putting aside his poor wife as a whore because he had married her under
the auspices of a sect with a slightly different theory of the psychological processes in the inner recesses of the Trinity. There was his shameful guilt over his boyhood adventures about which, as lots of analysts
have pointed out since, he couldn't even tell the truth. Worst of all, as
a young esthete, was I shocked by his idea that the great Greek trage-
dians were vicious depraved men who worshiped devils. Platonist or
no, I have never been able to take Augustine seriously, except as perhaps the greatest writer of "poetic prose," a neurasthenic medium.

Hegel I plowed through doggedly, although every page seemed absolute nonsense. The only book which wasn't was the *Philosophy of
History;* here I could find my way around in a subject I knew well
enough to know that it was simply wrong. Ever since those days with
Spengler and Hegel and Flinders Petrie I have been a reader of philosophy of history. It is a fascinating subject and all of its practitioners
are about as sound and few of them as interesting as Ignatius Donnelly
and Judge Cooling. Although eventually I came to accept most of
Marx's purely technical economic analysis, even then I spotted the
profoundly irrational Hegelian undercurrent of his system.

At this same time I bought a copy of Bradley's *Appearance and Reality*. I still have the book. It had belonged to an English colonel in the
Straits Settlements who had filled the margins with learned and acute
notes. The cover is spongy with mildew, the glue has leaked away, and
all the pages are badly foxed. Bradley introduced me to the English
Hegelians and they have never ceased to fascinate me. Even the
American Josiah Royce, in spite of his style, seems to me still to have

had some profound insights. I am not sure that I am at home in the strange metaphysical world of the English Hegelians, but I don't really think that they owe very much to Hegel. The Absolute as a community of love is not really a Hegelian notion. I doubt if I believe it, but it seems to me a more wholesome metaphysical metaphor than most.

What I was looking for as a boy first turning to philosophy was an explanation for the experiences that have been the determinative core of my life, occasional moments of vision, not very easily fitted into a world of scientific materialism, in which I had seemed to rise above time and space, and momentary flashes of perfect communion with others—these things had led me to a hope that a philosophy which put the foundations of reality beyond time and space would best account for my own most important experience. Unfortunately, this does not seem to be the case. Philosophical speculations, which concern themselves with such matters, I was to find, were uniformly foolish. Some powerful hidden good sense saved me from becoming an occultist. I read Ouspensky's *Tertium Organum*. I had enough sense to know that this was egregious tosh, but it did provide me with a reading list. I read all of Taylor's Neoplatonist translations, Mead's *Hermes Trismegismus* and *Fragments of A Faith Forgotten*. The Theosophists I was never able to stomach. Try as I would, I could never get through more than a few pages of Madame Blavatsky. The only philosopher of this persuasion who ever stayed with me and whom I can still read is Boehme; and, of course ancestors of mine had been reading Boehme for hundreds of years. I am still moved by the tremendous beauty of his picture of the universe.

I went around with my head in the clouds thinking only the most elevated thoughts and with the sense that at any moment the ultimate mysteries of reality would reveal themselves to me. Gradually I discovered that philosophy, certainly philosophy since the Middle Ages, has never made anyone wiser or happier, and that the most extensive acquaintance with, and habit of, philosophical speculation has never imparted an iota of wisdom to anyone. Still, that sense of exaltation, that feeling of being on the brink of discovering the Absolute, is really a habit of living. I formed it then and never lost it and I am not sorry, although I have long since ceased to believe that there is anything to discover which doesn't meet the naked eye.

What I was learning, of course, is that philosophy is a work of art; the best philosophers were the ones who wrote best; the best systems were the prettiest. Nothing could be less like the real world than Plato's *Timaeus,* or Leibnitz's *Monadology,* or McTaggart's timeless, spaceless universe of love. Their virtues are of the same order as a fugue or a Cubist painting. I cannot understand why the practice of philosophy never imparts wisdom but rather the opposite. Imagine a college student going to the head of the philosophy department for advice about a pregnancy or venereal disease, or a decision to refuse to be drafted. The subject seems to have as deleterious effect upon good sense as the practice of poetry.

I learned that intelligence has nothing to do with wisdom. Leibnitz has always impressed me as being by far the most sheerly intelligent of philosophers. Few works of art ever impress you with the intelligence behind them. I have never stood in the Scuola di San Rocco without being overwhelmed by what Vasari called "the greatest mind ever to lend itself to painting." There is plenty of evidence that Tintoretto was a very wise man; there is no evidence that Leibnitz, in spite of his superlative intelligence and the beauty of his system, had any wisdom at all. Nowadays, wisdom in philosophy has gone completely out of date, and with the exception of Bertrand Russell and John Wisdom, contemporary philosophers are not even very bright.

I did respond to the only wisdom philosophers of the West, the Stoics and Epicureans. Fortunately, it was Marcus Aurelius and Epictetus whom I read, not the systemizers, except Lucretius. Still, I did find, amongst all those atoms, wisdom in Lucretius. I learned by heart his description of *taedium vitae* and his sermon on the senselessness of the fear of death.

I guess Aristotle is a philosopher for grown men. As a boy struggling with the horrible Bohn Library translations, I was unable to get anywhere with him.

Through reading about Plato I discovered Walter Pater. Although he is an ideal writer for adolescents, I am afraid he set me back, because it was through him as well as through the two homosexual boys in our high school set that I started reading the literature of the English Decadence. I still think that Pater's *Plato and Platonism* is one of the best books on Plato. The soundest way to approach Plato is via the English Decadence. In late Victorian England, I suppose, the upper classes realized his program on a larger scale than anywhere else except in a few Muslim courts.

About this time, under the stimulus of Plato, I started to teach myself Greek. I got some help from Mrs. Manley, but mostly I did it on my own. Eventually I was able to read the lustrous opening pages of the *Republic*, the starlike watchfires of the Greeks before the walls of Troy, and a poem of Sappho's. In spite of the crossword puzzle method by which I ferreted them out, I can still relive the ecstacy those words gave me.

Having taught myself the rudiments of Greek, I sat down to translate what are left of the poems of Sappho. One of the great experiences of my life is a long evening spent with a friend who was an undergraduate student of Paul Shorey's. Working on that Japanese-like fragment about the apple orchard, we analyzed and weighed and discussed exhaustively every word. A whole night was spent in a kind of fury and for the next few days I wandered around in a trance, overcome with joy.

About this same time, I ran across an early book of interlinear Romaji and English translations of Japanese poetry, possibly Clay MacCauley's *Hyakunin-Isshu*, and then Arthur Waley's *Japanese Poetry*, with its elementary grammar and fairly extensive vocabulary. I mastered this and then learned a handful of Chinese characters, and in the same year in which I puzzled out Sappho's "Apple Orchard" I did the same for "The deer on pine mountain/ Where there are no falling leaves/ Knows the coming of Autumn/ Only by the sound of his own voice," with the same results. This was the first thing that my daughter Mary ever read and the first thing that she ever printed out, and it is still her favorite poem, as it is certainly one of mine.

No poem of my own, for the obvious reason that no poem was even remotely as good, gave me the same thrilling rewards of artistic accomplishment as those two did. It is a wonderful thing to have been able when only a child to have partaken, however distantly, in the creation of a major masterpiece, and nothing would ever come up to it again. They are wonderful, those first kisses of the muse, and the memory remains, brilliant and poignant for the rest of life. Like a girl who never gives her heart to anyone else as she did to the boy who took her maidenhead—you have been ravished by eternity and you never quite recapture that sensation. More than my own poems those two translations were the first intimation I had of what it meant to be a creative artist. No painting was to give me these rewards for some time, because, as I say, nothing, poem or painting, of my own was very good. The abstract, rather Lissitsky-ish "Annunciation" I mentioned before was thrilling, and more so were the abstract portraits (so-called) I was doing of my friends, especially the ones of Naomi Fitzgerald and my social-worker girl friend who is due to turn up in a few pages. But their satisfactions didn't compare with the days of bliss left by those two four-line translations.

CHAPTER 17

Not long after I came to Chicago to live with my aunt, my father's mother died. Although while I had lived with her she had treated me with such violence as to cause a scandal, when she died she left me a small amount of money to be spent each year for clothes and other necessities.

I lived with my aunt's family for a year or so and then we decided that I would be happier if I rented a place nearby where I could come and go as I wanted and study, write, and even have a studio for painting.

At this time there was also a breakdown in the administration of my estate. My uncle had a friend, a dentist, a rather mealymouthed character who had volunteered to be my guardian. Unbeknown to my family, he had been defrauding me, and the probate court took the estate away from him and adopted me as its own ward.

After a conference with the judge, he decided to appoint himself my personal guardian, and from then on for several years he took a close interest in me. This was Judge Horner, who later became governor of Illinois. He was one of the few civilized men in Illinois politics, and a good person for a young boy to know. I visited at his home and went on a couple of trips with his family, and after he had visited me it was he who advised me to move.

I rented two rooms with a separate entrance and a kitchenette, quite a little apartment, on Calumet Avenue near Fifty-fourth Street. The people were Jewish garment trade unionists and Socialists, and more than typical. I took dinner with them and learned to cook Jewish dishes, and even to speak a little Yiddish. I got a larger stock of paints and a big studio easel. There was an old roll-top desk in their basement that we moved up. I moved out some of their more conventional furniture and built or painted other pieces. I decorated the walls with my mother's Medici prints, and there I was at sixteen with a genuine studio. They had a square piano that no one played, and I moved that in, too. I couldn't play it, but I could pick out the scores of my music

class and get at least a faint sense of the cadences of Thomas Tallis and
Orlando de Lassus.

Although I was still registered at Englewood High School, through
some kind of pull which I've forgotten, I started visiting classes at the
University of Chicago High School, which was incomparably better;
in fact, one of the best secondary schools in America. I was excited by
the way things were taught there—all languages by the direct method,
synthetic mathematics, the techniques of the best period of progressive
education. I bought the textbooks and started boning up. They were
certainly a great deal more fun to read than those of the public-school
system.

The only classes I continued at Englewood were Mrs. Manley's
Latin class and, in a hit-or-miss fashion, an advanced French class, because I had a crush on the teacher. Looking back with more experience, I suspect the teacher had a crush on me. She taught me tennis
and had me home for tea, her roommate at first chaperoning us. I
have forgotten her name, but I can still visualize her with the greatest
clarity. She was very handsome and very French. She looked almost
exactly like Irene Bordoni, and had a similar personality. For a little
while she invaded my life and more or less took me over. This passionate friendship began one day in class when she discovered that I
was reading Remy de Gourmont while I was supposed to be studying
grammar. She came up, looked over my shoulder, and said, "What are
you doing reading a book like that?" and I replied, "What do you think
I'm taking this class for, to learn to read *Sans Famille?*" She laughed
and said, "I'll see you after school. Perhaps I can help you." And she
did.

For several weeks we played tennis, sat in the park, read each other
Verlaine and such, and generally carried on like people in Colette. Her
roommate was an Alsatian from the University of Strasbourg, she herself a Parisian, and they both felt out of place and homesick in Chicago. They made me a mascot, and showed me off to their little set of
French people and French-Americans who lived by themselves and
few of whom I ever met anywhere again. They were cultivated enough
but they took no part in their own kind of life in American Chicago
and only appeared in public when the Symphony played Debussy or
the Art Institute had a show of post-Impressionists.

Finally the two girls took me up on the Near North Side to show me
bohemia, and discovered that I knew everybody in it. Then for a while
I took them around. I'm afraid it wasn't good for them. Slowly they
ceased to be passionate, Continental intellectuals and became Middle
Western bohemians. I have no memory of how this grand affair ended,
but as I look back now it seems to me that the gift of passionate Gallic

intimacy from what seemed to me to be a beautiful but middle-aged woman, although of course she was only a young girl, was too much for my intolerant adolescence and gradually came to exasperate me.

Shortly after this I was walking down the corridor in the high school when I ran into the principal, who called me into his office. He was a tall, thin, gray-faced, sunken-chested man, then about seventy. He looked like a bigoted Scotch dominie, straight out of Burns. He said, "You aren't coming to school. What is the matter?" I said, "Well, I don't find anything here to learn. I pass all the examinations, and even all the tests, if the teachers bother to give them to me, so I don't see why I should attend classes. I have better things to do with my time. I don't see that it makes any difference." He said, "What do you think would happen if everybody did as you did?" I said, "I think America would be an infinitely better place to live." This made him angry and he said, "But you don't go to anything any more. You made a tremendous fuss to take military training as a major subject, and you're the captain of the crack company. Now you've stopped going to that." I still wonder if my answer was genuinely naïve or if I was smart enough to have said it with malice. "Oh," I said, "you see, when I was young and fresh out of grammar school, like Lenin I still believed in turning the imperialist war into a civil war, but I don't believe that any more. I have become a pacifist."

He finally recovered enough to chase me out of the office and expel me, and said he would never allow me back in school. This created a terrible uproar amongst my teachers. They went to him and raised Cain and demanded that I be taken back. Finally he agreed to let me enroll again and in fact help me to graduate in three years, if I would first apologize to him. Teachers came and wept and pled with me, but I could see nothing to apologize for, and I never went back.

A couple of years later there was an investigation and scapegoats were immolated to create a smokescreen. The principal was arrested and charged with fantastic peculations. It was revealed that through him one of the South Side gangs of the pre-Capone epoch controlled the school and all its supplies and finances. He was sent to the penitentiary when in his seventies and there he died. As for me, I felt just like Elijah and the bears.

I still remember the effect on my English teacher. I suppose all English teachers live for the day they catch a budding writer. She was prostrated. She came to see me and had hysterics, and after that she gave me all the help and guidance she could. For several years she would come to see me and go over my manuscripts with me. Mrs. Manley, on the other hand, called me up and said I was perfectly right, and wished me luck. The two French girls thought it was all just hilarious.

Judge Horner had already got me the promise of a scholarship, I think for Oberlin, and he also got me a full-time scholarship at the Art Institute, neither of which I used. His attitude was "Oh well, the hell with it." He called me into his chambers and told me that if I went into business it would be better if I went on through college, because by the time I grew up a college degree would be a business requirement. But since I was going to be an artist and writer, conventional education would only do me harm, and the sooner I got out and started educating myself, the better. My aunt and uncle were terribly shocked. Most everyone I knew was sure I had ruined my life.

So instead of getting a good education and living a life which would have consisted largely of seminars in John Donne, about whom I would have written until I was old and gray, I had to go out and live, and so I had something to write about as the years went on. And, as it happened, due to this very expulsion I discovered John Donne.

As a ward of the probate court I suppose I was on record as a problem child. One day the doorbell rang. I went downstairs in a dirty apron with a paintbrush in my hand. Here was a girl who looked exactly like Katherine Mansfield on the dust jackets of her collected works—thin, exophthalmic, overbred, sensitive. I was nonplused.

"Are you Katherine Mansfield?" I said. She laughed and said, "No, but I wish I were. I'm from the Institute of Juvenile Research and I'm looking for a little boy named Kenneth Rexroth." "That's me," said I. I was standing in a rather dim hallway. She said, "Oh, I mean your son." I said, "I'm all the Kenneth Rexroth there is. Come up, you can sit and talk and entertain me while I work on a picture."

She came upstairs and sat down in the studio and looked around at the pictures. They were great big things, mostly geometrical abstractions or free improvisations. It was obvious that she had never seen anything like them, and she looked a little intimidated and embarrassed. I was scared to death, but I acted as cool as Lou Tellegen.

She said, "Well, now that I'm up here in the light, I can see that although you aren't a little boy, you aren't old enough to be your own father." And I said politely, "I can see you aren't Katherine Mansfield; you're much better-looking."

I made her some tea and we talked about the problems of my finances and education, and suddenly the atmosphere in the room became insufferably tense. Since I was only sixteen years old, I didn't know the proper things to do under the circumstances, or rather I did know them theoretically but I innocently believed that if I had done them she would have fled. I had already offered her a drink of wine, which seemed to take her aback—so I suggested we go out in the park for a walk and continue the discussion of my problems in the open air.

We walked around Washington Park and over to the Midway, and bought some groceries in a shop on Cottage Grove Avenue and walked back through the park to the island in the midst of the boating lake, near the purple-martin houses on their tall poles. We sat down under the twisted half-dwarfed pine trees which leaned over the water. This is one of the great romantic sites of American literature. Here Studs Lonigan first caught sight of the little blue panties of his childhood sweetheart. We sat and ate buns and salami and talked about Katherine Mansfield. My social worker was a poetess and short-story writer, and had already started to model herself on that affected and unhappy woman she resembled so much.

Just like Studs Lonigan, I sat and stared at her body as it revealed itself moving back and forth passing the mustard and leaning over for a light for her cigarette.

And I thought, "Within a few hours I'm going to be this girl's lover."

But I thought something much more important than that—I thought, "I guess this is what you do when you're grown up. This isn't anything like any of the relations I've had with girls before. I'm falling in love. This is the first time for the real thing. Nothing like this early autumn evening will ever happen to me again."

I had no doubts about what was going to happen. I knew this was going to mature into something of the greatest importance and last a long time. Not just the space between us but all the blue air of the park, full of watery lights and leaf smoke and swooping purple martins, was charged with overwhelming power.

Although she was about ten years older than I was, I was perfectly confident that she felt the same way. Whatever triviality we talked about, we made no pretense with each other, even in those first hours. I made a date for the next week, kissed her good-by as though I'd known her all my life, and went back to my studio and started to lay out an "abstract portrait" of her that is still one of the best pictures I ever painted. It was sold long since, but I have reproduced it several times from memory, and could do it again. I remember every color and detail perfectly: the blue light, and the slow rocking motion like the windless sails of a yacht at anchor.

CHAPTER 18

Not long after this I moved to the West Side. Much as I like Jewish food, my landlady wasn't a good cook nor an imaginative planner of menus, so I got out of the habit of coming to dinner and ate out or cooked in my own studio. Since I was no longer going to high school, I spent most of my free time up on the North Side and I'd get hung up by the lateness of the hour and spend the night in shakedowns on people's floors and davenports. The operation was costing more money than I had. I still had a part-time job as a drug clerk, and the income from my estate of seven to ten dollars a week bought a great deal more than it ever has since. In fact, you could get pretty good board in a boardinghouse for ten dollars a week. So I decided to move out.

I had been spending a lot of time around the Green Mask, a tearoom on Grand Avenue and State Street across from where Jazz Limited was later. It was in what Chicagoans call an English basement. Upstairs was a row of limestone-front houses which had been knocked together to form one immense brothel run by the Greek Syndicate. Alongside, in the other English basements, were marginal businesses like key makers and petty coal merchants. The Green Mask had nothing to do with the enterprise upstairs and neither the patrons nor the employees ever came in, although the madam was a fairly frequent visitor. She was stage-struck and had intellectual pretensions. However, the Greek Syndicate afforded the place free protection, and it was not subjected to shakedowns and payoffs. Also, State Street and Grand Avenue were in a neutral zone between the territory of the North Side and the South Side gangs. Also, the madam upstairs was the mistress of the boss of detectives at the East Chicago Avenue police station. These details are important to the success of an enterprise in Chicago.

The Green Mask was run by June Wiener, a slightly plump girl with a black Dutch bob, a large white nose, a rather beautiful face, and a most harum-scarum manner. She had been carnival performer, burlesque queen, chorus girl, and snake charmer. Her partner, Beryl

Bolton, had been the leading lady of the famous old heavy Frank Keenan. They had made a *Garden of Allah*-type movie, perhaps that very picture, in which she had ridden a camel on a treadmill all day into an airplane propeller at which two men continuously shoveled sand. This had removed the skin from her face, and she lived the rest of her life on the damages. They ran an extraordinary bohemian tearoom, quite the best that I have ever seen. Somebody else in the family died, so I got a few hundred dollars, and I invested it in this enterprise. Here I was, just kicked out of high school, part operator of a joint.

Both June and Beryl wrote poetry and painted pictures, all of a pagan sort. Around the walls were blue nudes dancing with silver fauns under crimson trees and shelves with books of free verse and books about the sexual revolution, and all the current little magazines. These in the course of time withered away as the customers stole them.

The place was a hangout for bona-fide artists, writers, musicians, and people from show business. June and Beryl seemed to know everyone of importance from Mercedes the Strong Woman to Little Mercedes, the Strong Woman for Singer's Midgets, and from Eva Le Gallienne to Bert Savoy. After the show the place filled up with headliners from the *Follies* and the Orpheum circuit as well as people from the burlesque shows. The girls had a friend, Gertrude, who was a concert pianist devoted to modern music, and she brought everyone in serious music who came to the city—composers and performers. So in a couple of years I met everybody in show business and in music who was of the slightest importance, and in addition the great female impersonators Bert Savoy, Julian Eltinge, who was not supposed to be gay but who had huge natural breasts, and Carole Normand, "The Creole Fashion Plate," known to her friends as "The Queer Old Chafing Dish." The latter were more than welcome but lesser fry came to stare and grew disorderly; and almost every night I had to kick out a savage little Mexican fairy known as Theda Bara, and her knife-toting pal, who weighed about four hundred pounds, the Slim Princess.

We gave poetry readings or lectures once a week. The chairmen were people like Ben Hecht and Sherwood Anderson. Once we had Clarence Darrow.

After we'd been in business a few weeks, in came a gaunt man with a bald, scabby dome of a head, banjo eyes with great pouches and irises like spittle, broken teeth and pendulous blue lips, a turkey neck which seemed stuck with pinfeathers, an immense Adam's apple, and huge, nicotine-stained hands with spatulate fingers that had thick, gray, broken nails. He took off his coat. He had on a dirty fancy vest, a candy-striped silk shirt with garters on the sleeves, and a black patent-leather snap-on bow tie. He sat down at the piano and started to play. And there he stayed from then on. He came in just as we were clearing away the dinner dishes every night and left when we did after the joint closed. He had either no bladder or a motorman's bottle, because he never left the piano stool. Each night he'd start off with a tumbler of gin and a sniff of coke. Once he got going, he'd open a cigarette case full of big cigarettes of marijuana made on a Russian cigarette machine, and smoke them chain fashion all night long. We provided the gin and he had his derby upside down on top of the piano for a kitty. He was known as K. C. Frank or just plain "Kansas City." For years I thought he was K. C. Frankie Melrose, but this man, I discover, was about my own age and came up years later and played almost entirely in the joints and roadhouses around South Chicago and northern Indiana. This K. C. put his name on a record date, probably in imitation of our man, who was no small-time bum. Our K. C. had once been a pianist with Joe Frisco, who was in the place almost every night when he was showing in town.

K. C. Frankie attracted many early jazz musicians to the place. I suppose all the ones that have since become legendary figures were in and out all the time, cornets and trombones under their arms. To us, I'm afraid, they were just a social problem and few of them seemed as good as Frankie himself. The Mask became the nightly after-hours spot for the inner core of the Coon-Saunders band who were straight out of a bad imitation of *The Sun Also Rises*. They made the early hours of the morning miserable with a constant racket of mayhem, drunken tears, attempted suicides, and fits of the horrors. They were kept together and kept functioning by a very pretty girl who looked rather like Norma Talmadge in her young days. She spent most of her time giving them psychological warm bottles and patting them so they could burp.

The first jazz musicians who started hanging around the Mask were members of a band which had played at Schiller's Café, where I had gone with my father. It was run by two brothers whose name I think was Stein, and then there was a very tall, emaciated clarinet player who used to eat in the place every night.

One night a skinny little boy came in with a whole mess of drums. For once we all realized we had a great artist. It was Dick Rough, the first and greatest of the hipsters and one of the few really great musicians in the history of jazz. It turned out that he also wrote poetry no better or worse than my own, a precocious kid's poetry. He and I became friends. In spite of the entire repertory of minor vices which were to become part of the jazz-man stereotype of a generation later, he was always welcome in the place. High, sick, gone, lushed, or just plain scared, everybody still loved him. He's been dead these many years, but I understand that a manuscript of his poetry still survives somewhere, and I wish some publisher would find it and take a look at it.

June Wiener had been a friend of Emma Goldman, and both girls were friends of Margaret Anderson and Jane Heap, the editors of *The Little Review*. I believe June came from an old Jewish Anarchist family. So we got the leaders of all the various radical sects in Chicago, a slightly more aristocratic crowd than hung around the Dill Pickle—editors of radical newspapers and publishing houses, strike leaders, and theoreticians. For a long time June managed to replenish the book stock as fast as it was stolen. On the shelves were all the early books of the poetic avant-garde and the theoreticians of revolution. Their authors were around the place if they lived in Chicago or when they were passing through town.

June and Beryl had both lived in France, and amongst the books in the library were French poets that I met for the first time. June was very fond of Alfred Jarry, on whose spirit, if not on his exact example, I think she patterned her life. She was always discovering wonderful poems in German, French, English, or Yiddish, chanting them over and over, staining them with coffee rings, tearing the books apart, and pinning them up on the wall. For a while all the literature of the avant-garde in the heyday of Dadaism was as available as the newspapers in an old-fashioned French restaurant. The stuff in foreign languages was stolen much more slowly than the stuff in English, and not only did I get a chance to read it if it was French, or to have June translate it for me if it was German or Yiddish, but now at last it wasn't just something in a book. Here I was, living it out, part of the scene, just like Tristan Tzara, even if it was only on Grand Avenue in Chicago.

In the Mask there gradually formed a small, permanent family of oddities who were there every night and never paid for their coffee. There was a hermaphrodite violinist: a tall yellow-faced youth with slit eyes, a prognathous jaw and a shock of hair that looked like a wig. He played the violin while his mother and father did a contortionist turn in carnivals and cheap vaudeville. His name was Aldebaran—they'd really named him that. There was a still very beautiful but quite demented ex-show girl and now unsuccessful prostitute—she scared all her tricks away—who looked exactly like a slightly faded blonde Gibson Girl. Her name was Angela d'Amore. There was Willy McCauley, a mediocre, "decadent" sculptor and worse poet, but a boy with a special talent for an outlandish, adventurous life. There was a very light, freckled-faced Negro, what Negros call a "marino," who claimed to be the illegitimate son of a British admiral and a Haitian princess. Since there aren't any Haitian princesses, there was something wrong with his story. He had dyed red hair, ultraconservative clothes in the height of fashion, and wore an egg-shaped eyeglass without ribbon or rim. There was Mick McCann, the beautiful, dark Irish captain of the Boston Bloomers and the world's champion lady boxer, with whom I fell in love; Louis Rosenberg, a beery hobo tenor with a bouncing belly who got odd jobs as a burlesque comedian; and, last, a spectacular redheaded burlesque queen known as Lorelei, although she was Irish.

Gertrude, the concert pianist, was a close friend of Chicago's leading Negro banker, and an even closer friend of his two mistresses, "Black and White." One was very dark and always wore white clothes, and the other was white and always wore black. They brought a lot of South Side high society, music, and underworld to the place. Another close friend of Gertrude's was Lillian Hardin, Louis Armstrong's first wife. Lil was a young woman who had been valedictorian of her class at Fisk and had started out as a concert pianist with ambitions to be a composer. Contrary to legend, the music of the bands that she played with in those days was not blown spontaneously into the air, but was composed, written down, and carefully coached on the piano by Lil. I have little memory of others of the Oliver band around the place; possibly this was before its formation. Just before I left Chicago I met Louis, then an innocent youth too big for his collar, with a farm-boy manner. He was eager for culture and busy absorbing all the education Lil could give him. I developed quite a crush on Lillian Hardin and used to go out to the South Side to the places she was playing. However, the Sunset, Dreamland, and later places were terribly expensive. In the first years our favorite hangout and the hangout for most musicians who weren't working was a dirty little dump called the Fiume, the customers of which were very sinister characters indeed. It had been a spaghetti joint in the days when Eighteenth and State was an Italian neighborhood and nobody ever bothered to change the sign. It served nothing whatever except moonshine made of potatoes in dirty white coffee mugs. The stuff had the stench of an ill-kept morgue, but it was guaranteed never to leave you with a hangover. All the early musicians and singers of the kind the discographers now call primitive played there.

We got a few of these people back up at the Mask, but mostly more educated and sophisticated Negroes like Alberta Hunter, Isabel Du Cagne, and Jimmy Yancey. Irene Castle was a regular visitor to the Mask and she was always showing up with people who had been in Jim Europe's band, the men who founded the New York school of jazz. Fenton Johnson, who remains one of the best Negro poets, was a close friend and I suppose could be called one of my early teachers. I don't think he was any relation, but he knew the Johnson brothers and always brought them around when one or the other came from New York. Bands were already appearing on the road with Frisco and Jimmy Durante and I believe there was a colored band in either the *Scandals* or *The Passing Show* of those years. Anyway, they all came to the Mask after showtime and we used to pile in cabs and take over the Fiume along about dawn.

Joe Frisco was billed in Palace Time first as the "American Apache" and then as the "Jass Dancer." He had a little girl partner who looked just like Moreau's "Salomé." With her, too, I fell in love; all the pronounced types seemed to attract me in those days. I used to take her out when she wasn't working and desperately tried to learn Frisco's routines. These were the first "air steps" anybody in the North had ever seen and resembled the most advanced jitterbugging of the end of swing. I presume that Frisco had learned them by watching the conniptions in Congo Square. Imitating him, I was always getting chucked off dance floors for hurling around some foolhardy girl.

I'm afraid that I can't provide any inside information about the formative years of jazz, for the simple reason that none of us knew that this was what was happening. We didn't know we were making history and we didn't think we were important. People were always trotting in and out with horns under their arms—Dick Rough played something else beside the drums, although for the life of me I can't remember what it was. Great as he was, we weren't very enthusiastic about the services of volunteer drummers. Jazz was pretty hot and made a lot of noise. People talked loud to be heard above it, got thirsty and drank too much and made trouble, so we tried to keep the jazz small and cool. "Cool" is far from a new concept. I remember many nights going over to the piano and saying, "For Christ's sake, cool it or you'll get us all busted!"

Then, even as now, some jazz musicians were difficult types. The best musician in the Coon-Saunders group had been shell-shocked, and at the sound of an automobile backfire or a fire engine he would go into a fit like *furor epilepticus* and start throwing chairs and tables at people. Another one in the group was always jumping out of windows, although he usually picked low ones. The girl who was the mother goddess and Great Mother of the group, and kept them alive, dropped out when they went to New York, and as I remember the group broke up in a rash of suicides and psychoses.

Those were the days before entertainment licenses and unionization, so that we had a continuous free floor show. Many nights when the *Follies* was in town Bert Savoy would keep the crowd entertained from one to four in the morning with an always new stream of drag-queen jokes, far filthier than any he ever pulled in the *Follies*, although those were filthy enough. Alberta Hunter used to sing, and I realize how long ago this was, because she is the only singer still in the business left from those days. Alberta, of course, has long since ceased to sing blues. She plays mothers and old servants in the movies and sings lead parts in chorales of Bach and Mozart. Bert Williams was another free entertainer and he, too, had a private repertory which never got on the stage, although in his case these numbers were simply authentic Negro humor. There were a lot of great burlesque and circus clowns who used to come and go, but I don't remember now who they were.

There was a beautiful and wealthy Negro woman who used to sing excessively modern salon songs, like Milhaud's settings of Tagore. I wrote some words for her to a couple of the *Sodades Do Brazil*, "*Leme*" and "*Botofogo*," which I wish I had today. As I remember, most of this stuff was a bit thick. Back in those days there was a huge repertory of vocal music of the *Pierrot Lunaire* order, of a rather theo-sophical cast, very mystical, like female unicorns (female unicorns do not exist—the unicorn is only male, but he doesn't exist either) bleat-ing, lost in a dense fog. It seems to have gone out of favor. Cyril Scott, Leo Ornstein, Van Dieren—all the heart-rending settings of Maeter-linck and D'Annunzio—where are they now? It was before the shawm and the clavichord had invaded night clubs, but we had disciples of Arnold Dolmetch, who played Bull and Byrd on the piano with all the archeologically correct mordents in the right places.

In spite of this array of talent, by far our most successful evenings were the Thursdays given to poetry. We got everybody to read, even Chicago's most seclusive and asocial poet, Edgar Lee Masters. There was a succession of Negro poets, of whom the best was Fenton John-son, locally, and Langston Hughes from New York; also Countee Cul-len, Claude McKay, as well as many others of the leaders of the New Negro who started out in life writing verse and later became sociolo-gists, anthropologists, politicians, trade-union leaders. It's remarkable how many of them in those days were poets. In fact, the Talented Tenth of the Twenties all seemed to have started out on their careers writing verse, not unlike Chinese mandarins.

A lot of the poetry readings were trash, but all the important poets around Chicago read there, too. Here happened the first reading of poetry to jazz that I know of. The readers were several people I can't recall and Mark Turbyfull, Sam Putnam, Louis Rosenberg, and myself.

I suppose it was Dick Rough who brought down a whole lot of drums of a kind I had never seen before. I guess they were congos and bongos and such. I remember some Chinese and Japanese drums. Anyway, there was a most exotic percussion battery, and to this and a piano and a horn and once in a while a bass I read some poetry. The percussion makes it sound frightfully arty, but it couldn't have been too arty with K. C. Frank at the piano. Who the others were, I don't know. The horn was so drunk he could hardly stand, and eventually blew very nicely sitting down on a backward kitchen chair. About this time Langston Hughes was doing the same thing in New York. I read the poems I had read on the soapbox, a lot of Whitman and Sandburg and popular low-life poetry to what nowadays would be called primitive piano as accompaniment. That is, the piano took the line most of the time. Besides this we did more pensive numbers to slow and solemn music—like Matthew Arnold's "Dover Beach." And then, too, I read translations of contemporary French poetry to modernist improvisations by Gertrude, full of tone clusters and hand- or table-knife-plucked piano strings, just like Leo Ornstein or, years afterward, Henry Cowell.

There was never any dearth of poets. In fact, some of the leading ones of those days, like Vachel Lindsay and Maxwell Bodenheim, had to be forcefully discouraged. Bodenheim and his wife Minna, who was the office secretary for the IWW, ate in the place every night. On Saturdays Minna helped out as waitress. Minna was busy feeding Max up because she was anxious to have a child. We provided the high-protein diet.

Sandburg was just beginning his career as a folk singer, and he came down several times with his guitar.

What all this activity meant was that I had no sooner left home and been kicked out of high school than I was thrown into a world of celebrities as though I had suddenly become Texas Guinan or Toots Shor, except that our celebrities came from a much wider world than the limited one that patronized Toots Shor, let alone Texas Guinan. This was before the speak-easy had developed a clear pattern and before the night club had grown out of it, and somehow we managed to keep the Green Mask for ourselves.

No rubberneck buses unloaded at the door. June simply refused to seat tourists, and if they got past her she had such a devastating way with her that they quickly left. Also, the myth of the Twenties falsifies history. In its early days Prohibition worked fairly well. Liquor was hard to get and most people drank relatively little. We did not serve liquor, only setups, and the customers were not allowed to put bottles on the tables or even on the floor. If they got drunk they were thrown out. I think the place was probably too serious to attract tourists, although we didn't think we were being serious at all.

Another thing, everybody in Chicago in those days of any importance in the arts considered himself a Red, which doesn't mean a Bolshevik. The city editor of the *Herald and Examiner* and the highest-paid reporters on the *Tribune* carried Wobbly cards. Most people called themselves Anarchists. I have no memory of anybody who believed in capitalist society, its values or its political parties. In fact, I can't even remember anybody, except a few aged leaders, who was bourgeois enough to call himself a Socialist. This radical atmosphere kept out the squares and scissorbills.

The citizenry stayed away from places where Negroes were seated at their tables and where somebody might burst into "I'm a stranger in your city, my name is Paddy Flynn," or one of the Joe Hill songs, or, after midnight, "The Three Old Whores of Canada," and the whole room take it up. This scared people back in those days and we were left to ourselves. That was fine, because there were plenty of us.

What I was witnessing was the development in a few places in Chicago, New York, and Paris of a culture pattern that was to spread all over the world. In another generation all professional people of any pretense to bohemianism in Sydney and Oslo did the things we did, but back in those days we all knew one another.

Even the riffraff who hung around the place and ate the free dinners were far from being plain bums. Aldebaran wrote fair poetry of a decadent cast. Angela d'Amore was writing her memoirs, *Born and Raised a Prostitute*. The only trouble was she was a psychopathic liar, so instead of writing a record of the fascinating facts of her life, she invented and produced just another "kidnaped into white slavery" tract.

The Lorelei was a burlesque star, and could even sing and dance. I used to go to the Haymarket or the Star and Garter and watch her come down the runway in one of those wonderful old burlesque costumes, all red velvet and gold fringe and tassels, like a circus pony. That was before strippers, but she used to do the Dance of the Seven Veils at smokers, and I used to go along as escort, since her husband was incapable of punching his way out of a wet paper sack.

Mick McCann really was a terrific boxer, fencer, and lady rassler, although on the stage these female fights are always fakes. I used to go with her to the same burlesque shows where matches were staged between the acts, and act as her second. I wore a big bright yellow wig and a pink tie and camped as no fairy would dare do. I beat her with a towel, pumped her arms and legs up and down and blew water in her face between rounds, and tied and untied her tin tits in a long comic routine. Later I got a job as a general relief man and filled in mostly for the candy butcher, but also for the comics and straight men. So my first real job in the theater was at the Star and Garter. Once you've been in burlesque you can always pick up odd jobs, and I did this sort of thing off and on for years.

The Lorelei had a husband, Jimmy Feely, who decorated lamp-shades and made plaster figures of the kind you win at carnivals. He looked like an overgrown spaniel in an advanced stage of distemper. His great brown eyes were straight out of Landseer. Although I knew him for years afterward and his relations with other women were not of that sort, with the Lorelei he was extremely masochistic. I remember him in those days whimpering and often weeping, and following her around half doubled over in a state of semiprostration.

One off night the little set of oddities were all sittng around the fire having a nice naïve conversation about what makes a really sophisti-cated bohemian. I was standing there silent and intimidated by all the wit and beauty, but I guess looking very cool, scared to open my mouth. The Lorelei leaned back on the davenport and looked up at me with a good deal of cleavage and said, "I think Rex is the most sophisti-cated person here!" and then proceeded to describe what she thought were the cool inner recesses of my most sophisticated personality. I was so terrified I almost fainted away.

A few nights later we were shutting up the place and I was talking about how much trouble and expense it was to go out to the South Side every night. The Lorelei said, "Why don't you move in with us? Jimmy and I would be delighted to have you. Wouldn't we, Jimmy?" While I, scared once again, was fumbling for words June said, "Oh no, he doesn't need to do that. He's got a nice place out on the South Side and there's plenty of take in this joint. We can always afford cab fare."

I should say in parentheses that we had no cash register, or even cashbox, and nobody ever kept track of income or outgo. June just stuffed the money down the front of her blouse or in her stocking until bills began to peek out like straw out of the Scarecrow of Oz, and then she'd go back and empty it in a large coffeepot.

I didn't realize that June was trying to protect me, and after I had recovered sufficiently from the great honor of this invitation, I agreed, sight unseen to move in. Nor did I realize that my tiny income seemed like a fortune to the Lorelei and Jimmy.

My uncle and I loaded the South Side studio—easel, paints, books, typewriter—onto his truck and unloaded it into the best room in the Feelys' English basement apartment over on West Adams Street. The Lorelei stood about in an advanced state of negligee, smoking black Mexican cigarettes while my uncle ogled her as he came and went.

It wasn't at all a bad place—a large, dry, sunny room with two bay windows, a small side room, and a private shower and toilet. I un-packed my paintings and very modestly inquired if I could hang some

on the wall. I was quite sure from Jimmy's conversation that he was another Picasso, and that my childish efforts looked very unskilled to him.
Later I discovered that they were the first paintings of the kind he had
ever seen.

After a few minutes of rather self-conscious conversation the Lorelei
took a quarter out of a garter purse—something I don't believe is worn
nowadays—flipped it up in the air, and said with a fine sadistic curl on
her proud and curtal lip, "Jimmy, hop out and get a pack of Humps."
After an Oriental bow and scrape, Jimmy vanished, and the Lorelei
teetered over toward me, hands on rolling hips, long bright orange hair
down her back, black lace over pink and white baby skin, and said,
"What a heel, what a heel!" I sat with my precious copy of Lawrence
Binyon's *Painting in the Far East* held meditatively in my hand, just
kicked out of high school and finally definitely moved away from home,
and thought, "Ah—life is beginning."

CHAPTER 19

I had a good enough life in my own chambers, as they call them in British novels, and I soon learned to keep the communicating door locked. The Feelys' orgies were more noisy than violent. They seemed to be mostly ritual, but the Lorelei was a consummate ritualist. Their whole life was a little sad. She was ill a good deal of the time, and when she wasn't ill she spent the afternoon entertaining an assortment of shady friends. Born in Georgia, she was a passionate—in fact, paranoid—Negrophobe. She never came back from a streetcar ride without complaining that the stink of the dirty ——s made her sick. She was a pushover for any *café-au-lait* charmer with straightened hair. Her clandestine guests were putative Cubans, Mexicans, Portuguese, and she accepted them all at face value, although most of them had stronger accents than her own strong redneck one.

Although he could certainly have got a better job, Jimmy had a nice masochistic position operating a loom in a rug factory. He worked from 1 P.M. to 11 P.M. and came home at midnight completely covered with lint, as though he had mildewed in a cellar for weeks. Hair, face, clothes, shoes—he was one uniform fuzzy gray. This gave him the appearance of the three-toed sloth in whose fur lives a symbiotic fungus —or the abominable snowman. The Lorelei was an incredibly bad cook, but she usually had some scorched floury mess fried for him to eat, and after he had spent an hour cleaning up they had dinner and went to the Near North Side to relax. I took my meals at the Green Mask and stayed downtown for the rest of the evening. The few midnight dinners I had with them are among the most gruesome repasts in my memory. The elaborately acted-out liturgy of sadomasochism never stopped, but as far as I was concerned the really horrifying thing was the cuisine, a subtle blend of whorehouse, shanty-Irish, and Georgia, always burned.

At last the job got too much for Jimmy's pleasure in self-torture. The lint caused first a static pneumonia, and then a chronic lung infection from which he never fully recovered and which killed him three years later. He was sick for several weeks and we lived on my seven dollars a week and the Lorelei's rare earnings. Most of her work was for charity. As soon as Jimmy got out of bed, emaciated, with enormous eyes, blue lips, and a baying cough, the Feelys started on a career of high-class beggary and petty thievery. The Lorelei was an expert shoplifter. One time she rented an open touring car and parked it in the alley against the Hub, one of Chicago's better-class men's furnishing stores. Jimmy went up to the third floor, where the best ready-made men's suits were, and threw half a tableload of them out of the window into the car. Another time they showed up with three sable coats. I never did find out how they got them. Christmas, Jimmy took her picture and went from door to door along Chicago's fashionable Astor Place. Somehow he got past the butlers and housemaids and told the grand rich a story of how his beautiful wife was blind and pregnant and he was dying of tuberculosis and had nothing to give her for Christmas. She waited down at the corner with a car and they filled it up with everything from pearl necklaces to scarcely used vacuum cleaners to several complete sets of baby equipment, diapers, cribs, sterilizers, and hundreds of bottles. Whoever they fenced all this stuff with must have cheated them, because as far as I could make out the principal source of income remained the money I paid for board.

When they decided to go into the badger game, I decided this was too dangerous. It might cause more trouble than I could keep on the other side of my locked door, so I moved out. For a while the Lorelei brought home aged, harmless suckers, and they made quite a bit of money. One night she got a little drunk and picked up a dark-skinned, marcel-haired handsome plug-ugly who called himself Rocky Alvarez. It would seem that she wasn't quite sure whether he was a john to exploit or a new lover to cuckold Jimmy, but she was too tipsy to care and brought him home to bed. Jimmy burst into the room, Irish-setter eyes blazing, cough baying like a bloodhound, in his hand an immense .45 with a broken action and no bullets. Rocky got out of bed in his BVDs, took the gun away from him, slapped him silly, and put him out in the snow. When he got back into bed he reached over and took his D. J. (Department of Justice) card out of his pants, and showed it to the Lorelei. For a week they kept Jimmy locked out of the house, and then one night moved out and took everything of value with them, including the three sable coats that Jimmy had been afraid to sell.

About six months later the Lorelei disappeared for good, this time with an unquestionably Negro boxer, Tiger Flowers. They were both found stabbed to death in Oakland two years later.

Jimmy ran to me for rescue and I had him on my hands, uninterruptedly prostrated with hysterical grief, for the rest of the winter. He carried around her dirty underwear and wept over it in public places. He stuck up pedestrians, bought bunches of four-foot roses, and tried to break in the underworld speak-easies where the Lorelei was drinking with Rocky. He broke into their hotel room, and they found him full of veronal, snoring on the bed with a sheet of bad poetry pinned to his chest. Worst of all, he kept me awake or interrupted my work with his fits, vapors, and tantrums.

To go back to the beginning of this episode, shortly after I moved in, Judge Horner came to see me and scared the Feelys out of their wits. They shook and trembled and bowed and scraped, and the Judge made knowing, sly, sarcastic remarks to the Lorelei. That night he took me to dinner at the Saddle and Sirloin Club, and told me he thought I was going about being a writer in the correct way but that I should be careful to keep out of jail. "Let the other people do it," he said. "Your job is to record it. Let your characters do your sinning for you—at least the kind that will get you in trouble. What would you think of a de-tective-story writer who had to kill somebody every time he wrote a book?" We spent the rest of the evening in the Green Mask, where the Judge had a fine time, and when his chauffeur came to pick him up he gave me a card and said, "Here's a number that will always get you through to me wherever I am. Try and keep out of trouble."

It was through the Feelys that I first met the cheap and unsuccessful underworld, the fumbling pickpockets and stumbling prowlers and bumbling, implausible con men who can be found any morning in the lineup. Through the Lorelei—but not through Jimmy—I also met a pretty mess of high-class stool pigeons, crooked detectives, and embez-zling gangsters, like Rocky Alvarez. In addition, there were plenty of tramp bohemians from the bottom rungs of Near North Side society always about the house. I soon learned to be ruthless. I kept them on the other side of the door.

The door wasn't enough. My bed was in one of the bays and I slept with my head in the wide-open window. One night one of the worst female problems in the Feelys' select circle, Maggie McGinnis, the daughter of a police-court judge, climbed drunkenly through the win-dow and straight into bed with me. I would hardly say this began an affair. It was my first encounter with that ever-recurrent pest of the artist who ventures into bohemia—the incurable, unshakable case of female trouble. For a while I had Maggie on my hands, getting her out of jail, bailing her out of speak-easies where she'd get drunk with-out any money, saving her from various petty crooks who blackmailed her, and taking her to a doctor for real troubles. All this time she had a husband, a solemn, courteous young Swede, so brokenhearted his com-pany was unbearable. He had lost the emotional strength to help her any more. One night long after I had stopped seeing her, I got a telephone call from a dick I knew at the East Chicago police station. I called up her husband and we went over to a cheap hotel on Dearborn Street where she lay on a dirty bed in a pond of blood—her head practically cut off her body. Nobody ever found out who did it, or why, or any of the circumstances. As the years have gone by I have met a good many pitiful psychopathic personalities like her, girls hell-bent for self-destruction, but after her I've never been able to take them as seriously as they wished. She really meant business.

Other than this episode, which really wasn't a part of my own life—however harrowing it was—I managed to keep from getting involved in the Feelys' shifty, petty, and dangerous world. Once Jimmy was free of the Lorelei, he escaped from it himself. He remained a bohemian intellectual until his death, but his orgies with his redhead seemed to have purged him of more dangerous tendencies and appetites.

By this time the Green Mask had begun to wear on me, and I used to escape by taking one or two close friends and going to one of the Levantine coffee shops then dotted along North Clark Street, to spend the evening drinking moustike, smoking a narghile, and watching the belly dancers. These were fine places to dodge the pressures of organized bohemia. No one ever went there in those days but Greeks, Turks, and Syrians. The music and dancing were splendid, the girls were beautiful (they were never Levantines themselves, but American girls who could wiggle and who memorized the songs without understanding the words.) The liquor was the safest to be found during Prohibition. In the next year or so they became the favorite hangouts for Chicago newspapermen, but in those days they were still unsullied.

CHAPTER 20

Shortly after I left the Feelys I became a newspaperman myself. I started where all Chicago journalists start—I got a job on the City News Bureau, a local press service like Associated Press that covered the petty courts, the morgue, and the police stations for all the Chicago papers.

I don't think I kept the job on the News Bureau very long. It paid almost nothing, eighteen dollars a week, and was deadly dull, especially the divorce court. Cub reporters are sent to the divorce court either because what happens is so dull and repetitious that it would interest no one or so filthy dirty that it couldn't be printed—it's just dumfounding the things people say in divorce courts—or because it's big, hot, and important, a Society case, and the paper sends an experienced man, or more often woman, to cover it. I suppose I learned some more about the great American sexual sickness, but it didn't interest me very much.

I quit and went over to the *Journal of Commerce*. On this job I covered conventions—a dreadful occupation. However, conventions are entertained by strip teasers, naked dancers, and French circuses in order of importance of the convention. If one of the major industries throws a convention they provide a call girl for each delegate and a five-act show with top models in *flagrante delicto* with armadillos and other beasts of burden, while the Hyde Park Plumbers have to put up with one elderly, unemployed burlesque stripper. Since conventions become rather savage as the evening wears away, it is an accepted custom for the entertainers to ask the newspapermen present to escort them to safety. So I met a lot of nice girls, those I hadn't met already around the Mask, where most of them hung out.

The editor of the *Journal of Commerce* was a pacifist and poet by the name of Hi Simons. He had done hard time as a conscientious objector and had written a book of prison poems called *Orioles and Blackbirds*. I don't know who owned the paper but I have the impression that he was a rich man who didn't have very much use for the war either, and had given the job to Hi as an award of merit for courage under fire. A nice bunch worked on the paper. The offices were just down the street from the Green Mask, and I opened it up at noon and put out a lunch. I had a good enough time—banquets every night, good liquor to drink, and an endless succession of sad and beautiful women to take home. Since I was expected to be around the Mask part of the time, I found I wasn't getting any work done. Also, of course, I was drinking too much for a young boy. From the *Journal of Commerce* I went to the *Herald and Examiner*.

On the paper there was a girl who called herself Mitzi Duclos. She was tiny, almost a midget, with a large, spherical head, yellow skin and Dutch bob and perpetually raised eyebrows. She looked like a wobbly-headed Japanese Kokeshi doll. She had a flair for trouble and dissipation, which made her a most successful newspaperwoman while she lasted.

One night we were sitting in an expensive low dive, a remodeled mansion, called the Radio Club, with the Lorelei and Rocky Alvarez. Our table was at the back, separated from the garden by a kind of half-conservatory, a glassed-in bay with a little fountain and potted ferns and rubber plants. Suddenly there was a terrible racket, exactly like it sounds in the movies, and most of the glass was shattered by a zigzag stream of submachine-gun bullets. Rocky tipped up the heavy oak table and got down behind it and started plugging away with a Police Special. The Lorelei, Mitzi, and I crawled away to safety on our bellies. Nothing happened. Some of the customers ran away, but the owner straightened up the place and business went on as usual. The police never came; Rocky swore convincingly that he hadn't the faintest idea who'd done it. Drinks for us, for the rest of the night, were on the house. That was the last I ever saw of the Lorelei. I suppose that haughty, high-borne behind, flaming hair, and heavy sneering lips of the professional sadist drew violence and bloodshed as bad meat draws flies.

Mitzi was exactly the opposite type. She looked as though she had been born to be dropped in the Bosphorus in a sack, and so she was. Her life, too, was filled with senseless violence and in a couple of years she was killed.

My high school chum Aloysius Gonzaga Murphy had shown up on the Near North Side, a hotshot reporter. He had two inseparable companions, a sarcastic young Frenchman named Ted Boudin and a large, lean, sallow Irish drunk, Bugs Riley. Of course, they were known as the Three Musketeers. I don't know just how they managed it with the city desk, but they seemed to show up on big stories together.

One night I came in to one of Joey Aiello's speak-easies and they were all sitting there with a very drunk and excited little woman in a short imitation ermine coat. "Meet Francie," said Riley, with a large drunken gesture. "She just blew the brains out of her old man." (Before I go on I should warn you this has been turned into a movie—nevertheless it's basically true.) Francie tittered and said with housewifely politeness, "Won't you please sit down?"

Everybody started to tell me the story at once, except Francie. Riley had been loafing around the East Chicago Avenue station, sampling some of the liquor the captain had reserved from the last couple of raids, when the phone rang on the captain's desk. In the fashion of the newspaperman of those days, Riley languidly leaned over, said, "Allow me!" and picked up the receiver. The voice on the other end said, "This is Mrs. Frances Winson. I have just murdered my husband." Riley remained steeped in languor. "Why hello, honey," he said, "this *is* Francis X. Riley speaking. I'm sure glad to hear from you. Don't do a thing. I'll be right over. Where are you?" he went out to a phone booth, called up a lawyer and the paper, located Boudin and Murphy and a cameraman, and arrived at Francie's, ready for work.

It was two hours and more before anyone notified the police, and by that time Francie had been filled with the best liquor, and not just coached but completely hypnotized into the role she was to play. I don't know how they managed it, but she never spent any time under lock and key. She went over to the station and out on bail as though she was guilty of a traffic violation. So began one of Chicago's more uproarious murder trials. I suppose, considering the circumstances, it must have been a trial for manslaughter. Murderers are not allowed out on bail, unless they are gangsters, even in Chicago.

Francie and her husband had owned their home, a dignified brownstone front on the Near North Side. The boys took it over, and in seventy hours it was a total shambles. There were open cases of liquor in the hallways, smudged blondes sleeping in the bedrooms, the plumbing was broken, the phone rang without interruption, cops and newspapermen played poker in the kitchen, other smudged blondes in their stepins played the piano in the parlor, everybody ground out their butts in the rug. The dog wouldn't come in the door but bayed in the backyard day and night. One by one windows got broken.

Every day in court was rehearsed beforehand by practically the whole cast on both sides, prosecution and defense. These dramatic sessions usually lasted until well after midnight, when one by one the participants passed out. It was a murder case straight out of the Marx Brothers, and like the straight woman in the Marx Brothers, Francie, until she had been filled with liquor and hypnotized by three comic Svengalis, was an ordinary, middle-class housewife, gentle and puritanical. For all I know, she may actually have killed her husband by accident. She was acquitted, and immediately vanished. I hope she was pensioned off by the newspaper, because the Three Musketeers had made a wreck of her goods and chattels.

It's hard to believe the Chicago of those days. Not only is every episode in Ben Hecht's *The Front Page* based on fact, but every character is a portrayal of some Chicago newspaperman of the time. Furthermore, this stuff wasn't isolated and occasional; it went on all around you all the time. One day I was eating, I still remember, baked whitefish in a restaurant at State Street and Chicago Avenue. This was a half-basement place; the windows look out on Holy Name Cathedral. Suddenly there was a familiar roar and rattle overhead. A man from the district attorney's office and a couple of other gangsters, just emerging from a funeral, tumbled over on the steps of the Cathedral and a line of machine-gun bullets punctuated the pious Latin on the cornerstone, "To the Glory of God and the Most Holy Name of Jesus."

One morning, about six, I woke up to find the room full of Law. Willy McCauley and the poet Ray Larsen were sleeping on the day bed and davenport. We'd been up all night talking about art and letters. They took us down to the Detective Bureau, mugged us, fingerprinted us, and worked us over—showed us the goldfish, as it is known. It was a little like the Moscow trials, because nobody told us what we were to confess to. About ten o'clock that night, having had nothing to eat, drink, or smoke, with black eyes, split eyebrows, torn lips, sprained fingers, burned toes, and missing a tooth or two, we were kicked out the door, literally kicked, with no explanation. When we got back to my place we learned that the boys in the back room had missed a wallet and called the cops. They discovered it in a couple of hours behind the dresser, but neglected to notify the police until the police called them fourteen hours later. For those fourteen hours we had been kept uninterruptedly busy. One thing you can say for the Chicago cops, they liked their work.

Newspaper work was far from being romantic. Most of it was dull. It was far from being a school for good writing in those days. In fact, long addiction to city-room journalism had practically incurable deleterious effects. Journalism classes tell you the papers demand the utmost compression and concentration on pure facts. Nothing was less true in the Twenties. All important local news in a city the size of Chicago could usually be put in one column. Nobody really cared much about facts, just the appearance of factuality. One of the signs of a good journalist was the ability to work at least one serious misstatement into every three sentences. Everything was puffed and padded out of all recognition, and it was puffed and padded with sentimentality. The

Chicago writers of my youth—Anderson, Hecht, Sandburg, Sam Putnam—all might have been good writers if they hadn't been corrupted by the awful sentimentality of the police-court reporter. Sob-sister journalese was the distinguishing characteristic of the Chicago Renaissance, and its effects last as late as Nelson Algren and James Farrell. You weren't even permitted to organize your sentimentality in dramatic, or melodramatic, form. A news story was written so that it could be cut upward from the bottom. I foresaw all the bad effects this could have on me as a writer, as well as the effect all the drinking would have on my health, and worked only sporadically at it, mostly for fun.

The best thing about a newspaper job is the press card. Theoretically it should have protected me even from minor arrests, but it never did except when I was actually working on a paper. It not only gets you through fire lines and into theaters and up to the bedsides of the violently dying, but can be used as a key to open up sections of society normally impenetrable by a writer. At least it does if you have sense enough to shed the distinguishing coloration of your caste. You learn nothing if you carry with you a journalistic system of values, which is invented to save reporters from experience. As a newspaperman you see so much of life, so much of politics, so much of the real organization of society, you discover the hidden unbelievable rascality of men. This makes you a cynic for the rest of your life, but I should imagine that year-in, year-out confrontation of the Social Lie would destroy you. All reporters' jobs were like those in Nathanael West's *Miss Lonelyhearts*. The working reporter looks at the naked behind of society every day, for a living, and he dulls the sight with cynicism (in the cheap sense of the word), sentimentality, and drink. This is not for a writer.

So I used these jobs to make friends with the leading Chicago writers of the time, almost all of whom were newspapermen, and to see life. "Where is Athens now?" said Ben Hecht of the Chicago of those years. The comradeship of these men did make the city rather like Athens. We all ate lunch every day in Schlogel's old German restaurant, and the conversation was a good deal more intense, creative, less phony, and better informed than the similar Algonquin circle in New York.

I think there must be a demographic element in these regional renaissances. Once a city gets so big that its leaders in all fields can no longer candidly know each other, and the social structure settles so that, for instance, a writer's curiosity is no longer negotiable all through the society, it is impossible. The culture of a great capital is quite a different thing. Very likely there is some critical point in the population which insures the best conditions. Some years ago there were flickerings of such a regional upsurge in the intermountain area, but something aborted the promised renaissance. When I came to San Francisco in 1927 it was the worst city in America for a writer. It had gone through one such critical point, with its attendant renaissance, and on this it lived. The city was so ridden with native son-ism that it was literally impossible to get anywhere in the professions, let alone in the arts. Suddenly, after the Second War and a sharp increase in population, it erupted and started throwing off artists, writers, entertainers, jazz musicians, Nobel prize winners, all sorts of creative people in all directions. In San Francisco was established the world pattern of post-War II culture, and in exactly the same way Chicago, rather than New York, created the style of the Twenties.

I was fond of Sherwood Anderson, but most of the literary greats didn't impress me much. The two men I liked most were Jack Molloy, the wild, drunken city editor of the *Herald-Examiner* and the even wilder and more drunken Lionel Moise. I spent a considerable amount of time with Moise. I don't think he really was of much help to me, because his violent, imagistic realism was far from being what I was after. I think Hemingway, on the other hand, does represent a perfect realization of Lionel's theories. What I absorbed from Moise and Molloy was just the hard-boiled attitude, and, I hope, their considerable courage and great appetite for life. Lionel had something that Ben Hecht did not, a massive mind. He was able to take in all of the complex and unending evil of the world, with which, as a newspaperman, he had to deal, and absorb it and organize it. All that was wrong with Lionel was that he couldn't write himself and so he drank too much. His hard-boiled magnanimity was just the trait to make the greatest impression on an adolescent, and I did my best to imitate him. Lionel was always stumbling into situations in which he was forced to exercise his courage. I once saw him punch his way out of an alley full of hoodlums, while somebody from behind busily thumped him over the head with a pair of bowling pins. I was not so well built or so hard-skulled, so I carefully taught myself to keep out of mischief. I learned to be cool, and if a situation was such that I couldn't talk my way out of it quietly, I avoided it. Anyway I would like to think that I had been influenced by Lionel, and in this way. I realize now that, with a name like Moise, he was almost certainly Jewish, but he gave the impression of being Irish, and of being the die from which all real and moving-picture hard-boiled, softhearted, hard-drinking, hard-fighting, hard-wenching Irish newspapermen were stamped.

It is not a bad thing to have grown up in a circle in which practically the only virtues were loyalty, magnanimity, and courage. Sometimes they exacted a rather heavy price. It was about this time that John

Loughman volunteered to go up and talk for the strikers in the Montana copper mines. He got into Butte in the night in somebody's car, spent several days speaking four or five times a day. Anaconda was closed and the sheriff's posse and the company's nobles kept everybody connected with the strike from either entering or leaving. Loughman disguised himself rather superficially as a drummer—he was a hard man to disguise—and went up on the train, accompanied by a bodyguard of Seattle and Chicago Wobblies scattered inconspicuously around the car. Two of the biggest got off first with Loughman immediately behind them. Two deputies came from between the cars and without a word sandbagged them, and, in the next motion, pulled the porter's stool from under Loughman as he stepped down, and sandbagged him. He woke up spread-eagled across the door of his cell, his hands and feet handcuffed to the bars and a pair of handcuffs with the chain tight across his throat. The sheriff had wakened him by putting matches between his toes. He said, "I'll fix you so you'll never talk again, you dirty Red bastard," and proceeded to ram a weighted night stick into his mouth until he had broken all but two or three teeth, broken the lower jaw in two places, and smashed the palate into the sinuses. They then stripped all his clothes off and threw him out into the desert. He walked to the nearest ranch house and got a ride back to Butte. None of the doctors in Butte would touch him, but after he had been patched up by a sympathizer, he went back to Chicago where a leading specialist was one of our group and carried a Red card. This man did a complete job of restoration, a silver plate inside the roof of his mouth and an extraordinary set of lightweight dentures. All this took about four months to heal, the strike was still on, and John went back to Anaconda. This time he got off the train in the center of eight men with Springfield rifles. This was the generation of Wesley Everest, Frank Little, and Joe Hill, and it's just an accident that these friends of mine didn't get it, too. Jack Molloy and Lionel Moise were as much members of this circle of agitators as they were newspapermen.

When the *Daily Worker* was founded in Chicago, the leading newspapermen of the city, under pseudonyms, wrote for it. This only lasted for a year or so; soon they were all bitterly disillusioned. This was the time of the Michigan raids and other foolish catastrophes, which revealed that the Communist Party was ridden with stool pigeons, and that almost all the top leadership were agents of the police or the Kremlin or both. It didn't take a corps of old-time journalists long to discover that the Communist Party was morally indistinguishable from Big Bill Thompson and the Chicago Republican Party, or the Organization. For a brief period the *Daily Worker* was probably the best-written newspaper in America. I wrote for it myself but I have no memory of it. I remember only the disagreeable personalities of the Party bosses in charge—petty, covetous men, full of the most absurd bureaucratic pretension. It is amusing to think how Communist writers and fellow travelers, from the days of the "failure to implement Khrushchev's speech" back, always think theirs is the first generation to be disillusioned, but this has been going on since the first year after the founding of the Communist Party. I suppose that today, as an impotent veterans' club of a couple of thousand old men and ladies, it is morally a more respectable organization than it has ever been. At least the newspaper business taught me how to find my way around. I learned that Chicago was a conspiracy of corruption and mediocrity and that the most mediocre and most corrupt squeezed their way to the top. I learned that there was no such thing as an honest cop or politician. I learned that their dishonesty and brutality passed the wildest dreams of *New Masses* cartoonists—with one strange exception, which demonstrates so well the use and function of the square in society. Almost all police forces, and not the least that of Chicago in its worst days, included a sizable group of earnest young officers, most of them with degrees in criminology from the Jesuits, who took police work with the utmost seriousness. They were incorruptible, courteous, no more brutal than the next man, and their captains usually sent them up narrow staircases to bring out insane murderers armed with machine guns.

So my distrust of the State and its minions was reinforced, and I faced the moral question of what would happen if everybody thought as I did; if my judgment and behavior were universalized. Once again I could only answer as I had answered my high school principal: "I don't think that's a valid dilemma. I am responsible neither for the evils of society nor for its consequences, pro or con." If any widely accepted system of morality were actually put into practice, say the Ten Commandments or the injunctions of the Koran, society would tumble down overnight. I learned this early: that the only effective action of a moral man takes place within his actual reach, on persons he sees in front of him, and inside himself.

It was close contact with individuals that was most valuable to my newspaper experience. I did a lot of interviewing that was never used, a lot of tracing of the ramifications of cases that turned up in police courts, and over a few years of sporadic newspaper jobs developed a web of contacts with the saddest and most submerged people of the city. Curiously enough, this kind of human-interest journalism actually pleased city editors and they did their best to use as much of it as possible. I suppose, eventually, I might have made a good living doing it, but I don't see how I could have stood it.

I have never lost my appetite for this lowest low life, with its terrible innocence. No virgin saying her rosary in a convent is as innocent as an elderly debauched whore and pickpocket, who, as you buy her beers, spins you a long fantasy about her daughter, who thinks her mother is a schoolteacher, and who is a virgin novice, saying her rosary in a convent. I suppose the CPA, trapped in a fashionable suburb, is as pathetic and as innocent as a hard, foolish, three-time-loser cannon-guy (the ironic name the underworld calls a pickpocket), but the CPA is not as interesting to an adolescent. To this day I greatly prefer hustlers and grifters to bohemian intellectuals, and, as a place to relax, a saloon frequented by prostitutes and thieves to a coffee bar full of bad poets. The trouble with the Tenderloin is that society has outgrown it. People like this are vanishing away. The Tenderloin of Los Angeles is the Sunset Strip and Las Vegas, and these I can't afford.

Whenever I went over on North Clark Street it had usually been to one of the Oriental cafés to smoke a water pipe and drink and watch the belly dancers—and incidentally to dance Greek folk dances with the customers, an activity that consists of holding on to a handkerchief and lunging about like a bear. Newspaper work out of the police station got me in the habit of frequenting the lowest dives on North Clark Street, on State Street just south of the Loop, in the red-light district at Twenty-second and Wentworth, and over in Little Italy around Oak and Orleans Streets. It would be possible to fill a book much larger than this with anecdotes of the people I met there, and their dirty, warped images rise up in memory in an endless procession.

One I used as a kind of reporter's handy man. He could always be found in one North Clark Street bar or another. He was a flabby, shriveled, bony little man with a gray skin blotched with raw patches. His clothes were in rags, he seldom wore socks, and his shoes were broken. So were his teeth and his fingernails. All three were equally dirty. I have never understood how men like him manage always to wear a three-day growth of gray stubble. Is it possible they trim their whiskers with scissors to just that length? He had pale gray eyes, and since he was usually full of some kind of drug, they seemed to have no pupils. The whites were not bloodshot, but bluish-gray. He looked as though he had dirty rags stuffed in his skull. On first meeting him, most people thought he was blind. He was a total physical wreck, not from narcotics so much as from the constant punishment of kicking the habit, getting back on, kicking it again, running out of money, and using all kinds of poisonous substances instead of morphine. Although it's a common kick with aged, broken whores, he is the only male I ever knew who chewed nutmegs. When he couldn't get marijuana, he smoked chervil, and was full of information about the comparative effects of green chevvy and gray chevvy. When he couldn't get liquor, he drank Jamaica ginger. When he couldn't afford jake, he'd get three large cans of Sterno, mix them thoroughly with dry bread, and squeeze the alcohol out through a clean—more or less—sock. This is called "smoke."

He was an informer but, as far as the police were concerned, an unwilling informer, although he'd tell me the inside dope on the whole Chicago Tenderloin all afternoon for a couple of drinks. He was so loquacious and he was obviously in the last stages of addiction and alcoholism that you would assume he had what is called Korsakoff's syndrome. This is a passion for confabulation that comes on terminal alcoholics and leads them to tell long, disoriented tales, inventing anything they think will please their listeners. Louie's information was elaborately detailed and perfectly accurate. The police used to pick him up about once a week and beat him until they got out of him whatever they wanted to know. He almost always knew it, and he always cheered, as they say, but he never wanted to. It had to be pounded out of him.

Most informers are queer, but although Louie had everything else wrong with him, including ulcers in his stomach and on his shins, he was a heterosexual of sorts. His girl was pretty, fairly young, and a cripple. She had curvature of the spine and one leg shorter than the other. These defects were not so obvious as to be grotesque, but they were sufficient to make her sexually undesirable to ordinary men. They made her desirable to others, however, and many of her customers went with her simply because she was crippled. However, she made most of her money as what they call a dump girl, hiring herself out to be beaten. You could always tell when she had had a big, successful party. Not only did she have a couple of black eyes, but she and Louie filled themselves up on all the dope they could stick into them and capered around North Clark Street happy as mudlarks. Most of the time they were broke. They sniffed ether, took veronal—then the only common barbiturate—smoked marijuana, and finally went on the meg, chewing up packages of whole nutmegs from the grocery store.

Although it may be true that most prostitutes are frigid, most of them get a kind of kick out of their relations with men, whatever they may be and however much they may protest their disgust and contempt. But this girl had an absolute horror of what she did to make a living, and never went on a date—and I've seen her go off to many of them—without showing all the physical signs of stark terror. I suppose this is what made her attractive, and I suppose that such a tremendous amount of affect does show a sort of subconscious satisfaction. She often got quite badly hurt. You see, girls in this branch of the profession always insist that there be a group of men. It occurs to me now that this is probably for safety. Three or four men, no matter how rough they get, police one another, whereas a single man might well kill you.

Except for the dope habit, and the resulting terrible poverty, her relations with Louie were a model of normality and even respectability. She couldn't keep him clean, but she kept herself and their house-keeping room spotless. She was a good cook and seamstress and she was always talking about getting off the habit and adopting a lot of children.

I met her long before I met Louie. Late night out on the South Side I was writing by the open window when I heard a frightful animal scream. I ran out and down to the vacant lot at the corner. She had been beaten, her clothes torn off, and she'd been thrown clear across the sidewalk into the lot from a speeding car. I was first on the scene and notified the police and the ambulance. Several weeks later she came up and offered to buy me a drink in a North Clark Street speak-easy. Louie I met when I was working around the police station. They were named Louis and Louise and were both called Louie. Mr. Louie and Mrs. Louie.

Lives like this fascinate intellectuals. When they read about them they have wonderful fantasies of living the same way, of having girls like Mrs. Louie or lovers like Mr. Louie, and having terrible, exciting, degrading, and painful things happen to them. They even write novels about it. But the significant thing about Louie and Louise was that they were overworked, impoverished, and harried. Their lives were the lives of a dishwasher and a char, except they were more disagreeable, and all their values and attitudes toward life were as conventional as could be imagined. Like most petty criminals and cheap hustlers, they were the utter fag end of the working class, and had none of that gaudy splendor which novelists and Bakunin attribute to the *lumpenproletariat*.

Every once in a while Louie would get a job. Racing people would give him something to do around the stable—or he'd get a job as a pearl diver or swamper in a bar. The jobs never lasted very long because he'd get sick, not because of the job; he just broke down physically every couple of weeks regardless. But he was always so proud of his paycheck, and he'd buy cheap presents or flowers for Mrs. Louie.

He loved to keep his jobs secret from his wife (she was his legiti-mately wedded wife) and surprise her with a string of fifty-cent pearls or a pair of mules decorated with pink ostrich plumes. One day he showed up in the office of the dentist who had fixed John Loughman's teeth, and gave him quite a little pile of money to fix Mrs. Louie's teeth as a birthday present.

I'd come over to their room and find them eating dry bread and half a can of California sardines and drinking lemon extract and water. Mrs. Louie would scuttle downstairs to the Italian grocery and pan-handle a pint of red wine and some cheese or pastry to offer me. Although everybody knew that Louie was an informer, and all hustlers pretend to despise dump girls, everybody liked the Louies. I rather doubt if Louie ever divulged much specific incriminating evidence. That isn't the way the cops work. When a crime is committed they don't ask somebody like Louie, "Did you see Big-Nose Jack stick up that bank?" They ask, "Did you see Big-Nose Jack last night? Where? When?" They use informers to envelop a likely prospect in a mass of circumstantial evidence, rather like working an alibi in reverse. But since Louie's philosophy was "Only a copper-hearted son of a bitch would ever tell a copper the time of day," they'd have to show him the goldfish just as though they were working for a confession of murder. What the cops got out of this is pretty obvious. This is not some iso-lated instance; most police work consists of exactly this activity. There are dozens of Louies in every Tenderloin.

The Louies became by way of being intellectuals. They were de-voted listeners to my soapbox poetry recitals in Bughouse Square. The cops were always chasing Louie out as a pickpocket, although he was so shaky that he couldn't have picked the pocket of a corpse. He got a big library of five-cent Haldeman-Julius Little Blue Books. He used to read Mrs. Louie selections from "Hiawatha" and *The Rubáiyát*. They even got started coming to plays at the Pickle. I could look out over the footlights and see them sitting hand in hand, watching Strindberg with rapt attention.

Most morons are rather stupid, but Mrs. Louie—whose mental age could not have been more than seven—was extremely bright and alert. Like a raccoon or fox, she made the most of her limited intelligence. It was this alertness, along with her generosity and loyalty, which gave her poignant sweetness.

I suppose a lot of their touching efforts at self-improvement came from their acquaintance with me. I remember sitting in a North Clark Street bar, drinking needled beer and talking with a friend about the Chicago Annual. The Louies came in and sat down and listened like little mice. After a while Mrs. Louie whispered in Louie's ear and he said, "Say, do you suppose if we went down to the Art Institute on one of them free days, they'd let us in? You know, I've never seen any real pitchers and I'd sure like to see a whole building full of them." So off they went and spent Saturday afternoon going through the place systematically, and talked about it for weeks afterward.

Not long after this Louie was found sitting in the doorway of an empty shop, with his head leaning against the doorjamb, quietly dead. Mrs. Louie was taken care of by a couple of the girls around the Pickle. At first she was as silent and morose as a bereaved dog. Then she brightened up and was full of plans, as optimistic as they were unrealistic. Then one day she simply vanished between breakfast and lunch and was never heard of again. I have never thought of them before or since and never written anything about them, but it was knowing people like this—dozens, even hundreds of them, although few so intimately—that was the best thing I got out of newspaper work. For that, a real and not a literary knowledge of the world far beyond the end of night, I am grateful.

Then, too, newspaper work may not have taught me how to write well, but it literally taught me how to write. How to sit down and hammer out three thousand words when I wanted to. I learned that if I were given an assignment to turn in half a column about last year's measles epidemic among the Eskimos inhabiting Chicago and get it in at three o'clock in the afternoon, I didn't have to know anything about Eskimos or measles to begin with, but at 3 P.M. could produce an accurate and competent story. It taught me to write under pressure, to sit in a courtroom or convention and write about what somebody is saying while he is saying it, and not just a shorthand transcription. I learned to write without mechanical or technical difficulties, as fast as I could hit the typewriter, and I never had any trouble with style except in the period which I'm going to talk about next, when I underwent a revolution of taste under the influence of a girl.

CHAPTER 21

As I foresaw, I fell totally in love with the social worker Shirley Johnson who had called on me just before I left the South Side. Maybe it was an adolescent infatuation; to me it seemed the first fiery blast of adult love. In a sense, it was. There's nothing very adult about adult love, and, my childhood erotic life seems to me now so much more mature than this affair.

She, too, got an apartment on the Near North Side, and I spent much of my time there. Although she was born in a small town in western Illinois, she, like my paternal grandmother, to whom she turned out to be distantly related, came from an ancient, thoroughly decadent upstate New York family. In many ways she was more British than the British and more county than a Shropshire cattle baroness. To three furnished rooms in an old mansion on the Near North Side of Chicago she transplanted all the atmosphere of Bloomsbury Square. She didn't just look like Katherine Mansfield; her friends looked like Virginia Woolf, the Stracheys, and the second generation of the Fabian Society. Her sister had been without question the best poet of the group which included Glenway Westcott, Yvor Winters, and Elizabeth Maddox Roberts: the group that grew up around William Vaughn Moody at the University of Chicago shortly before his death—the refined reaction against Middle Western poetic populism. Shirley's library included authors like Edmund Blunden, Charlotte Mew, Edward Thomas, Vita Sackville-West, and Viola Meynell, and there was always the latest issue of the *London Mercury* on the table by the chaise longue. Also, for its brief life, there was the Sitwells' magazine, *Wheels*. I later discovered that Katherine Mansfield came from New Zealand and was vulgarly affected. She wore Chinese gift-shop gold-embroidered pajamas and swooned over the delicate aroma of jasmine tea and thought Arthur Machen wrote beautiful prose. Up the valley from Rock Island, the leading families did things better. Shirley wore greenish-lavender Donegal homespun and drank English breakfast or gunpowder from Cauliflower Spode. Here, for the first time in my life, I became the recipient of the intimate maisonette dinner with candles on the table, *bifteck au poivre*, browning claret, and a meal ending with a savory. Even my father and mother had never had the temerity to finish a dinner with sardines, butter, and radishes.

From the worldly eroticism of precocious childhood I slipped back into puppy love. This had a dreadful effect on my taste. I, whose head had been full of Blaise Cendrars and Louis Aragon and who knew that the best prose in English was *Robinson Crusoe*, developed nasty habits of reading. I learned all of Ernest Dowson by heart, and how well his poems seemed to apply to my stricken life! I lay for hours in hazy autumnal parks, and in winter by what the British call a good fire, with my head in Shirley's lap while we read aloud from Walter Pater's *Marius the Epicurean, Greek Studies, Gaston de Latour,* and *Plato and Platonism.* I read them all that winter but, even I, infatuated as I was, balked at Pater's *Mona Lisa.* No more Balzac; now it was all *La Princesse de Clèves.* The first Prousts were coming out and we read them aloud together, mispronouncing the French. No more Tristan Tzara; now it was Verlaine, Renée Vivien, and Germain Nouveau. Through Shirley I did rediscover my father's favorite, Francis Jammes, which was not so bad. So many of these poems remain in my memory attached to her—Francis Jammes making love to his girl while the old servant coughs for dinner at the door; Toulet, undressing his girls before the murmuring fire; Tristan Derème feeding his girl strawberries, and all of Dowson's easy heartbreaks. "They are not long, the weeping and the laughter . . ." but mine gave certain infallible signs of going on for years.

At least I had something to write about. Every week I erupted with poems. Fortunately most of them were not in the idiom of the *Yellow Book* but a quiet imagistic free verse compounded of Richard Aldington, F. S. Flint, Toulet, and Tristan Derème. Fourteen of them survived, to be published in my middle age. As I got deeper into the affair, these world-weary imitations of French men about town were not sufficient and I started on my first long philosophical epic, or really reverie, entitled *The Homestead Called Damascus,* a book I finally published only the other day. Shirley provided one of the feminine poles of the narrative, and figures in it very little overdrawn. I doubt if these poems are really bad, but the prose that has survived those days was dreadful stuff, modeled on Arthur Symons, the Keystone novelists, the short stories of the *Yellow Book,* and of course—guess who—Henry James. Our affair was an elaborate acting out of the most cobwebby passages of *The Golden Bowl, The Wings of the Dove,* and *The Ivory Tower.* Sometimes I doubt if I saw Shirley except through the glass darkly of *The Portrait of a Lady.* It was always late afternoon, and the leaves were always falling and we really did wander up and down on disconsolate terraces debating whether to offer each other cigarettes. Like the breathing of Shiva, the universes fell to ruin and were reborn as we stirred each other's tea. My letters to her were full of sentences introduced with four qualifying clauses and weighing for pages the contingencies of sentimentality.

I am afraid I am giving the impression that this affair was something ridiculous. It was nothing of the sort. In the first place, I was full of young blood and new ideas, and the girl, who had a pronounced exophthalmic goiter and enormous protruding eyes, was, as my friends on North Clark Street would say, "hotter than a two-dollar pistol." So, our respective organisms insisted on their own sanity and we had a lot of wonderful, simple hours together. And then, too, there are a hundred pages of surviving poetry for some of which I got a prize when I was past fifty. Of course, there were some hundred dreadful imitations of Cynara which I destroyed shortly after their birth. It just goes to show the difference between theoretical and real learning—at fifteen I had been sure that I could have handled Pola Negri with the finesse of Adolphe Menjou.

The effect on my painting was nothing but good. The girl's personality haunted me with a color chord—gray-blue, sienna, yellow ochre, pale umber, gray-lavender, terre-verte, coral, and silver, and a kind of motion, a slow, hesitant tilting like a becalmed yacht. It was not until I was grown up and saw again the great Tiepolos that I realized how befitting these colors had actually been. I painted dozens of pictures. At first they were all abstract, and later many of them were of various aspects of the Blessed Virgin, Saint Teresa of Ávila, and the Catherines of Siena and Genoa. I didn't know much about Tiepolo then, but there was a lot of him in Shirley. She didn't look anything like his models, who are all chubby Venetian tarts with bleached hair, while Shirley was close to emaciated, but she had the same lassitude and lasciviousness and the same well-bred decadence. Take off thirty pounds and she looked not unlike "The Immaculate Conception" in Vicenza, one of the least immaculate-looking women in all art. I have never recovered from this taste. These are the colors I still like and the same indefinite reticulated space and the same wavering motion.

We used to meet for tea on winter evenings in the Art Institute, and we agreed that Pissarro was the best of the moderns then on view and that the loveliest painting in the building was a little field *croquis* by Cazin—dove-gray skies, pale sienna, and terre-verte withered grass rising in a faint swell to, in the middle distance, a *cabane* with silver and peach cob walls and pale, mottled, coral tile roof. It still satisfies me more than any other painting in the Art Institute, precious as that may sound.

Indeed, all our responses to life were as precious as we could make them, but many things in life really are precious, and if you can just outgrow preciousness in your own response, perhaps a system of esthetic values based on these precious things is a pretty good system. There is certainly nothing invidiously precious about Tiepolo or Pissarro.

Since I could not handle my own inner picture of Shirley with the simple geometrical painting I had been doing with compass and ruler, I was forced to loosen up my formal asceticism. The paintings of those days were narrow, fanlike, and saillike forms whose edges were defined by the outside of parabolas and hyperbolas. In some ways they looked a little like Gleizes, but they were all completely abstract, whereas even in his most advanced Neocubism, Gleizes remained essentially figurative. These paintings must have been fairly competent and modestly original because they were the first that I felt were accepted by others as paintings in their own right and not as the work of a prodigy. Not only were they accepted, but they sold, and I hope that some of them are somewhere around Chicago today. That key form, like a series of half parabolas applied to the letter F, haunts me still. From then on, for several years, I painted steadily, never losing the ground I had gained from the impact of Shirley's person.

What this affair did was to break up all the rationally learned responses and controls of a precocious boy and throw me back to start over from a natural, instinctive basis. I suppose that is why my writing, the more rational and verbal form of expression, went to pieces, whereas the painting surged ahead. I was able to look at it fairly objectively, even while going through it, and much more so as soon as it was over, so that I learned right away, confronting my first great emotional experience, how meaningless any rational synthesis is for living. Since then I have seen so many people who thought they had laid streetcar tracks for themselves from birth to death discover themselves derailed by the first really significant experience they encountered. I was lucky not to have become frozen in the mold of intellectual precocity. Had it not been for Shirley I might well have become one of these dreadful unaging young men, like Jean Cocteau or Marcel Duchamp or any chess wizard.

I don't want to give the impression that the effect of this love affair was what you might call purely liquidating—far from it. There was not all that tempest, sentimentality, or acting out. We shared deeply a great range of experiences, and learned much, not just about the significance of life but about ordinary matters of information, from each other, and I, for one, could do with considerable refinement of my tastes and responses. We didn't spend all of our time reading Arthur Machen and listening to Cyril Scott.

I was never able to get from Shirley any kind of definite commitment. I was too young and she was too involved and too exposed, so that, although I was always begging her to marry me, I never lived with her, and I have suspected that from the beginning, however much she loved me, she was anxious to get out.

One June day we were canoeing in the park and she said, "I won't be seeing you after this month. I have a fellowship to Smith College, and I'll be going to Northampton to summer school." As usual in such situations, I was just full of *sang-froid.* "Oh, that's all right," I said. "I'll meet you at the train." "I'm not going by train," she said. "I'm driving to New York with Betsy and taking the train up to Massachusetts." "I don't mean the Chicago depot," I said. "I mean the one in Northampton." She smiled wanly and managed to convince herself that I wasn't serious. But so I was, and there I was when she got off, linen dress and trembling lips, her huge eyes under a cartwheel panama hat. When she saw me she burst into tears, very likely tears of defeat and frustration. I felt proud of myself.

So I went to Smith College. This was the first long trip, pulling up all my roots and taking off, that I had even taken on my own, though God knows I had done it énough with my family. All I'd ever done alone was to take brief trips out into the country to make a particular harvest, to pick cherries or cut corn, with a few long hikes and canoe trips. I had no idea of what Northampton was like; in fact, no idea of what New England was like, and no surety that I would survive the adventure. For all I knew I might never come back to Chicago. In fact, I hoped that once we were isolated together in Northampton we would get married and a new kind of life would start. But it didn't.

On the way, hitchhiking across the country, in Erie, Pennsylvania, I had seen a sign in the window of a restaurant, "Fry Cook and Counterman Wanted." I didn't know anything about restaurant work, but I could cook, so I went in and said I was a fry cook. In a couple of days I got fired, as I expected I would be, but meanwhile I had learned some of the more obvious tricks of the trade, like breaking eggs in one hand, or even slicing tomatoes with the knife and tomato both held in the same hand, a manipulation not unlike rolling Bull Durham in one hand. Stunts like this are all you need to know about most jobs, and any bright and handy person can pick them up in any trade in a couple of weeks.

When I got to Northampton I was smart. I went down to Springfield and got a job in a restaurant. That lasted about a week, and I had picked up a lot of learning. Then I went over to Greenfield, where I couldn't get fired, and after about two weeks I quit because it was too far away, and I knew that a job was coming up in a dairy lunch in Northampton as graveyard-shift fry cook and counterman. I was, in fact, the only person in the restaurant all the latter part of the night.

I should explain that there were no restaurant unions of any importance in those days, and no real standards. You were much more likely to get hired if you could talk a certain lingo and wore a snap-on bow tie and a striped shirt than if you could cook. Almost all restaurant help was hired from floaters straight off the street. Even chefs and bakers were migratory.

It turned out that this was exactly the same as the Kinsolving & Granisson job. The baker came to work in the early hours of the morning and had a break and then he put to bed whole ovens of hot breadstuffs of the sort they eat in Massachusetts for breakfast, mostly muffins. He got ready the lunch and dinner baked goods. It turned out that he needed sleep so he used to pay me out of his own pocket to take care of the muffins, and sometimes he'd take a morning off, once he had shown me how to handle the pies and cakes. The chef was an alcoholic. He was supposed to start some of the heavy cooking for lunch and even dinner before I went off. One day he showed up with a severe hangover, offered me five bucks to do the work, and lay stretched out on the potato peeler's bench eating oranges and giving me directions.

In addition to this, of course, part of my job was getting the porridge and such stuff ready before I went off. This is not hard to do. Restaurant mush is cooked in the steam table. I was learning everything in the business except dishwashing, one of the few things in life I've always been too proud to do. So I learned a trade. It wasn't really such a hard job because the counterman part of it amounted to almost nothing. It's just that at five o'clock in the morning after I had been up most of the day and all night and was very sleepy, I was hit by a sudden demand for a couple of hours of fast and tense skilled labor. It was fine with me. I knew that I was investing in something that I could use to keep me the rest of my life if I wanted to.

For a while I even had a day job. There is a thing called the Eliot Service Company which still sells news photographs in a frame with advertising copy alongside, for display in store windows. They had just started a special industrial service. It offered several news photographs, a batch of inspiring mottoes and other pernicious bosses' propaganda, and a lot of safety and health and similar posters which they picked up from sundry agencies. This was on a big board with a cork bulletin board attached for use by the customer. The service cost a pretty penny and paid an extremely high commission. For several weeks in a hit-or-miss fashion I lugged samples around through the sweltering Connecticut Valley summer. Then one day I called on Mc-Callum Hosiery, the principal business of Northampton, and got to see Mr. McCallum himself. He was a learned and eccentric man with paternalistic ideas of his own about employee-employer relationships, and told me definitely that he had no use for the service. Then as I had gone out of the door, his receptionist called me back, and he said, "Oh well, we can use six of them. They are nice-looking bulletin boards and we can modify them to suit ourselves." The commission on this deal alone made a tidy income for the summer, but I kept my restaurant job as long as I could.

Somewhere in here—I have forgotten the sequence—I got a job with the Florence Manufacturing Company running a stapling machine sticking bristles into prophylactic toothbrushes. I stood with my midriff pressed against a steel guard plate and fed brush handles onto a drum and staples and bristles in packets into two different conveyors, unsnapped the staple handles, and fed them into a trimmer which went off to a man at my left. For eight hours, with a half hour for lunch, I stood pressed against this machine. The effect was just like Charlie Chaplin. All night long I twitched and throbbed and still had subcutaneous jerks when I showed up at the factory next morning. Maybe this reaction would have died down after a few weeks or months or years, but I didn't stay around to find out. I quit at the end of the week.

Worse than the physical effect of the machine was the vicious psychological and moral atmosphere. It was piecework, and rigged in some way so that the men were all pitted against one another, and you didn't dare ask the man next to you for advice or information, because he would be sure to tell you something that would break the machine and might cost you a finger. You had to hurry back from lunch to make sure that nobody sabotaged your machine. Not only were you not making money while it was being repaired but after a low maximum all repairs were charged against you. This is my only experience with machine tending, and I find it absolutely inconceivable that a sane human being would do it voluntarily for more than a couple of hours in his life. Whenever anyone has asked me to give the fundamental reason why I'm opposed to the so-called profit system I think of the hideous moral atmosphere of those rapacious and vindictive men, more than perfect examples of what Marx meant by human self-alienation. I know that this sort of thing is no longer so bad today, but it's bad enough and I want no part in it.

I had one other employment experience, so to speak. Next door to me in my hotel lived a naïve and earnest young man who came to my door one dawn and offered to take me to work with him and guaran-

teed me a job. What was it? Digging onions. How much? Oh, good
pay—fourteen cents an hour. "Son," said I, "I don't have to take jobs
like that, because my father isn't President of the United States." It
was one of Calvin Coolidge's sons, a sweet and callow youth who died
a few years later of blood poisoning. Most evenings he was too tired
from digging onions, but I seemed to fascinate him, and whenever he
got a chance he would question me wistfully about what he obviously
considered my extremely glamorous life. He was sweet and earnest
and full of fatuous observations like his father's "When a large number
of men get out of work this is liable to result in widespread unemploy-
ment." It was hard to tell if young Coolidge was dumb or just stunted
by his family environment. Everybody in Northampton felt sorry for
him, just as everybody hated his father, certainly the most disliked
man the town had ever produced.

Young Coolidge was destined for Amherst in the fall semester, and
this had led to one of the greatest scandals in American academic history—the expulsion of its president, a famous progressive educator,
Meiklejohn. The lengths to which the administration went to get rid
of this man pass belief. His colleagues were bribed and intimidated to
testify against him, and the Department of Justice investigated every
moment of his past, ransacked his library while he was out, and spied
on his wife. They planted rumors that she, who believed with her husband in making their home a social center for the students, carried
on mass sex orgies. I was offered a job by a faceless intermediary to
investigate faculty members of the pro-Meiklejohn faction and draw
up a little report, for which, as the man said, I'd be able to take it easy
for the rest of the summer. The leader of the Meiklejohn faction was a
young sociologist whose wife had played with me in the Little Theater
in Chicago. When I turned the job down, Amherst and Northampton
were mysteriously flooded with false tales that I was her lover, a dangerous Anarchist from Chicago; that she was the reason why I had
come to Northampton; and that we were carrying on lewd and lascivious relations with the consent of her husband.

I learned several interesting things from the Meiklejohn case. In the
first place, all the civil libertarians and progressive academicians believed that he was certain to win out and keep his job. When I pointed
out in meetings of his supporters that he didn't stand a chance, and
that the only reason he was being kicked out was that Cal was sending
his son to school and didn't want him corrupted, I was scorned as a
dangerous Red, an outrageous cynic, and a depraved juvenile. These
people had to believe that the case was an issue—that it made some
kind of sense. Furthermore, although the whole countryside was filled
with carefully manufactured nasty rumors and obscene innuendoes,

Meiklejohn's defenders refused even to admit that these existed. The pitiful thing is that I believe the sociologist thought there was something in the slanders which were circulated about me and his wife. The case was defended on the squarest, most idealistic, and most foolish level imaginable, and on the other side the dirt was so filthy that the defense refused to admit it existed, or, as in my case and probably in others, actually believed it. Once again I had learned something. If you don't want to embarrass yourself, keep away from the do-gooders and people who wear Phi Bete keys.

I don't know just when I slept. I guess while the girl was at classes. We did a great deal of walking around the country. In fact, since we were unable to use either my hotel room or her student apartment, we spent an undue amount of time in the woods. There I wrote some of my best poems of those years. A long poem, which is an expansion of Sappho's "Orchard" in the manner of Michael Field (it appears in *The Phoenix and the Tortoise*), is a record of what we always referred to afterward as our pinnacle—lovemaking in a ruined orchard on a steep hill overlooking the Connecticut River.

Although Shirley had her classes and I had to work at least eight hours, it seems in memory as though we spent all of our time together in totalized, utterly self-abandoned intimacy. This is the wonderful thing about lovemaking off somewhere away from responsibilities and intrusions, out of this world, far away on your own planet, given to your own love. This is what honeymoons are for and what people find in affairs in summer resorts or Venice. We had it.

Scenes from those days come back in total recall. Every detail is stored, and yet there's nothing to them. Late afternoons lying side by side on the bank of Paradise Pond behind Smith College, reading Georgian poetry, throwing sticks in the water, and watching the ducks with strings of ducklings swim about. Here I discovered John Donne, and "I long to talk with some old lover's ghost" will always bring back, not an Elizabethan, but myself, a boy, chanting poetry in the hot August by a pond in Massachusetts, a girl's body curled into mine. I think we discovered John Donne via Arthur Symons, and I still think this is the best way to do it. You get so much more out of John Donne if you first come to appreciate him as an incomparably more noble Ernest Dowson than as a primitive T. S. Eliot or William Empson. Once we had discovered him, Donne became an obsession. We read him over and over to each other every time we met. Soon we knew all his love poems by heart, and they seemed rather emanations or secretions of our own love than the work of a third person, a strange and long-dead man. Through Donne, or possibly through the same essay by Symons, we discovered Marvell and Henry King's "The Exequy,"

Waller, Kynaston, and all the metaphysical heartbreak. To this day, when I read the lines "At my back I always hear,/Time's wingèd chariot hurrying near," I see the broken, ancient apple and pear trees of our pinnacle, and I see them again when Kynaston says, "Though the tree die and wither/Whence the apricots were got."

One of the nicest things about going to Smith College was the town itself and the countryside. This was so much more civilized, bore so many more marks of human tenancy than the Middle West. West of the Connecticut Valley itself, it was hilly, something that my native country was not. I was entranced with the place, and even if it had not been for the demands of lovemaking, would have spent as much time as I could out of doors. We got bicycles and rode all over nearby New England.

Western Massachusetts in some ways is more civilized than eastern. A much larger proportion of its settlers were not Puritans. The tradition of Merrymount is still strong in the land. New England people are supposed to be much less hospitable than Middle Westerners, but everyone was wonderful to me. Northampton had one of the best small public libraries in the United States and one of the best bookshops. On the English faculty at Smith was the editor of a little magazine, *S4N*, which was without doubt the most open to modernist poetry of any that have ever existed. In it were first published many of the most important writers of my generation. The editor and I became good friends, and he got me library privileges and various other things—admission to concerts and such at Smith. The hotel I lived in was a rambling old mansion, with a wide porch and chain swings and a parlor filled with relics of the China trade. My room was in the attic, pure white with handmade birch furniture and a lovely desk in the deep dormer built by some long-dead carpenter. Next to the windows, which were held open with pegs, hung a knotted rope for a fire escape. All night a little fountain chirped and tittered out in the rose garden.

I spent a couple of weekends down in Boston, where Hays Jones, whom I had known in Chicago, was working for the Sacco and Vanzetti Defense Committee. I did some work for him, and was able to visit Vanzetti, who I believe was then jailed in Dedham. Sometime later I was able to meet Sacco, too. It is hardly necessary at this date even to bother to describe the overwhelming effect they both had on me. Everyone knows the force and, as things came to their terrible climax, the grandeur of their personalities. This was the first time in my life that I had ever encountered true saintliness, and not only have I never forgotten it but the persons of Sacco and Vanzetti are for me one of those memories like the memory of one's most precious lovers:

a memory that does not have to be recalled but is always there, all the time, just under consciousness.

Altogether that summer in Northampton was one of the finest things that ever happened to me. It was vacation from the madness and strain of life in Chicago. It gave me a chance to recollect myself. I learned a trade. I could wander relaxed in a gracious, mellow countryside. I met a lot of gracious and mellow people—which were not terms applicable to my friends in Chicago, whatever their vintage. On the other hand, for relief I met the rather proper but very talented bohemia of Boston's Common Cupboard, one of the historic tearooms, where—lo and behold!—sat Max Bodenheim. I met Sacco and Vanzetti, one of the major factors, one of the ten most important events, as they say, in my life. I loved and was loved.

CHAPTER 22

At last school was over and it was time to leave. Shirley went down to a job as a social worker in one of the suburbs of New York and to take courses at the New School of Social Research. I followed her to New York, not to her suburb but to the Village. I even followed her to courses at the New School—which, love or no, were too square for me. I did, however, take classes at the Art Students League.

I got a room at 201 West Thirteenth Street (the building is no longer there). This was one of the important bohemian nests in the history of the American intellect. My next-door neighbors were two young former conscientious objectors, just out of prison, William and Earl Browder. Down the hall lived Mike Gold; next to him, Bill Gropper; in front of me lived a young girl, Masha. Upstairs lived a man who never became famous but who was the leader, patriarch, and father-confessor of the group of radical intellectuals who later ran *The New Masses* and were the most important figures on the literary front of the Red Thirties. His name was Morris Pas. Several girls lived in the building—Minna Green, Helen Black, Frances Midner, and Morrie's wife, Ruby. I think Dorothy Day stayed there for a while. Masha, Morrie, Mike, and Bill Gropper were all products of the Lower East Side, and although they were thoroughly Americanized, there were plenty of other purely Yiddish intellectual visitors—Moishe Nadir, Moisaye Olgin (once Trotsky's closest friend in America), Yusel Cutler, and a lot of people from the Yiddish theater whose names I've forgotten.

With the exception of the purely Yiddish group, almost everybody around 201 had spent a great deal of time on the West Coast, especially in Seattle, where the cultural life of the community was gingered by the intellectuals who worked in the IWW office or on the Seattle Wobbly paper. They'd been in the great historical fights—Everest, Centralia, Wheatlands. A lot of them had done time.

Morrie Pas had been imprisoned as a war resister, and had done very hard time indeed. His face was beaten permanently out of shape, and his upper lip was broken so that he looked like an elderly benign

Jewish camel, although he was in fact still quite a young man. There is only one explanation for Morrie's great influence on all his friends. He was a sculptor and painter, but a very poor one. He knew an immense number of folk songs but he couldn't carry a tune. He was an indifferent lover but a good husband and father. He made a living as a signwriter but he wasn't even very good at that. In spite of his conspicuous lack of talents he possessed something which was much more conspicuous, which was in fact unique in bohemian radical circles—namely, wisdom. Everybody knows about Eugene O'Neill or John Dos Passos, and plenty of people even know of Mike Gold and Bill Gropper. But nobody outside of our own circle ever knew that it was upon the foundation of Morrie Pas's courageous and magnanimous character that a generation of radical intellectuals was reared.

Things like this don't just happen. It is true they are conditioned and even evoked by economic development—there would never have been any proletarian Thirties without both the world economic crisis and the Bolshevik revolution; but in each country this movement took a distinctive form, however much in its decadence it was forced to imitate the Russians. The earlier, more libertarian set out of which the first years of *New Masses* and the John Reed Club developed had its own specific character, ultimately a complex web of what couch slang calls "interpersonal relations" of a distinctly American kind. Webs of interpersonal relationships are made up of persons, and almost always groups like this are sustained in meaningful relationship by one or a very few individuals, like bees or wasps.

In this case the individual was Morris Pas. He was the man who had the answers, who knew what to do till the doctor came, and who could always raise bail. Even though he was an abominable artist, he was a sound critic and teacher. He even had good ideas about writing, and a budding poet could trust his advice. Mostly it was just himself. He wasn't the wisest or most stable man in the world, but he had so much more equanimity and so much less foolishness than anybody else around. I could draw his portrait today—tousled hair; bronze skin; deep horizontal wrinkles on his forehead and deep furrows on his cheeks; broken, beetling eyebrows; broken nose; cleft lip from which always hung a sizzling butt of a homemade, wheat-straw cigarette; battered chin; long arms; long waist; short legs; and twinkling brown eyes full of animal humor and cunning. I always think of him as a wise old animal. He didn't really look like a camel except for the lip, but more like a chimpanzee or orangutan that had sometime or other almost been beaten to death, but who never allowed the beating to bother him—*c'est la guerre.* The Proletarian Thirties were bad enough in Greenwich Village. Without Morrie as principal ancestor they would have been awful. But this wasn't yet the Thirties, it was the Anarchist Twenties and life was still lyrical.

Another focus of the group, the lyrical pole, so to speak, opposite from Morrie, was the youngest person in it—Masha, who was even younger than I. She is the best folk singer I have ever known, with an infinite repertory in a dozen languages. This was in the days before Café Society Downtown had discovered the Folk, and people sang such songs then quite unaffectedly. Pete Seeger had yet to be born. In fact, one of the curious things about the singing habits of the old revolutionary bohemia is that they never sang "songs of protest," except, as a joke, some of those in the Wobbly songbook. Even the gang of soapboxers I knew in Chicago bellowed Negro spirituals; their favorite was "I'm Gonna Walk and Talk with Jesus One of These Days."

Many evenings around 201 West Thirteenth were spent in what might be called an extended family life class. One of the wives would take off her clothes and everybody would sit around and draw, while the nonartists played chess. Sometimes we danced to records, but mostly we sang.

It was an interregnum in the history of American revolutionary bohemia. People were dear friends and devoted comrades and passionate lovers who have been the bitterest enemies now for over thirty years. Around 201 West Thirteenth came and went Max and Crystal Eastman, Hayes and Zenith Jones, Manny Gomez, the Becker brothers, all the bunch that had been in Yucatan during the war when it had been a socialist state. There were students from Columbia who became philosophers; other students, like Joe Freeman, who went to the top of radical letters and then got out; Scoop Phillips, from Seattle, who was one day to be hunted out of the university there; Daniel De Leon's son, Solon; Carlo Tresca; and the New York American Scene painters who for the next ten years dominated the Art Students League. There were all kinds of girls, but most of them were rather fugitive and came and went on their way through the Revolution to Vedanta or marriage. Mark Tobey was then a young commercial artist who was about the place but was never a real member of the group. However, it was probably through 201 that he first learned of the easy life for the artist awaiting any talented New Yorker in Seattle.

Marsden Hartley of all the artists was the one who impressed me most both as painter and as human being. He was also, it is almost forgotten today, a fine poet of the utmost modesty and simplicity. We became good friends and I have always felt that Marsden is one of the people in my life who had great influence on me. Perhaps I just hope this is true, because I believe his influence was a moral and spiritual one, rather than literary or physical. Other people writing of this period have commented on Marsden's homosexuality. In fact, there is a silly and almost certainly false story in the autobiography of one of America's leading poets, all about how Marsden was always making passes at him. Whatever he did for sexual outlet, he never made advances to his friends. This, in fact, was Marsden's greatest virtue. He had an inexhaustible capacity for the deepest and most solemn friendship, and I am sure that anyone who ever enjoyed him remembers it as one of the finest possessions of memory. Since the episode in my colleague's memoirs is unquestionably false, I feel that the record should be made straight. It wouldn't have made the slightest bit of difference to me if Marsden had indulged in the most shameful relations with his friends or offered them to me, but the fact is his friendships were platonic in the noblest sense of the word. He is one of America's four or five greatest artists of any period. That is exactly the moral quality that his personality gave off like a perfume—the true magnanimity which belongs only to the very great.

Maybe it was good for a young boy to be able to associate on terms of fancied equality with painters like Boardman Robinson, Bill Gropper, Hugo Gellert, and sculptors like William Zorach and Gaston Lachaise. The ones who understood what I was trying to do were Morris Pas, who couldn't paint at all, and Marsden Hartley, who was certainly the best painter of his generation. From the others I learned very little, except how to carry on an impressive conversation in old-fashioned artist's shoptalk.

Those were the days when there were still long-winded arguments of technical economics in the radical movement. Most of the participants have since become reactionary professors, and would not like their names in this context, but in those days they were specialists in the inner recesses of the third volume of *Capital,* doctors of the Law of Falling Rate of Profit, and bitter partisans of rival theories of imperialism. These theories included the Left, which thought imperialism was a good thing, and the Right, which, like Lenin, had borrowed from the Victorian reformers the notion that imperialism was very bad indeed and the primary solution to the contradictions of capitalism. The curious thing is that the Indians and Irish and Chinese were on the Left. In those days they thought imperialism was fine—they just wanted to take it over. I kept my ears open, read the books I heard mentioned, and eventually came down on neither side. Even then it was beginning to dawn on me that there were forces operating in the relations between imperialist and subject peoples which were not accounted for by Marxism.

Egmont Arens, who later founded *New Masses,* ran a bookshop and also manufactured Early Modernist lampshades and lamps. He was rather solemn, with no time for me, but he had a girl employee, Frances Midner, with whom I became great friends. She was a little older than I, but she had grown up in the Village and had probably gone to kindergarten classes at the Rand School. She was very knowledgeable and more or less took me over and managed my initiation into New York's revolutionary bohemia. She told me whom to meet and where to go and what to see, whom to trust and whom to distrust, what girls I could make and whom I should be sure to stay out of bed with. She was pretty, with tawny, candy hair, green eyes, and a heart-shaped cat face. Almost everything she said up to, but not including, final intimacy was more or less ironic. I've seldom met a woman that young and that bohemian with that much good sense. It didn't do her much good. She went off to Europe on a tour with Margaret Anderson, Jane Heap, and Djuna Barnes, and then back again to Europe with Harold Loeb, Arthur Kreymborg, and his wife to function as the general secretary and art editor to *Broom*. According to Harold Loeb she was not very good at this, and had just come back to New York when I met her.

This is a whole set of new names. The people whom I had met through my father were dead, had been deported to Russia on the Red Ark along with Emma Goldman, or had, as they say, sold out and disappeared into success. Almost all the people round 201 West Thirteenth Street had been part of the Anarchist movement. Many of them had been active in the IWW in the great Eastern mill strikes, or in the Northwest. The New Yorkers tended to jump over Chicago to Seattle. Chicago had its own cadres and its own particular interpretation of the Wobbly Preamble. In fact, the Chicagoans rather frightened the people from New York.

Now Anarchism and Anarchosyndicalism were on their way out. However glorious their ideals and their history, it was apparent even then that they were the expression of a dying epoch. The Bolsheviks had already alienated their first mass base in America. The Workers' Party was coming out from underground, and a new Bolshevik movement was being created one step nearer to the Kremlin's orthodoxy. In those days, in America, Kremlin orthodoxy with all its bigotry and moral violence meant not the dying Lenin but Trotsky.

Young and old were veering around, most of them unknown to themselves, and becoming Bolsheviks. This meant that the evenings that weren't spent playing chess, drawing the girls in family life classes, or singing were spent in violent arguments. "Where two or three are gathered together . . ." Once five or six people got into a room, unless something was done to distract them, the place took on all the turmoil of a committee meeting at the height of a bitter strike. From the vantage point of thirty-five years it seems our best hours were spent singing.

All of us however, unlike the Proletarians of the Thirties, were interested in upholding and defending the rights and standards of the arts against the pretensions of the pompous and ignorant bureaucracy, which is, probably by definition, characteristic of all Bolshevism. They believed it was up to the artist to judge whether a work of art was revolutionary or not. In fact, they believed that in most cases only the artist had any clear idea of what revolutionary means in the arts actually were. A few years later, under the inspiration of that great aesthetician Dugashvili, there was much bloodstained argument pro and con on the relative claims of form and content. In those days, none of us was so naïve or unlettered to believe any such dichotomy existed. Kandinsky was a revolutionary painter; Upton Sinclair was a reactionary novelist, however they marked their ballots.

As the years went by I watched the radical artists and writers of my youth either leave the movement and become virulent anti-Bolsheviks or go under and voluntarily embrace the militant vulgarity of the hacks and hatchet men of the Communist Party. Those who stayed in liked to speak of themselves as Progressives, leaders of the vanguard in culture as well as politics. The fact is that from 1932 to the eventual collapse of their movement they were the champions of every vulgarity and obscurantism in the arts, and the enemies of all vitality and originality, and the appalling thing is that to a man, they knew better. I knew them when they knew better and I watched them throw away their birthright for a mess of blood pudding.

At the Art Students League I took life classes and Weber's course in "The Materials of the Artist," which I had looked forward to for several years. I am afraid I didn't learn much. His palette was entirely of earth colors and his use of materials was conservative and cranky. For instance, he urged his students to paint on pebbled aluminum. To me this was making permanence an end in itself. He had yet to work out a permanent palette of high chroma, and it was this I was interested in. I knew the pigments were there because I had discovered some of them in experiments of my own. Also, I was interested in learning the chemistry of the synthetic media which were just then coming into use. I adopted Weber's palette for a while and painted quite a few pictures in it. Most of them were abstractions or Cubist still lives, but some of them were heavy portraits of charwomen and Negroes in the Art Students League style. One thing to be said for this palette, it gives a painting something that learners find difficult to achieve—cohesion. A picture always looks as though it were painted all in one piece. The students of Kenneth Hayes Miller and Schnackenburg all painted totally indestructible objects which looked like they had been built of variously tinted mud. At first sight these pictures seemed the products of the most refined color sense; the chemical unity created its own easy plastic unity. I, for one, quickly tired of iron oxides and started painting in pure spectrum colors.

It's hard to believe today that the most powerful broadcasting center for nonobjective art was Russia. The kind of painting I was interested in, later to acquire names like Suprematist and Purist, in those days was called Constructivist, after the Russian movement, by practically everybody, including its practitioners in all countries. With few exceptions these ideas were completely over the heads of people around 201. They may have been political revolutionaries, but most of them were docile followers of the Art Students League academicians. Their heroes were Goya and Daumier. Little did we think in those days, painting and arguing, our naked girls and wives perched on the tables, that not very far in the future as the two schools alternated in power in Russia they would be killing each other over differences that we found it easy to abandon for a game of chess.

Possibly this all sounds like bohemianism of the Murger type, but I can't imagine anything less like the lives of Mimi and her boy friends. There was a constant, almost unrelieved artistic activity, or at least conventional interest in the arts. Nobody drank very much. Night after night it was a scene of group domestic bliss. Nowadays you can't go into an *espresso* bar in Osaka without having a chick in Jeanmaire *maquillage*, stretch pants, and bare feet come up, sit down beside you, bang on a guitar, and start bleating, "Why does your brand sae driep wi blude, Edward, Edward?" but in those days folk songs came more natural. Amongst these people were several who later became famous as collectors, but almost all of them had learned an appreciable amount of their songs from cowboys or lumberjacks or sailors, or in the ghetto. Since they were themselves the people who later wrote the books, almost no literature on the subject existed in their youth. This must be about the date that the first race records were issued, yet even then dozens of my friends, both black and white, had large repertories of both blues and spirituals. Two of the regulars were the Larkin sisters, singers and collectors of cowboy ballads, but the best of all was the young girl Masha.

She had a rare sense of the modal structure of American folk songs, and back in those days when musicological literature on folk songs was very rare indeed, she was one of the few singers who appreciated the widely varying harmonic structure of the folk song's melodic line. Her delivery was of the purest type, very simple and direct with no flourishes and drama, but whenever there were dramatic possibilities in unusual intervals she made the most of them. I suppose I learned more about the musical structure of folk song and about the methods and means of popular poetry from listening to Masha than from anyone else—including my grandmothers or any Southern mountain singer.

Masha had come into the group as a model. She had been an athlete in high school, and when we all first met her she was a student at Savage's, a school for physical education instructors. She had the body of a champion swimmer and that kind of young Jewish beauty which looks very Polynesian: high cheekbones, broad face, full lips, a great mop of wavy dark brown hair, and a rather broad nose. Her spit and image occurs time and again in the paintings of Gauguin. At this time I didn't know her terribly well. We were of an age and therefore I suppose more or less antagonistic. Later she was to become one of my best friends. We'd all be sitting about reading, playing chess, arguing about what Rosa Luxemburg really meant, or drawing and Masha would start to sing quietly so as not to bother anybody. Sometimes she would sing alone for a good part of the evening, sometimes other people would join in and we'd sing until early morning.

One warm September night we had a picnic supper on the roof, about fourteen of us. I remember Mike Gold was there and distinguished himself by eating a whole kosher salami. Haridas Mazumdar showed up with a leash of beautiful girls; this time, unusually, one was an Indian. She was introduced as Nanda Devi, which at the time meant nothing to me (it means the goddess of joy, the white goddess, the wife of Shiva, and the mountain which is the favorite daughter of Himalaya.) She was extremely beautiful, with three little black lines and a red crescent on her forehead, a ruby in her nose, and a milk-white sari. Haridas seemed anxious to wish her off on somebody else. This struck me as stark madness, so I immediately fastened myself on her, brought her sandwiches, poured her drinks, and peeled her fruit.

After we had eaten and told the usual quota of stories we started to sing. There were a number of good singers present; a couple of sailors, a French Anarchist, one of the Larkin sisters with cowboy songs, and Yusel Cutler with Hebrew and Yiddish Hasidic songs. Eventually Masha was leading the singing.

There was a full moon, and the sky had been full of nighthawks—"bullbats"—screaming and plunging and zooming up again all the early evening. I sat in the corner of the coping, with Nanda Devi in front of me. I was unaware of it, but leaning back against me she gradually pressed my body not into anything as uncomfortable as the lotus posture, but at least cross-legged like a Westernized Buddha. About midnight the moon was overhead and Seventh Avenue had quieted down for the night into the deep stillness that once was characteristic of nighttime in lower New York. Everybody had run out of songs. Nanda Devi without any warning started to sing. I don't think any of us in those days had heard much Indian music. The effect of the first notes was not just electric, it was literally stunning. Everyone gasped for breath, and especially me, with this beautiful woman sitting with her vibrating back pressed against me.

She sang until daylight, needless to say without interruption. We hardly dared to breathe. At four o'clock she stopped abruptly and said to me, "I'm really frightfully tired, do be a good chum and take me home." So I went with her to the old theatrical hotel on Eighth Avenue and Twenty-second Street. It turned out that she was an Indian revolutionary, one of Gandhi's closest associates, and was touring America giving concerts to raise money for the movement. Unluckily, she was halfway through her tour, but for what was left of it I followed her from place to place on the East Coast and never left her until she took the boat for England.

I suppose the thing to say is that this was one of the great love affairs of my life, but it wasn't, because it was so utterly out of context and bore no relationship whatever to anything that happened to me before or since. I was like Thomas the Rhymer, rapt away by the Queen of Elfland. In fact, I used to lie in bed in the early morning in some provincial show-business hotel that would accept a colored woman traveling with a white man, and think that maybe when the tour was over I would turn away from the Cunard Line dock and find that several hundred years had passed over New York while I was gone.

At last she did go, and I turned away, and New York was still there just as it had been a few weeks before, and I'm not sure, in spite of the tremendous character of the experience, that I was changed. It's hard to say what she left with me, except the knowledge that it is possible to find absolute bliss in another person's company and the rather bitter knowledge that this is probably always easier to do with someone you'll never see again. Northampton with Shirley had been a honeymoon in a romance. But it was a respite. Chicago and New York with their hangers, their responsibilities and claims, were always in the back of our minds. The weeks with Nanda Devi were like science fiction—as remote as another universe. Since I can't carry a tune, she didn't teach me any Indian ragas, but she did teach me what Westerners call sexual Yoga, the sort of erotic gymnastics that dark gentlemen in Hollywood make a fortune imparting to cinema stars. I never got the impression from Nanda Devi that this sort of lovemaking *was* gymnastics, let alone anything like Yoga. She just acted as though that were the way all Indians made love. I certainly didn't want to disappoint her, so I bore up manfully and did my best, and tried not to let on that it was all quite the most extraordinary thing that had ever happened to me, and that I had never heard of such refinements. For years afterward I was under the impression that all Indians made love with such learning and skill. Alas, I am afraid it is not true.

Of course her real name was not Nanda Devi, and I never learned what it was. Nowadays when I see handsome middle-aged women in saris in the corridors of the UN Building, or on the Place de la Concorde, or the streets of Washington or London I often wonder which of them is her. I am sure she is an ambassadress at the very least.

During this episode I never gave my girl a thought. But when I turned away from the Cunard dock I went straight to her, just like Dmitri when he sees Katarina off on the train and turns and shudders in his greatcoat and says, "Grushenka!"—only, so to speak, in reverse. Unfortunately all the wonderful skills I had learned have turned out to be just a little too much for most Occidental girls I have known since, so they didn't do me an awful lot of good.

While the experience lasted it never lost the quality of those first hours when she was singing. It was not a love affair but I suppose a kind of mystic experience, a transport that went on for days. I wasn't in love in the least; we never talked about love; all of the conflicts and agonies of an Occidental in love were stilled. I didn't even have any anticipatory regrets that it would be brief and soon over, and when it was over I didn't feel bad about it. It was a remarkably impersonal thing, rather like a very great and grave theatrical performance.

When I saw Shirley again she said she was leaving for Chicago, so back to Chicago I went.

CHAPTER 23

I moved into two rooms in an old gaslit brownstone house at the corner of Ontario and Michigan. I fixed up a studio in the latest Greenwich Village fashion, with batik curtains and couch covers, an accomplishment that I had learned in New York, and furnished it with the Victorian furniture which had survived from my grandmother's home and which had been decaying in the cellar and attic at my aunt's. I went back to the Green Mask, which was booming.

I was much more serious about the theater that winter, and whenever I could got local fill-in walk-ons in plays that came to town. This was the year, I believe, of *Aphrodite*—or was it *Mecca?*—anyway, I carried a spear or something similar in both of them. I took a more active part in the theater at the Dill Pickle and tried very hard in my juvenile way to turn it into a serious experimental theater.

From the pages of *Broom* I took Pirandello's *Six Characters in Search of an Author*. I did the costumes, masks, and sets. The "characters" were outlined in milliners' white wire, which was painted with fluorescent paint and glowed when the lights were turned on it. The masks were gaunt, sickly-looking things, rather in the style of Munch. This was the American première of the play, although we probably would have been sued if Pirandello's agent knew we were putting it on. I was inordinately proud. After we had been running for a week or so, I got a letter from Charles Ray, then probably the most popular semijuvenile comic in Hollywood. He had a little theater in Hollywood called the Pot-Boilers, and they were putting on *Six Characters* and wanted to exchange advice and information.

Many years later I was at a party in Beverly Hills, and a middle-aged man next to me was introduced as Charles Ray. I said very modestly, "You probably don't remember me but I had some correspondence with you once, when you and I put on *Six Characters in Search of an Author* in the same season. You at the Pot-Boilers and me at the Dill Pickle." "Oh yes," he said, "I remember very well. In fact, that is something I am never likely to forget. For years my name was in lights from Iceland to Singapore, and I played opposite all the greatest stars of the time. But nobody ever seems to remember; nobody ever says, 'Oh, you're Charles Ray, I saw you in a wonderful comedy with Bessie Love.' Instead they say, 'Oh, you're Charles Ray; I remember you—you put on the American première of *Six Characters in Search of an Author* in Hollywood.' I only wish they'd been around when the play was on; most nights we played to audiences of about twenty. But now I know the nature of fame." This all sounds important, but as a matter of fact I am dead certain that, to say the least, my *Six Characters* would seem a childish, flimsy thing today.

(Most amusing: when this story was broadcast on KPFA, I got a phone call from the actual director of the Pot-Boilers, who told me that Charles Ray was only a rich hanger-on around their theater. Ah, Hollywood!)

As I look back now these productions strike me as ridiculous. Most of the action of *Six Characters* took place behind a heavy scrim with green and violet make-up and different colored lights from either side. The people looked as if they were moving around in pea soup and the whole thing was far more modernistic than the text of Pirandello warranted. Other plays of a quite conventional nature I tried to put on the tiny Pickle stage with the mechanistic esthetics of a Meierhold or a Piscator. They must have been hilarious, but I had fun and fancied that I was changing theatrical history.

It was this winter, too, that I had most jobs in burlesque. I worked as a relief candy butcher in all three of the big burlesque houses and then, as is the way with burlesque, people were always failing to show up and I got chances to fill in as a straight man and a few times as a comic. I've never forgotten any of these routines. The butcher's patter selling cheap chocolates and purportedly filthy pictures I can repeat word for word today without pausing for breath. The chance at bit parts in the legitimate theater appealed to my vanity but the real fun was in burlesque and with few exceptions the people were both smarter and better actors. Lots of people have the fantasy that they would make great burlesque clowns. I certainly do. I was lucky enough to have a chance to try it out. Most important about this kind of work is the knowledge it gave me of the fundamentals of the theater. I don't think anyone can be a good critic, let alone a good dramatist, unless he has had some theatrical experience and that preferably at the lowest level.

About this time I met a girl who had been a Wave in the First War. I think they were called Yeomanettes. She was a part-time model and any time I want to go down to the drugstore I can still see her. She was the girl on a well-known shampoo wrapper. The wrapper has since then been redesigned and there is a more modern-looking girl taking up most of the space, but Nancy is still the trademark—delicate Irish-looking face and a long banner of light chestnut hair. I had never known well anyone like her. By the standards of my friends or even of my family she was petty bourgeois. She was also a publicity woman and lived the fast, expensive, high-bohemian life of Madison Avenue a generation removed.

We roamed Chicago night-clubbing and dancing. She had once made her living as an exhibition dancer. This meant that we had to be very careful not to drink too much or we were sure to get thrown off the dance floor. We made all the places from the mass dance halls at Sixty-third and Cottage Grove to Marigold Gardens, Ike Bloom's Midnight Frolics, the Sunset, the Dreamland. One was a place owned by Jack Johnson, who could be found there every night, suave and handsome, although he was supposed to be living in Cuba, a fugitive from a framed Mann Act charge. I don't know precisely where I got the money for this activity because it was expensive even then. Nothing is sillier than the modern notion that jazz grew up in the resorts of the proletariat. Nancy was the kind of girl who usually does not appeal to me at all: hard, fast, in the money, and terribly bright. I don't really know what I found in the relationship. I guess exercise, because we certainly did an awful lot of dancing.

She was a good feeder, too, and every night we went out we ate in one of the best restaurants. Finally we settled on the old German restaurant in Northside Turner Hall and ate there every night. This was run by Charlie Apfel, the father of Lila Lee, then a reigning movie star. She was in and out, off and on during the year, but on her birthday she always came back to Chicago and Charlie threw a stupendous banquet. Not only did he have one of the best chefs in Chicago, but he had the largest and by far the best cellar. He sold beer made by what later became the Capone Organization but the wine and cognac in the cellar he gave away to his friends. Every night Nancy and I had wine of the first growths of the best years. Charlie had been not only a wine connoisseur but a wine collector, and we had things that I've never seen before or since. Wines of Persia, Lebanon, the Caucasus, Romania, Serbia, and best of all a light white Hungarian wine slightly *pétillant*, something like a Johannesburger, which I have never forgotten and which is the best wine of its type I have ever drunk. It ceased to be bottled some years before the First War.

Since Nancy and I ate there for the better part of the winter, we soon became part of the family and used to play chess or cribbage with Charlie almost every night. One night Nancy and I were playing cribbage and Charlie was kibitzing and a couple of characters straight out of the movies came in and nodded him over to the bar. When he came back he looked pretty disturbed.

"What's the matter?" "They offered to buy my cellar." "What did they offer?" "Oh," he said, "the offer's all right, about five times what it's worth. But I told them I didn't want to sell." "You better sell, Charlie," I said. "No," he said, "I'll wait and see. They say the Boss wants it for himself."

A few days later was Lila's birthday party—the last time, it turned out, I was ever to drink wine of the Year of the Comet. The Boss Himself was there, lavish with compliments for the food, the wine, and the beauty of Lila Lee. Charlie drew me aside and said, "He just personally doubled his first offer." "What did you say?" "I told him no, I was going to give it all to Lila." "Better sell, Charlie," I said.

The next day detectives from the East Chicago Avenue station pulled the raid in the dead hour of the middle of the afternoon. As they walked in the door three patrol wagons drove up to the place and the uniformed coppers toted the stuff out of the cellar like stevedores. Charlie meanwhile was taken over to the station, booked, and turned loose, and stood around chain smoking cigars and watching a hundred thousand dollars' worth of fine wines being loaded and lugged away. The paddy wagons didn't even bother to stop at the station but drove straight out to the suburbs to the Boss's home. Charlie of course was never prosecuted; in fact, he was paid the final offer and a couple of years later gave up the place in disgust. That left the Red Star Inn as the sole survivor of the great Chicago German restaurants which in their day were as fine as anything to be found in the old country.

One of the problems about Nancy was that she had an apartment on Astor Place in the same building as my regular girl, and wandering around the streets sentimentally late at night I was often confused as to who was who. There is a poem from this period on just this subject and even while I was writing it I wasn't sure for whom I was writing it, nor am I yet.

Relations with Shirley were getting difficult. I was continuously pressing her to marry me, and she with eminent good sense always refused even to discuss such a prospect. Meantime her two steady beaux from her home town showed up. One was a young surgeon, then still an intern, and the other was an accountant who was actually named Faithful Jones and looked it. The real reason she should not have considered marrying me was that I was ten years younger and most of our intense intellectual or spiritual kinship was due to my own imagination and power of projection. The reason she gave was that as an artist and poet I would never make enough money, and this I am afraid began the first subtle insinuation of disillusionment. Girls were always turning me down in those days because I didn't have the standard characteristics of a good provider.

I was beginning to feel unwelcome at Shirley's, and I can't say that I much enjoyed bridge games with Shirley, Faithful, and the surgeon, so I spent more and more time with Nancy, running about. I don't want to give the impression that we behaved like the mythological characters of the Jazz Age. Maybe there were people who lived lives like those in Hemingway and F. Scott Fitzgerald, but with the exception of my soapbox friends, who had the appetites of Skid Row, I didn't know anybody who ever got very drunk. Nancy and I got kicked off cabaret floors for taking up too much room and distracting the customers. I can't say I was ever very good at rolling her over my back or whirling her around by one foot, but we tried. She had a set of Jazz Age friends, most of them commercial artists whom I have not bothered to describe, but I have few memories of anybody being drunk. We drank only enough to be fairly elated and worked off our energies living it up.

One night we were doing a slow exhibition tango in a little joint called the Classic. The band switched to "Three O'Clock in the Morning" and the lights blinked. It was snowing outside. Nancy pressed up against me, buried her face in my shoulder, and said, "I'm getting married tomorrow." "Really," I said. "Who to?" "Someone you don't know. He's a broker." "Oh, go on," I said. "You're kidding." "No," she said, "I really am. Really a broker. We're leaving right after the wedding at ten o'clock and going to New York to live." I still only half believed her, but she woke me up about seven thirty with a splendid breakfast, smoked sausages and hotcakes, and sent me home. I never saw her again.

Not only was there relatively little alcoholism, but although practically all the people I knew were in show business, the revolution, the arts, or crime, I knew hardly any narcotic addicts. Marijuana was just coming in. Willy McCauley used to go out to a Mexican grocery at Sixteenth and State Street and buy a shoeboxful of it for a couple of dollars, put it up in Bull Durham sacks, and peddle those for fifty cents apiece. A few people around the Mask used to smoke it, but it has never had any effect on me except to make me slightly more sexy than I normally am. This particular winter there was a craze for it in bohemian Chicago which died down in a couple of years and never revived to any extent until the Second War. For a while everywhere you went there were muggles parties and people sat around and giggled over the patterns in the wallpaper and climbed laboriously over doorsills. I decided then that, like the conniptions of the Holy Rollers, the reputed effects of marijuana are largely group-induced hysteria.

Willy's activities brought me in first contact with Mezz Mezzrow, who was then a young kid. We used to get marijuana from the same Mexican grocery on the corner by the Fiume. That brings me to an experience which I shared with Mezzrow, although the circumstances of my experience differ considerably from his. He seems to have gone through the same thing at exactly the same time.

CHAPTER 24

One afternoon I came into the Green Mask and June was cleaning up. She was almost helpless with rage.

"What's the matter?"

"That bastard McGonigle was just in here, and you know what he wanted? He wanted me to give him Mei Wang for that goddamn whore of his." Mei Wang was June's stud Pekinese. He was not really a Pekinese but some rare kind of dog with the same lion face but about twice the size and with a coat colored like an Alsatian shepherd. He was one of the most valuable dogs in America. McGonigle was a detective at the East Chicago Avenue station. His whore was the blonde madam of the Greek Syndicate brothel upstairs.

"What did you tell him?" I asked.

"I told him to take his dirty Irish ass out of my joint and never bring it back."

"I'll make you a sign for the window: 'Fixtures for Sale'!"

"Go on," she said, "you're crazy."

"OK, you'll see, but you're the one that's crazy if you ever open the joint again."

For a week nothing happened. There was a fellow who had been hanging around the Mask who was a monologist on the Chautauqua circuit and did multipersonal impersonations—Saul and David, Joseph and Potiphar's wife, Solomon and Sheba, Jesus and Judas—acting out Bible stories before throngs of yokels. His wife was a big blonde who had been a bell ringer, not Swiss but Swedish.

One night while I was eating dinner in the Mask he came to me with a stack of poetry and asked if he could recite it the next Thursday evening. It was more or less like Robert W. Service's *Songs of a Wage Slave*, but if anything, better. I was agreeably surprised. I said, "Sure, if you want to." I later found out the poems were by, of all people, Damon Runyon.

That Thursday night I had dinner in Turner Hall and met a boy and girl from Englewood High School and invited them over to the Green

Mask. We came in late. The place was packed. The reading was ending, the air was full of smoke. My usual repugnance for the monologist
returned at the sound of his gravelly voice and I started back out the
door. Leaning beside the door was a big brute of an Irishman, obviously a dick. He put his foot up in the air against the doorjamb and
barred my way. "Where you think you're going to?"

"Out to get a little fresh air," I said. "I'll be back."

"Oh, you'll be back, will you? I don't think you need any fresh air.
You'll get lots of fresh air in the Bandhouse. They've got more fresh air
out there than they know what to do with in January."

Then he maneuvered me silently a couple of feet into the shadows
in the hallway and hit me full force in the mouth with his pistol. A
couple of seconds later a squad car pulled up screaming. McGonigle
rushed into the center of the crowded room and blew his whistle; his
partner Putz collared my monologist friend with one hand and June
with the other. I was still only about half conscious. Everybody was
taken in.

June and Beryl were booked as keepers of a disorderly house and
managers of an obscene exhibition. The monologist was booked for
lewd and lascivious conduct and for making an obscene exhibition.
All the customers were booked as inmates of a disorderly house. Their
bail was set at a thousand dollars each, and the customers' at five hundred. I shouldn't have to point out that even in Chicago in those days
in raids on brothels or cardrooms or speak-easies the customers were
never held, and if by some chance they were booked, their bail was
purely nominal or they were turned loose on their O. R. The audience
was such as would go to a poetry reading in a respectable teashop
anywhere. Male and female social workers and schoolteachers and
very square white-collar culture seekers generally. Few of them got
out that night. I got a hold of Spike Hennessy but he said there was
nothing he could do for me this time.

The next morning McGonigle and Putz presented as evidence a
stack of extremely obscene poems on mimeographed sheets, the sort
of things that are sold in high schools for two bits and are known
amongst kids as "four sheeters." They testified that this was what the
monologist had been reading and they had three witnesses, dubious
characters from North Clark Street, who testified along with them. The
judge lashed himself into a fury and told us we should all be horse-
whipped, branded, and sent up for life. He sentenced June, Beryl,
the monologist, and me to a thousand dollars and a year each, and all
the customers to fifty dollars each and thirty days. The cops led us
away.

I was in a serious fix. There was no question but what the rap was so phony it would be easy to beat, but I didn't dare make any waves. I was very much a minor and Judge Horner was in Europe or Florida on vacation. Spike Hennessy refused to touch it. If I stuck my neck out the law would discover my real age and I'd end up in a reformatory and have a terrible time getting out of it.

We were taken down to the Detective Bureau, mugged and processed, and generally slapped around just for fun, although we had already been convicted, and sent over to the Bridewell about nine o'clock that night, having had nothing to eat since dinner the evening before. The Chicago police showed everybody the goldfish on every conviction. You got no water to drink all the time you were in the Detective Bureau and no cigarettes while the coppers sat around and drank highballs or malted milks and blew smoke in your face. It was just like the movies. You sat on a kitchen chair with a couple of carbon-arc old-time photographer's floodlights blazing in your face about eight feet away. Within a half hour you were literally burned, as from a bad sunburn, with the heat. Periodically one of the coppers would get up and slap you across the face, at first with his fist and then with his sap. You were very lucky if you kept your front teeth. From several such workouts like this, two of my teeth are broken and both my eyebrows are divided into two tiers each. (The "Talk of the Town" in *The New Yorker* once said I had the most peculiarly peaked eyebrows they had ever seen. If the interviewer had asked I would have been glad to tell him how I got them.) Every so often a little sly one among the coppers would come up quietly behind you in the dark and with the skill of long practice snatch the chair out from under you. Then a couple of them would kick you in the head and nuts.

They weren't all so rough. When the rough ones tired, in came the fatherly one with wavy Irish-gray hair and the unctuous voice of a pederastic archbishop. He was your friend. He just wanted to get you out of a tough spot. All you had to do was make a clean breast of it. You could relieve your conscience which must be torturing you. You could trust him. The D. A. was his son-in-law and he would fix it up. You could cop a plea—it was your first time. You were sure to get probation. He looked on himself more as a social worker than as a policeman.

The ridiculous thing about all this crap is that it was completely unmotivated. They asked you questions about every unsolved crime of the last six months from "L & L," known to grifters as pee-hole banditry and to the statute books as lewd and lascivious conduct, to the embezzlement of banks. But they really didn't want to find out anything; they just wanted to work off their animal spirits.

About nine thirty that night I was moved over to the Bandhouse. I

waited alone with a copper in a reception cell for half an hour and then
was turned over to a punk. He took me across the hall and booked me
in and then took me to the bathroom and prodded me into a trough of
cold water mixed with some substance that smelled like Lysol and
kerosene and probably was exactly that and then stuck me under a
scalding hot shower and gave me a cake of Fels-Naptha Soap.

When I came out I said, "Where's the towel?"

He said, "Who do you think you are, Claire Windsor?"

He then handed me an assortment of clothes: an undershirt full of
holes, a pair of drawers shrunk stiff and still dirty in the seat, a couple
of socks, two surplus shoes from the war, a chambray shirt with all the
buttons torn off, blue jeans and an overall jacket, both dirty, and cotton
mitts. Not a single one of these garments bore the slightest relationship
to any other. In fact, the shoes were both for the left foot and one was
about a six and the other a fourteen. After I had sorted them out I said,
"I can't get these on."

"Oh, you can't, can't you?" says he, and knocked me naked over the
bench onto the stone floor. I let out a yell, the door flew open, and in
came a screw who took me by the hair and prodded me up with his
fist. He did have the decency to explain that you traded your slops off
with the other fish until you finally got stuff that fitted.

Then they shook down my clothes and found in my jacket pocket a
purse, containing lipstick, compact, and powder puff, which Shirley
had left in my room and which I was bringing down to give her, expecting to meet her at the Mask. This had immediate effect—attempted
rape. By this I don't mean a general, abstract proposition. I was still
naked, the screw got a half nelson around my head while the punk
went to work. Each time he'd come at me I'd double up my leg and
kick backward like a mule. This led to considerable roughhouse, pro
and con.

At last they gave up and took me over, limping in my misfit shoes,
through the sub-zero night to the oldest of the cell blocks. This was
quite a place. It had been built back in the Seventies or Eighties, with
long, narrow windows like the archers' slots in medieval castles, and a
warped and muddy stone floor where the water oozed up in winter
between the paving blocks. This was the only running water in the
place. Each cell was given a one-gallon pail of water once a day and
provided with a battered old bucket for a privy. It was a cage-type
cell house. The cells were all in the center about thirty feet away from
the walls, so the only view was through the heavy iron grilles and door
which looked out on brick walls and filthy windows through which it
was impossible to see anything. The inner cells looked out on the tier
opposite. The whole thing was built of iron, and any movement in it

resounded as though it had happened inside a bell; any cough or groan or cry was magnified as if by an immense megaphone. In each cell there were four iron-slatted bunks that folded up against the wall. There were no mattresses, and each fish was provided, along with his slops, with a filthy khaki Army blanket full of holes.

Mezzrow says the Bandhouse was segregated. I judge he was there the same winter. If he was, this is simply not true. I was put in a cell already occupied by five Negroes (for the four bunks.) They immediately took charge of me and my misfit clothes were passed up and down the tier. In each cell somebody wore a device to be used for such purposes—a hook on a long handle, under his clothes, strapped against his thigh. There was lots of equipment of this kind. Each cell had at least one shiv; in fact, most prisoners had one. Usually these were made out of board, whittled to a rough sword shape and the edge lined with razor blades or sharpened triangles beaten out of tin cans. They looked rather like the swords armed with fishes' teeth from the South Sea cannibals I had seen in the Field Museum, or like those dug up in recent years in Jericho armed with microliths, thus demonstrating the great age and wide provenance of man's basic technological advances. This is a nice question for the Diffusionists. Could any connection be traced in time or space between the Bandhouse or any other modern prison and the Solomon Islands or the mesolithic Near East? Not only could these things kill a man, they often did. Many years later Dick Loeb was to be cut to death with just such a razor-blade shiv in a shower in Joliet. In our cell there was even a hypodermic and several needles, as well as the usual equipment of safety pin, spoon, and medicine dropper. There wasn't, however, anything to put in them, but there was plenty of marijuana, which was purchased from the screws. This was before the days of modern so-called heroin, but the screws had plenty of M.S. However, it was too expensive for my Negro cellmates.

One of the fellows, a brawny six feet and very black, was queer, and he had a complete set of what is known as "gear." White silk stockings were fashionable in those days. He had a couple of pairs, high-heeled shoes, a fringed girdle with fancy garters, a brassiere and falsies and even a transformation of false hair, as well as several brightly colored step-ins. The peculiar thing about the rest of the fellows in the cell is that they weren't interested personally in his charms, but he used to rig himself out and strut and grind and bump and sing "If You Want It You Got to Buy It, 'Cause I Ain't Givin' Nothin' Away," while the rest of us blew on combs, beat our shoes together, strummed the iron slats of the beds, clapped, and sang. He was quite a sight. He made a lot of dough and he'd always bring it out in the evening, wreathed in smiles, and with it we'd buy stuff from the screw—candy, cigarettes, muggles, pulp magazines, and alcohol from the infirmary. He was a natural-born whore and he got much more pleasure out of giving the really substantial proceeds of his tricks to us men and making us happy than he would have had spending it on himself. I'm sure that if the screws could have smuggled them in he would have provided us all with silk shirts, diamond stickpins, braided double-breasted suits and long, pointy yellow shoes. He was a great guy and remained my friend until I left Chicago. His drag name was that of the reigning movie actress of the day. When he died years later he was buried in drag in one of the historic funerals of show-business Harlem.

I was welcomed by my cellmates with enthusiasm. They were proud to have a white boy to educate and protect. As long as I was in that cell nobody dared make a pass at me, no screw ever laid a hand on me, and, as far as it was possible, I was saved from the most punishing jobs of work. All sorts of things showed up: cans of fancy food, good socks and underclothes; even, eventually, a new pair of Army shoes which fitted perfectly. I could have anything I wanted. Nothing was too good for me, and none of my cellmates made any advances to me.

Since the old cell blocks were essentially unheated and we each had only one ragged blanket, and as it was a sub-zero Chicago winter, keeping warm was a slight problem. It was against the rules to have newspapers, but from somewhere everybody gathered plenty of them. In the first place you had to wear them under your overalls on the job to keep from freezing. At night a whole mess of them were crumpled up in the corner of the floor. We all curled up in them like snakes in a posthole, put other newspapers over us, and put the blankets on top. The bucket privy was kept on one unfolded upper bunk so nobody would tip it over; on the opposite bunk, a bundle of everybody's stuff. I'm still waiting for somebody to ask me, "Would you sleep with a Negro?" If I hadn't, I sure as hell would have died. In the morning we filed out taking turns carrying the bucket, which smoked vigorously in the winter dawn, and dumped the contents in the garbage pit. This is one of the clearest pictures in my memory—the shabby Bandhouse yard, which looked half ruined, as though it had just gone through a war, and every fifth or sixth man, like a thurifer, carrying a pot from which rose a pillar of incense. It had all the solemnity of a religious procession.

Then we went on to work. The Bandhouse was a very profitable enterprise, all proceeds of which, except for payoff to the Organization, went into the pockets of the warden. We did the baking and several other things for all the city institutions. It had an aggregate and gravel plant; it did the laundry for many city institutions; it made furniture, and it had a large pottery and brick yard. My cell worked in the clay pits of the pottery. In the fall of the year a large hole was filled with water and turned into a puddle of mud, and from this we mined frozen clay blocks. This was pretty hard work for a young boy, and as much as possible my cellmates saved me. I was one of the few white men on this job. It was wonderful to work with these fellows. To keep up their morale, they sang—never proletarian work songs of the type popular with Pete Seeger and Woodie Guthrie, but mostly the Dirty Dozens, of which they knew an infinite number of verses. If they weren't singing they cussed each other out. Any mistake or fumble would be greeted with a string of the most imaginative abuse which would last for several minutes without interruption and never repeat. When nobody did anything wrong one guy would just cuss out another out of good spirits—working-class solidarity. It's quite impossible to convey what this was like. It's not just that it would be unmailable, but I can't remember it, couldn't possibly imagine it, and could never convey the rambunctious joy of life with which it was delivered.

For breakfast we had musty cornmeal mush already sweetened and very thin. It was usually burned. Once in a while we had oatmeal. That was always burned, and often there were little cooked worms in it. And coffee. I feel I won't be believed, but the tea from the night before was dreened off into the pot, filled up with water, a small amount of coffee added and boiled for half an hour or so. The result was a gray fluid like Mississippi River water. In the evening the leftovers were dreened off the coffee grounds, water was added, a couple of handfuls of the cheapest tea were thrown in, and the mess was boiled up again. The result was browner, thinner, and had more bite. Since prison induces a constant nervous fatigue, I learned to drink it. Whatever it did to my stomach it seemed to pep me up. Everybody said it was full of saltpeter, but I was sure we didn't need any saltpeter. Unadulterated, the food and drink would make anybody impotent. Lunch consisted of the seconds from the bakery—loaves that had not risen or had been burned, or both. They would have gone over big in a Los Angeles health-food store, because they tasted like no breadstuffs ever made. Along with two big chunks of punk, we had two slices of "blue steel." Blue steel is bologna and this bologna was blue, and sometimes ambulatory. If we didn't have blue steel we had moldy cheese, which I suppose was bought as spoilage from warehouses, wholesalers, or ships' stewards. For dessert there was a dish of prunes, scarcely cooked and served in a thin, sickish juice peculiar to the half-cooked prune. These were always weevily, sometimes so much so that when you bit into the prune you got a mouthful of wet brown powder instead of prune. Supper was stew, each bowl with a two-inch cube of meat which smelled like a rendering plant, and a gray, amorphous mass of vegetables. These had the special flavor of frozen, mildewed carrots and onions. Nothing gives that rare aroma of prison cuisine like a peck of onions, brown and translucent inside. On Fridays we had fish which no one could eat.

Morning and evening there was no way to wash, but once a week we were herded down to a shower room, where a number of pipes which came out of the wall were hammered flat at the end into fishtail jets which sprayed cold water over us as we pushed each other in and out. It was great fun—one of the high points of the week. Three days after I arrived I had crabs, head lice, graybacks, and scabies. Although we didn't have any beds the bedbugs never missed them but kept us all restless all night.

There was little of the food that I could eat, because it was so rotten or so moldy that it made me violently ill. I ate the bread and the other people passed me pieces of theirs, even though the bread, being the only really edible food we had, was in great demand. Everybody felt sorry for me. As the days went by, going without food and working as a mucker in zero weather, I began to get pretty giddy. One morning we were all filing out, with me carrying the bucket, when I fainted. I didn't fall down. A couple of the colored guys held me up.

I was sent over to the infirmary and the first thing the infirmary punk did was give me a good breakfast and a delousing. A few minutes later the doctor, a famous radical charlatan, showed up. He laughed in my face, put me up on the table, and gave me, in spite of my protests, an extremely irritating irrigation for gonorrhea and told the punk to kick my ass out—there was nothing wrong with me but an old dose of clap. As an example of senseless, gratuitious sadism this little episode is probably hard to believe, but I can assure you it really happened that way. I didn't have gonorrhea or anything remotely resembling it in any part of my body. In fact, there wasn't anything wrong with me except that I was hungry.

When I got back to the clay pit everybody was having a little meeting. The Negroes were sitting around on their hunkers, smoking cigarettes (which was supposed to be forbidden) and talking quietly with the screw, who was sitting on the wheelbarrow, slapping his feet with his broomstick. When I came up I got a cheering welcome and everybody went quietly back to work. Just before the noon break a punk came over with a note which said for me to report to No. 2 cell block.

Several years before the whole Bandhouse had been condemned by some do-good commission and the administration promised to tear it down and build anew. They built four modern, thoroughly penological cell blocks, but they no sooner got them built than Prohibition came along and the Federal Government rented practically all the space in them. The only county misdemeanor prisoners they held were big-shot gangsters who were being squeezed to get more money out of them as part of the maneuvers of intergang politics, or who were held because of some personal, spiteful feud with a police captain or judge. Come to think of it now, I suppose that is really what my trouble was, because I was the only person in the Green Mask pinch who had been sent to one of the old cell blocks.

When I reported they said, "You don't need to go to work now. Take it easy. You've had it pretty rough, and you can go to work tomorrow morning."

After another delousing they put me in a cell and didn't even lock the door. I lay down and immediately fell asleep. A little later a punk showed up with a whole pot of real coffee, two soft-boiled eggs, and some toast made of real bread with real butter. I was overcome but I ate it quickly enough.

When I got through he said, "Do you need any stuff?" I was so rattled by the whole experience that at first this remark didn't register. Then I realized he thought by the looks of me I'd been stuck in the old cell block to cold-turkey and was just coming out of it. I said, "No," and he said, "How about a drink?" "I could do with a drink," I said, and out of one of the capacious pockets of his overall jumper he pulled a half bottle of Three Star Hennessy. I had a good stiff drink. He said, "Don't worry about it. It's on the house," and after he had flirted with me coyly, away he went.

About four o'clock the men got off work and my cellmate showed up. He didn't march in but sauntered along a few minutes after the lineup, just in time for the count. His name was Blackie and he looked like all the Blackies that ever were: dark Irish, very handsome, and extremely hard-boiled, with a yellowish waxen face and long, delicate hands, like a woman's. He was in there held for retrial on a Federal murder rap, a large-scale bank robbery in which, as he said, "some clown stuck his nose into a bullet." Blackie was a many-time loser, with all the folkways of such. The first thing he did was make a straight pass at me. I said, "No," and he said, "Okay," with an expression that intimated I'd be begging for it eventually. He said, "Well, suit yourself about that, but tomorrow you're going to have to spend six hours patting my balls." I must say this kind of startled me. It turned out that he ran a stamping machine that made red terra-cotta gardener's pots, and I was the boy that dug the clay out of a bin and rolled it into proper-sized balls and passed them to him. After this had been explained to me I felt better.

I worked making balls for him for the better part of two weeks.

Everything was fine, except that Blackie never let me alone on the job. The screw in the pottery was an old man and didn't pay much attention to what was going on. Also we worked at the machine and bench in a narrow space in which our bodies were always brushing against each other. I suppose this was pretty hard on Blackie and he pestered me constantly with sly gropes and feels and all sorts of lucrative propositions, both for the present in the Bandhouse and to set me up in life after we got out. At the end of the day I was felt like a hat. Fortunately, in the cell he didn't bother me. I think this was because the place was better policed, and if I had created any rumpus he would have lost a very good scratch.

A very good scratch he certainly had. Food was brought in to him from all the best restaurants, always packed in the same insulated picnic hamper. Most of the big-shot gangsters had private meals, too, but they had to rely on the restaurant that had the racket of supplying the place. Exclusive rackets seemed to mean nothing to Blackie. He didn't have a habit, but every once in a while he'd take a sniff of coke or a joy pop, and he used muggles as currency in dealing with the other prisoners. Another reason he didn't bother me in the cell was that he had a more amenable boy in the same tier about four cells along. I must say that I never had any real trouble, just annoyance. Everybody that I worked with was wonderful to me, and whether it was courtship or altruism, all of Blackie's meals, after the first night, came in double portions, so I began to get fat on the cuisine of the town's best restaurants.

One visiting day, in the morning, Blackie announced that he was so hot he was afraid he'd go crazy before one o'clock, but that when one o'clock came he'd have a great surprise for me. This sounded ominous and all morning he rolled his eyes and made mysterious remarks. At lunch we had sea food from Ireland's restaurant on North Clark Street (miles away and brought by cab, I guess), and he kept urging me to eat up—I was going to need it. When visiting hour came we both got a call to report to the infirmary, where we were shown into a private room. Sitting on the bed were two gorgeous babes, straight out of a gangster movie. One was Blackie's old lady from St. Louis, and he'd had her bring along a friend. We spent an absorbing two hours. When we left, the doctor was nowhere in evidence, but the punk passed us out two Red Cross safety kits. It is only in childhood and in the harder and brighter underworld that group activities of this sort ever seem to be successful. These visits were eminently so, and they continued every visiting day until I left the place. In fact, they were so enjoyable that after things loosened up a little and I dared to let my girl come and see me I wasn't so anxious to see her. I had to talk to her through three layers of heavy iron screen.

As far as Blackie's courtship was concerned our new-found hetero-sexual outlet didn't seem to make matters any better. If anything, they got more difficult. Blackie was certain that he was going to beat the rap. He said he had an ironclad alibi, and I really do think that he was innocent and in bed at the time of the robbery. He'd spend evenings planning a regular Damon and Pythias life for us after we got out.

"I'm smart, but I haven't got much brains," he'd say. "You've got a lot of brains, but you're just a kid and you ain't really smart yet. If we work together we can take this fucking country to the cleaners."

We owned fleets of beer trucks, we ran dozens of cardrooms, we owned Derby winners, we drove Duesenburgs, and as for the women, Blackie would lie in his bunk with a copy of *Photoplay* and say, "Here we are, me and Claire Windsor and you and Clara Kimball Young. We're driving that old sixteen-cylinder crate down along the Rive-era . . ."

The meals got better and better. We had lobsters and two-pound porterhouses. Blackie drank whiskey with his meals like a Chinese, and I had the Thermos bottle in the picnic hamper full of the best wine.

Once a week there would be a shakedown of all the cells. Blackie had a luer, extra needles, and a vial of M.S. which sat in a safety-razor box beside the sink. Under the mattress he had an old straight razor remade into a shiv. There was all sorts of other stuff in the cell and none of it was ever bothered. The one shakedown that I had witnessed in the old cell block was something never to forget.

It was a surprise shakedown and pulled right after a cutting in the bathroom. We were all locked up for the night when we heard the screws rustling around in the lower corner of the block, and everybody started to yell, "Shakedown!" Instantly the air around the cage was filled with flying objects: candy bars, cigarettes, marijuana, dirty books, mystery magazines (which were forbidden because they would corrupt the prisoners' morals), playing cards, dice, razor blades, shivs, blue bottles of cocaine, round tubes of M.S., needles and luers, high-heeled shoes, silk stockings, garters, corsets, brassieres, ordinary dresses, shake dresses and trick dresses, muggets, dingfobs, outlines for briefs penciled on toilet paper—this list reading, as it were, from bad to worse—filled the air with a regular blizzard. It would have been possible to have equipped a full chorus line, a gambling joint, a law office, and a couple of dope shops from the stuff the screws gathered off the floor. One of the punks told me afterward that a Chinaman down the line from us had a whole opium kit—pipe, lamp, *yuen hok*, and a bindle of the best gum.

Nothing like this ever happened in the aristocratic new cell block. I'm sure that if you could have got her past the door, you could have kept a whole live woman in your cell and nobody would have bothered you during a shakedown. You would just have had to cover her up with a blanket to save people embarrassment. As it was, there were a couple of dingfobs in the cell block that were kept inflated and busy most of the time. These were life-sized rubber women which were exported by the Kobe Sex Shop, probably to all the prisons in the world. They came in a nice black package, without label, and depending on the quality were filled with either air or water. By and large they were not used personally by their owners, who, just like human pimps, were usually queer, but were rented out for a dime or two bits, depending on the rigor of the circumstances. Many a bum in the old days followed the harvest and made a better living off a rubber woman and with much less trouble than he would have had to take from a live one.

I don't want to give the impression that Blackie spent all his time making advances to me. He told long sagas of his and his friends' criminal adventures, whole stir epics that went on for days—not only long stories of crime and its consequences, but all the history, sociology, and chemistry of dope. Although Blackie said he'd never had a habit, and showed no signs of addiction while I was locked up with him, he was one of the few users I have ever known who just took a joy pop every few days. A lot of people want to do this and think they can get away with it, but in my experience any opiate means full-scale addiction in short order. Like all old-time users, Blackie was pretty close-mouthed at first—the morphine kit was the only thing which he hid from me, not from the screws, the first days I was in the cell. Once he trusted me you couldn't keep him quiet. He'd talk about dope, dope peddlers, and dope fiends, and the really incredible disasters and dilemmas the stuff does produce, until I was sick of the subject and begged him to shut up. The old-time M.S.-user was under the impression that the fewer people knew about it the better, unlike the modern hipster with his bad heroin, adulterated with milk sugar, who can't be kept quiet and spends most of his time talking—to the police, the newspapers, and on television. This was the most intensive course of underworld memoirs I was ever subjected to, although God knows I've listened to plenty of them since.

One day somebody that I knew showed up in the joint. He had been a driver for Eddie MacMillan, an Organization bag man I'll tell about later, and had driven me around Chicago with Eddie a good many times. He had tried to heist, of all places, Lorimer's Pool Room, out at Fifty-fifth and the El, and they'd locked him up for his own good. You must understand that vice and crime are two different things. The Organization employs criminals, but very few Organization men ever permit themselves to become guilty of conspicuous crimes. As any self-respecting gangster will tell you most of what is called vice in America is a civil-service occupation in Italy, and in those days, of course, most of the money was being made in booze, normally a perfectly respectable occupation. It is only in recent years that the Organization itself has dealt widely in dope, and this has come about due to pressure from above, from people far more powerful than the Mafia.

It is true that in those days people like Al Capone were shooting their way to the top, but by and large, gangsters are businessmen and no more personally involved in murder than the owners of any large corporation. The hired criminals may think they are members of the Organization and may get a big play from the public, but they aren't. It's a little like the Communist Party, with its inner and outer organization, except that behind the lords of the Mafia is a hidden rank and file, which plays a similar role to a common stockholder. One thing a hired criminal is never permitted to do is to act up on the job in his own interest.

This fellow, Shorty, had got off work driving Eddie, taken the El to Fifty-fifth Street, walked into the poolroom with a silk handkerchief around his face and the Organization's .45—out of the pocket of the car —in his hand. He stuck it into the belly of young Lorimer but as he did so the old man reached under the counter, took out a sawed-off billiard cue he kept for just such purposes, and conked him over the head. He wouldn't have been arrested at all but there was a cop in the back room at the time it happened who took him in on drunk and disorderly, and to learn him the judge gave him a little time. Blackie was very scornful of him and gave me a long speech about what would probably happen to him.

Then he started talking about his own case and how the Organization was going to get him out of it. His appeal was just a formality. It was a sure thing. I'd never given it any thought before, but as I listened to his morning-long monologue while I passed him his balls it was borne in on me that there was no real difference between the two cases except for the relative magnitude of crime. Blackie had been a member of the Organization in St. Louis with connections in Detroit and Kansas City that later became the Purple Gang and were the first large wholesalers of dope in the underworld. In those days they occupied themselves mostly with booze, gambling in all forms, and women, and were tied in on a businesslike basis with the outfits operating in Chicago. Blackie had been in town staying at the Drake Hotel when a stick-up of a bank in one of the Cook County suburbs resulted in the death of a policeman. Everybody got away, but Blackie and two other people were positively identified by all the employees of the bank. He had a very flimsy alibi which depended on the fact that his key was out of the box at the hotel, and on other circumstantial signs that he was occupying his room, where he said he had taken a couple of goof balls and lain down to sleep off a headache. I am inclined to think that he really had no connection with the crime, but the jury to whom he had been portrayed as a notorious criminal and public enemy thought otherwise. (I haven't any idea why it was a Federal crime. This was before the Federal bank-robbery laws that followed the rash of stick-ups during the depression.)

I realized that Blackie was trying to exorcise fate. He was a big shot and big shots have no business getting mixed up in such capers. He knew that while he was waiting for his appeal—or possibly it was a retrial—the number-one big shots were weighing, not his guilt or innocence, but the expediency of springing him and creating a public scandal. It would be easy enough to corrupt justice, but would it be worth it? I'd never thought so before, but I knew then that Blackie was scared.

There was a lot of free circulation around the pottery. When the work was slack, people used to smoke on the job and even play cards. Right after lunch Blackie went over and had a long, animated conversation with Shorty. When he came back he smiled in a hard, affectionate manner and said, "Oh, Buddy-boy, why didn't you tell your daddy that you were in that tearoom pinch? Why you been holding out on me? More dough? There ain't going to be any more of them little champagne suppers from now on. Tonight we give, or I'm going to bruise you all up, and don't hand me no shit. I know you artists are all freaks."

This didn't sound very good, and I was just about to go over to the screw and tell him that I'd have to be transferred from my present cell, even if it meant going back to the clay pit, when he came over to our machine.

"Oh, so you're an artist!" he said. "Why didn't you tell them that when you came in? You could have had a scratch right from the beginning." (I had given my name as J. Rand Talbot and my occupation as gardener, which is probably why I ended up with a shovel.) "Can you do sculpture?" he said. "Sure," I said. "At least I guess I could do anything you wanted me to."

"Well," he said, "that's just fine. Come on in the studio." He opened a door back of his desk that I had never seen opened, and here was a whole little studio, complete to a skylight in the roof. There was a sculptor's stand, potter's wheel, a rack of clay-working tools above a bench, wires for armatures, and even, over in one corner, some chisels and a block of marble someone had long ago started to peck at. On a shelf which ran all around the wall slightly higher than my head were

examples of work of past inmates, some of them quite good. One shelf
was almost completely taken up with a row of heads. They were like
nothing so much as the plaster fossil casts on the wall at the Field
Museum, which represented the evolution of the horse from *Eohippus*
to *Hippus domesticus,* from a small, five-toed, foxlike animal to the
massive, single-toed, hoofed beasts of today. They were the heads of
the screw, from the time he was a young lad under thirty and had first
gone to work in the Bandhouse to a year or two back, when he must
have been about seventy. There they were, white plaster, with staring
sightless eyes, covered with dust, in various degrees of skill, but all
recognizable—the life of a man.

He took me over to the sculptor's stand and showed me a couple of
big pots on the floor. He said, "You see, after these pots get over a certain size they get hard to hold if they're smooth, so I like to put a kind
of rough frieze on the band around the pot so you can get a grip on
them. Can you make up some designs and make some plaster casts of
them? Then we'll have some dies cut." "Sure," I said, "that's very easy."
"That's fine," he said. "I like to have some nice fresh designs every few
years. I'm the only guy in this joint that takes his work seriously, but
nobody can say that we haven't always turned out nice work in the
Bandhouse pottery."

I took the opportunity to tell him the problem that had come up with
Blackie. "Oh," he said, "that's all right. You can have a cell to yourself.
I'll make you my assistant. Can you type bills and things like that?"

He went out and left me alone in the studio for a couple of hours.
I did an egg-and-dart design, and I took a couple of pieces of bark
which I found over in a corner, cut them the proper width, greased
them, and cast them so that when repeated they would make a continuous barklike band. I modeled a couple of other things out of clay
that I have forgotten. Along about three o'clock the screw came back
and said, "How you doing? Think you'll be able to make it?" I said,
"Well, I've done six designs so far." "Good Christ!" he said. "How much
time you got to do? That's all the work we'll need for the next couple
of years." He was tickled pink with the bark, which seemed to him a
stroke of absolute genius, and took it out and showed it to Blackie and
a couple of other fellows at the machines.

"I told you he was a artist, didn't I?" said Blackie. "He'll do anything you want. I can't get him to do nothing, but art, that's different."
"Well, kid," he said, "I'll miss you. But don't say I didn't get you a real
scratch." I went back to the screw's office and typed up a short invoice
of assorted pots. "Well," he said, "another day, another dollar. Can
you play checkers?" I was an incorrigible young snob. "Sure," I said,
"but can you play chess?" "Do you like chess?" he said. "I haven't had

a good chess player in the joint for five years. I'll bring down the chess set tomorrow." "Oh, that's all right," I said. "I'll make one out of clay right now." So I did. They were very *moderne:* "functional," as they came to call them later, but still recognizable as chessmen, and nice and big. There were some old pots of glaze in the studio and next morning after they had dried, I glazed them white and red and baked them and we started to play with them while they were still warm. The old man was a great admirer of Morphy and brought down a book of his games, along with another chess book of classic tournaments. We played games that lasted all day, and when we weren't playing our own games we set up other peoples' and had long arguments about them.

It was remarkable enough that the screw was a chess player but he was far more remarkable than that. In his young days he had been a member of the Knights of Labor, and he was still a sympathizer of the Socialist Labor Party. Every week he showed up agog with the latest number of *The Weekly People* and there were stacks of back numbers lying around in the studio, which was the way I found out his opinions. Telling the story now, I realize how improbable this seems, but it didn't seem at all so to me then. I took it for granted, having grown up in such a world, that radicals should turn up everywhere. It really isn't so remarkable. Socialists have always been great ones for getting themselves civil-service jobs, and old MacGregor, when he was a young man and full of penological idealism, had slipped in during some change in administration.

He had never lost his idealism. The pottery was the only efficiently run enterprise in the jail and it was run without violence or trouble, policed entirely by the men themselves. At the door there was a custodial screw who was armed and carried a stick, but MacGregor, who was far too old to handle anybody physically, acted only as an administrator and work boss. Nobody overworked himself, but the place turned out more work per man than any of the other shops, and probably made more money. I never saw any trouble or violence in the place, and prisoners notoriously, when left to their own devices, are always getting into fights.

MacGregor's radicalism was not an unmixed blessing. Life locked up with a doctrinaire chess player eight hours a day is wearing enough, but forced association with an elderly follower of the most rigidly opinionated sect in the Socialist movement can get pretty tedious. I was too young to have sense enough to agree with everything he said right off, but it didn't take me long to learn. I tried to keep the conversation on chess and to draw him out on reminiscences of the old labor movement. Eventually it developed that MacGregor did feel himself compromised by his job, had long since dropped out of all activity in the movement, and was no longer an actual dues-paying member of the S.L.P. This didn't make him any the less contentious. I'm afraid I am giving the impression that I didn't like him. Quite the contrary, he was a real joy, but he only had three subjects of conversation—the old Socialist movement, chess, and anecdotes about the prisoners who had passed through. After all, these were the only things that had ever happened to him. Like most Socialists, he'd had a henpecked marriage, and his children had grown up and moved away and had no use for their father's ideas. He was half German. His mother had been an immigrant of the '48. He read German and had known all kinds of sectarian German radicals of the turn of the century, and many long since forgotten oddities of the American labor movement. Not only that, he had known Parsons and most of the other Haymarket martyrs. I don't know whether it was because he was a screw and a political Socialist or not, but he was convinced that they had guilty knowledge of the bombing. This was about the most outrageous heresy I had ever encountered. I had sense enough to keep my mouth shut, but it made me acutely uncomfortable.

Sometimes I think that all this stuff follows me around. Here I am, locked up in the Bandhouse, and I get mixed up with a Negro female impersonator, a high-pressure thief and pederast, and finally, an old-time radical. I suppose that's the point of an autobiography. It shows the pattern of events that have made you what you are—people like MacGregor will occur often in this story.

I had a cell by myself, with a view over the warden's garden to which I was permitted to take a pottery-office typewriter and plenty of paper. MacGregor brought me books from the public, not the prison, library. The conversation was as interesting as that at the Dill Pickle, I was admired as an artist, and I had nothing to do but play chess. The only thing I missed was Blackie's picnic hampers.

One of the most ridiculous things about the whole situation was that MacGregor had just discovered Bolshevism. Every few days he'd come in with the latest publications of the Workers' Library, an issue of *The Liberator* or the *Daily Worker*. He was impressed that I knew people who wrote for them, especially the *Liberator* crowd, who were practically synonymous with 201 West Thirteenth St. As befitted a screw, he was pretty square, and I think he thought I was just a decadent, bourgeois intellectual, because I didn't want to argue about the subject and had only cynical anecdotes to tell about most of these people.

I spent a couple of more weeks playing chess, making things out of clay, and trying to keep out of political arguments. Then one day the

Judge came home from wherever he'd been. My girl showed up, dim as a fish under muddy water behind three layers of dirt-caked screening, and brought me a change of clothes. The next morning the primitive intercom telephone rang, and MacGregor came over and said, "Beat it. You're sprung!" Everybody crowded around and slapped me on the back, and Blackie held my hand and looked into my eyes like a girl.

It's a good thing I got a new outfit, because the clothes I had worn in had been sterilized and shrunk until they wouldn't fit a midget. Even the shoes were warped and cracked with heat. Money had come in to me through the grapevine, but everything of the slightest value and all money that I had left at the desk had been stolen—watch, fountain pen, and cuff links, although the cuff links were from the dime store. I like to think my portrait of MacGregor is still there on the shelf along with the others, although I am afraid the shop and all the rest of the Bridewell of those days has been torn down. Blackie lost his case and was hung.

CHAPTER 25

My girl had gone to work for a research organization, and when she met me at the gate she had a psychiatrist in tow. For the next couple of months I had weekly visits with him, mostly occupied with political arguments. As psychiatric therapy it was ineffective, but maybe I converted him to something, because years later he was investigated by the Dies Committee. Also, I gained a friend and a free doctor. Unlike most psychiatrists, he was a good medical man and a neurosurgeon. We have remained friends to this day. He was one of the first reputable American Freudians. A couple of years ago I saw him in Los Angeles, little changed from the old days, and when I asked him if he was still practicing psychiatry he said, "Hell, no. I gave up all that nonsense years ago."

Willy McCauley had kept the studio, so I even had a home to come back to, though it was gaslit and the plumbing didn't work. From then on the police decided that I was to be learned a lesson and they began a campaign of harassment that lasted until I left Chicago. It became almost impossible for me to soapbox and in the course of time I also drifted away from "sporting life."

Through the connections I had formed in jail I got a little closer to the underworld than I had been, and considerably closer to the Organization. Eddie MacMillan, whose driver had been pinched, hung around the Near North Side and he came to see me to find out if the fellow was all right. MacMillan looked like an intelligent, quiet, and conservative North Irish professional man. He had a high, balding forehead, carefully combed hair with no stickum—most unusual for a gangster, however nifty—white shirts, plain round gold cuff links, a black tie, a navy-blue or Oxford-gray suit, plain black shoes with simple toes and no punch work, black silk socks with white clocks in them, carefully manicured hands, and no jewelry. He never raised his voice. You had to listen to hear him. He was a bag man for Moran. In those days Moran was peacefully giving up—swapping joints with the South Side Organization, and retiring from the South Side. Eddie's job was to collect the take from the joints that remained under Moran's control. This was ticklish work. The big Organization didn't believe that the South Side was being given up quite so peacefully, and a rumble was liable to break out any moment. We used to drive around the Negro district and as far south as there were any joints, Sixty-third and Cottage, Blue Island Avenue, out to Calumet, and to a bar near where I used to go camping, beyond Argo on Western Avenue, which was a hide-out and club for petty gangsters. Sometimes we would pick up a couple of girls and go socially to the same places and nothing was too good for us.

Two things Eddie MacMillan said I never forgot. I was making a living playing poker in a setup with Willy McCauley and Max Bodenheim. I said, "You know, I can't lose. Unless the game is crooked I always win, so that I don't really gamble." Eddie casually commented, "Only customers gamble." I laughed and said, "Is that your life motto?" "Well, I never said it before," he said, "but I guess it could be."

Then he was offered a job in a gangster movie. It was before *Underworld,* but Ben Hecht had something to do with it. Eddie was offered a part through Ben and left for Hollywood. When he left he said, "Well, good-by, Duke. Keep your nose clean and don't volunteer, and that *is* a motto." I never saw him again. He went to Hollywood and became a specialist in gangster pictures. All he did was authenticate the material. He died in bed, not so long ago.

My monologist friend had never done any time on the Green Mask pinch, and when I got out he had already opened right underneath our studio a place which he called the Dragon Inn. It was rumored he was a police agent and it was a plant. Nobody would go there but the Wobblies. They drank and raised hell and refused to spend any money—deliberate sabotage. It didn't take them long to ruin the monologist, but meanwhile a terrific racket was going on downstairs all the time. Willy McCauley and I started a poker game to make a little money, and when the monologist had been driven out of business Willy and I ran the place ourselves. We decided to sell Turkish coffee because both of us had been in the habit of hanging out in Levantine coffee shops, and we had a supply of moustike that we could get very cheaply. It is *grappa* with some herbs in it, similar to what the Italians call *grappa aruta*—it was in those days, anyway; nowadays it is just dry anisette. We peddled it in bottles, not drinks, and the customers bought setups. We also had baklava, and chili con carne, which Willy was very proud of, and cake and pie like all the bohemian tearooms, and muggles. In those days muggles was not illegal—you could be arrested under some ordinance in Chicago for selling it, but it was not specifically illegal and the cops could not make a pinch stick.

We had a nice little setup for ourselves, but things went wrong. All the Wobblies who used to hang out in the place got arrested. They'd driven everyone else away. It was bitter cold and the plumbing broke and it was impossible to heat the place. We had to shut down. My income had been spent and Willy had no money at all. We used to go out and panhandle money on the street and go build it up in a penny-ante game someplace. Even so, it wasn't very much. We had box after box of baklava and a couple of big pots of chili con carne, frozen solid, and on baklava, chili con carne, moustike, and Turkish coffee we lived for four weeks until it got warm. I have never relished baklava since.

It was about this time that the pinch over the stolen wallet occurred, and when we got over that we decided that things were breaking down. I had a high school friend, a highbrow whoremaster and football player, Big Sid, a great fellow for picking up girls. He read Dostoyevsky but otherwise he generally comported himself like a fullback and he discovered where we lived. I made the mistake one day of inviting him up to the place, and he used to show up there at all hours of the night with a couple of other guys and three or four drunken girls, and they'd take the girls in and wallow and then get up and leave. We'd go out and walk around the block and smoke cigarettes. This was the sort of thing you were supposed to do for a pal and it was difficult to say no. It's not masculine ethics to refuse such a request, but it used to happen two or three times a week and then his friends used to come by themselves and then some of the girls. Just at this time the McGinnis girl reached the gory climax of her career, too—so I began to weary of being completely accessible.

I got a room by myself on the ground floor, on Superior Street, in one of the last rows of houses near the lake—a limestone-front house with a beautifully proportioned room. It had early Navaho blankets and rugs of the type you can't get any more, a square piano and a lot of lovely, modest Victorian furniture with crossed pears for drawer pulls, and marble-topped commodes and a whatnot. Unlike most squares, the piano was in tune. I kept my residence secret for a couple of months until I recovered my equanimity. It had been a hard winter.

There was a girl who hung around the Mask named Meta Laninger. As far as anyone could judge, she was a typical Jazz Age hot chick. She had a long Dutch bob and a plump face, a large and wicked eye and loose lips, and a considerable amount of casually distributed embonpoint—and she was a heavy drinker. Nobody knew much about her except that she played piano and ran around on the South Side. She was an expert ragtime pianist, almost exactly like Fats Waller in style, and she knew all the ragtime classics. She could play Scott Joplin's *School of Ragtime*, a difficult book of études, straight through without batting an eye. Besides, she had the ability to rattle off with a flick of the wrist all the ornaments of the pianola or a whorehouse piano—that sounded more whorehouse than anybody else could possibly play by hand. Everybody looked on her as a party girl and as a source of expensive liquor. She wore a coonskin coat that had inside pockets in it and she'd show up with them filled with bottles of Pernod and slivovitz or something else unheard of in the States during Prohibition. One stormy night she got locked out. She used to climb in the fire escape, but this time the fire escape was all covered with ice and dangerous. So she came home with me.

There were no other dwellings there—the rest of the floors were occupied by trade-journal offices and a commercial art studio. So she sat down at the piano at four o'clock in the morning and played Bartók. Then she played her own piano arrangement of Satie's *Gymnopédies*, and then the *Sechs Kleine Klavierstücke* of Schoenberg—the evanescent, one-page-each moth flights that are supposed to be the turning point, the pivot, of Schoenberg's career, and are the only Schoenberg that I have ever liked. I was dumfounded. This was my favorite music. I had never guessed the girl had any taste at all. After that she would come over and play the piano for hours at a time and I would lie on the couch on the Navaho rug and smoke my water pipe and listen to her improvise on the Scriabin tone row and dodecaphonic counterpoint and tone clusters and all sorts of stuff.

By and large in my life I have avoided people like her and Nancy. She was a person with several public personalities, all of them entirely defensive, not really fraudulent because, of course, no one can ever be really fraudulent with himself, and only adolescents think people pose. She wrote quite good poetry, though she never showed it to anyone and it took considerable effort to get it out of her. She had a series of adaptive colorations that she put on and took off, and in the middle of the personalities of a musician and a poet was the personality of a perfectly conventional young American woman.

She was engaged to an Army captain. Her father had been an Army officer. She had been born on an Indian reservation. Behind her life as an artist in Chicago lay Army life with all of its sterility and meaninglessness. Nowadays the military live the most peaceful and civilized lives, but that was not true of the Sioux Indian reservation of the 1900s where Meta grew up. Life was fast and empty.

She had another interest—the largest collection of pornographic books, except those owned by a couple of millionaires, in the city. She must have had a fabulous amount of money because she would get books delivered to her in sacks and read them on consignment, put wineglasses on them, have to pay thirty or forty dollars for them, and then give them to me. I'd read them, bleach the stain, and sell them. One night she came over with my favorite wine, Château Ausone, 1910, in the inside pockets of her coonskin coat. In her shell-rimmed glasses and her Dutch bob and her tilty heels, she rapped on the window about one o'clock in the morning. Under her coat there were only her garters and stockings and the bottles of wine warm with her body. She sat down naked at the piano in the dark room, red with the coal fire, and informed me, while I opened the wine, that she was marrying her captain next morning. I never saw her again. This was the second time this happened to me—but it would not be the last. As I look back, all the girls whose last bachelor night I helped celebrate were very similar. Perhaps, like the benedict smoker amongst men, it is a square custom.

I lived six weeks of a quiet life, doing nothing but writing and painting and being entertained by Meta on the piano. She is certainly the best pianist I have ever had for a friend. (Harold Bauer, I suppose, was the best pianist I ever met.) She had the deepest, not only feeling for, but personal identification with, musical expression. When she played, it was as though the piano weren't there but the music were being produced out of her; as though she were singing or had the piano inside her. It was pure organic expression, like the oyster's excretion of a pearl.

She's not the only person that I've known in my life who had a great talent and then vanished. A large percentage of the most talented people I have ever known have vanished, and I think the reason for this is that to be a successful poet or painter or a musician you've got to be a kind of fool, you've got to *want* to. You always arrive on an ass and the foal of an ass. Persistence as an artist seems to require a kind of folly. All through my life I have known smart and talented people who just seemed to feel that it wasn't worth the candle. For all I know the Eisenhowers may have Meta and her husband in to dinner and she may entertain them with Webern this moment, but she vanished as an artist, as have so many people of her kind.

This was also true of Shirley. She not only looked like Katherine Mansfield but she wrote like her and, in my opinion, wrote considerably better. Many years later I called on her. I asked her if she was still writing and she said, "Yes." I asked, "What do you do with it?" "Nothing at all. I just put it in a box, just like I always did." I said, "What does your husband think of it?" and she answered, "He's never seen it." "You mean you've lived all these years with him and he's never so much as seen your stories and poetry?" She said, "That's right." "Didn't Faithful ever see it?" And she said, "No." "Didn't your sister ever see it?" and she said, "No." "You used to show them to me."

"Yes, I know. You're the only person who has ever seen a line that I have written." "You still write?" She said, "Yes, all the time." She went upstairs in the palatial home of a most successful surgeon's wife and got a box of stories and poems, and I thought, "I'm going to get a terrible shock. I'm going to find that my twenty-years-gone estimate of this woman's talent was false—the projection of love and ignorance." On the contrary, she was not only better than Katherine Mansfield, but she was what Katherine Mansfield had wanted to be—a delicate, ethereal, female Chekhov, and, as a poet, a corrupt Emily Dickinson. No one but her and me, and I do believe her, has ever seen any of her things.

I had moved a few blocks away to escape bohemia for an interim, but bohemia came to me. Four doors away a young couple from Little Rock, Arkansas, opened a restaurant. Their names were Hal and Judy Swanson. They were both excellent cooks, something that was utterly unknown in bohemia then and has hardly become common since. Hal was a professional chef and one of the best I have ever known. The place was beautifully got up: the walls were rough plaster and the tables were scrubbed white oak, which were holystoned every day by a Filipino porter, and the floor was covered with fresh white sand. There was a large fireplace and several pipe racks and a big pot of tobacco, which came from Bond Street or some similar source of good tobaccos, and they served to their close friends who stayed after dinner small amounts of wine and very good brandy. I started to eat there every night. They attracted the kind of people I had met only through Nancy and Meta—successful publicity girls, writers, advertising executives, and slick journalists. I'd seen them around the offices of places where I had worked but they weren't my dish of tea and I had never known them before. I don't mean people like Ben Hecht or other characters who have survived in the popular estimation from those days, but James O'Donnell Bennett on the Chicago Tribune, who I think was then the highest-paid reporter in America, and individuals of that kidney—publicity women with expensive clients, and top commercial artists. In those days these were the only heavy drinkers, except for the IWW circle, that I knew. They drove Stutzes and Velies and Marmons and Moon roadsters, and one of them had a Locomobile, and they generally comported themselves as the Bugatti and Land-Rover sets carry on today. Almost all of them were mildly homosexual. They doubled in brass and were paired—or tripled—off, each with a steady male and female. I never got much out of this association except Hal Swanson's cooking. I'm glad that I saw this particular kind of fauna at play, but I don't think it taught me much. About all I learned was that I'd had it, and I've never had much interest in such people since.

Possibly they gave him free dinners, because every night *The Dial's* young modernist poet, Olaf Olson, was to be found in Hal and Judy's. In those days he was called Olivier, and he was called Olivier because he sent a poem to *The Dial* and it was signed Ole Olson. He was a farm boy from Green Bay, Wisconsin, when they accepted it. They changed, as they had a habit of doing, nearly every line in it. When they came to the last line they said, "Well, of course, we can't have as distinguished a poem as this signed by such a name as Ole Olson, so we suggest that you spell your last name with two s's and I think we'll change the Ole to Olivier." (He was informed of this in a letter, not asked.) So the poem came out signed Olivier Olssen, an impossible name. Ole Olson remained Olivier all the years that he contributed to *The Dial*, and when he became a Catholic he became Olaf Patrick Olson, after the saints who were invoked at his baptism.

Ole had gone to New York from Green Bay, Wisconsin, and had met Carl Van Vechten and Muriel Draper and the set that Van Vechten had given brief immortality in *Peter Whiffle* and *The Blind Bow-Boy*. He was often said to have been the model for *Peter Whiffle*. This is not true, however—the book was written before he showed up there, but he was the perfect embodiment of Van Vechten's nonsensical chichi. When he came back to Chicago he was living in chastity with a girl who had also run away from Green Bay and come to the Near North Side to live the life of literature and art. The first time I met him was at the home of Fred Ellis, an ex-Wobbly and the cartoonist for the *Daily Worker*.

Buck Ellis was an ex-house painter, a friend of Loughman's from the days when they were boys in parochial school together. Although he was only about five feet two inches, he was one of the toughest individuals I have ever met and one of the best fighters. After Robert Minor had given up cartooning to become a Party official, Buck carried on for many years the dramatic conté-crayon cartoon style Minor had developed on the St. Louis *Post-Dispatch*—a style characteristic of all Red cartooning in its best days, and still, incidentally, the tradition of the capitalist *Post-Dispatch*.

Buck had started an "at home" in competition with the various other radical and artistic gatherings around Chicago, and this was presided over by his mother-in-law, a large, blowsy Mother of the Revolution.

I came up one night—everybody was sitting around drinking bathtub gin—and a mild and meek and innocent boy with a home-grown English accent was introduced to me as Ole Olson, the *Dial* poet, and with him was Peggy. He said, "This is Peggy." And then, "Show Rex your breasts, Peggy." The girl reached in and took out two strange objects, like slightly thick, pale pink garden hoses, and about seven inches

long. They looked like anything but breasts. She exhibited them and
I looked at them as though I were looking at the statue of St. Agnes,
and smiled and said, "Very interesting." Then she put them back.
Whatever happened to Peggy and her breasts I don't know. She moved
on from Chicago to Greenwich Village and then to the Left Bank and
disappeared. Probably made a successful marriage.

Ole attached himself to me. He was the kind of person who is totally helpless. He didn't know how to live at all—how to get his socks
on, how to get his eggs fried or get up in the morning and get to work—
a complete innocent. His extraordinary accent gave most people the
impression he was a homosexual, but he was not. He had no sex whatsoever, and for as long as he was around no one ever knew him to have
any kind of an affair with man, woman, animal, vegetable, or mineral.

A few nights later we were at a party at Morrie Fishbein's, and Ole
and I were standing at the punch bowl talking. We had a great deal in
common, as we were the only people in Chicago at that time writing
in anything resembling the same style, except Yvor Winters, who even
then was not very friendly with anybody. While we were standing
there a rather Babbitty-looking individual came up and talked to me
for a little while and then he turned to Ole and said, "Did you have a
good crossing?" and Ole asked, "Crossing?" He said, "Yes. How long
have you been in the States?" Ole said, "Why, I was born here." "Oh,
really," he said. "Where were you born?" Ole said, "Green Bay, Wisconsin." "Well, where in hell did you get that British accent?" And Ole
said, "Really! I'm sure it's ninety-nine per cent affectation." This seemed
to infuriate the man, who burst into a paroxysm of rage, tipped over
the punch bowl, and started pounding on Ole. I pulled him off. Ole
was completely demoralized, with bleeding nose, broken glasses—only
half conscious. I took him outside and said I'd get a cab. He said, "I
haven't got the money for a cab." So I said, "Well, I'll take you home—
I'll go home with you. Where do you live?" He said, "I haven't got a
room." Since he was in rather bad shape—shaking all over, and gray
with shock, and couldn't see at all, I said, "I guess you'd better come
home with me," though I foresaw the future.

I took him home and put him up on the floor and the next day I got
him an extra day bed to sleep on, and so I got a star boarder. I'm afraid
I'm giving the impression that Ole was a tramp, but he wasn't. He was
just completely unworldly and full of saintly intentions. The moment
he'd get any money, say a check for a poem, he'd spend it on gifts for
other people. He'd get money from home once in a great while, and
on my desk there'd be a bottle of wine and some Stilton cheese or something else he knew I liked. All his friends would get presents, and then
he wouldn't have anything to eat for a while. He wrote constantly—

every day a poem or two. His poetry was mellifluous like that of Archibald MacLeish or St.-John Perse. It resembled the lighter-textured poetry of Apollinaire, and it was certainly among the best poetry being written in the States at that time. For several years he was one of the better poets of *The Dial* and then of *transition*.

He has spent the last twenty-five years in a state hospital. In those days he was not what I would call a serious neurotic, let alone a psychotic. I think that in a well-organized society not only would there be a place for such an unworldly personality, such a highly strung and delicately balanced sensibility, but that such a person would be one of the leaders of the society—not in the sense of pomp and circumstance, but one of the spiritual leaders, one of the true growing points.

He has continued to correspond with his friends and still writes the same kind of poetry, which has not changed at all since he entered the Catholic Church in 1927. Even at that time it didn't change very much. He was in the process, then, of approaching the Church, and we used to go to the nearby Anglo-Catholic Church of the Ascension. The rector, Father Stoskopf, was a barren and rigid Thomist but Father Vaughan, the curate, was mildly literary in his tastes, effeminate in his manner, and sympathetic to the bohemians who made up an appreciable part of the neighborhood over which he was supposed to have the cure. The trouble with a personality like Ole was that, by and large, the Church could do him no more good than any other aspect of society, because the brutalizing effects of the society are to be found in the Church as well as everywhere else.

I used to try to talk to him about the fundamental difference between his poetry and mine. I had already begun to feel that unedited Wyatt was better than Surrey, and that Marsden was better than Beaumont and Fletcher, and Donne's *Satires* were among his best verse. Although I was not writing it, I was trying to feel my way intellectually toward a hard, rugged, and anti-mellifluous verse. It was impossible to discuss things like that with Ole. His mind didn't work that way. Our conversations about poetry consisted mostly of appreciative gossip about the people we admired. Still, behind the gossip went on an unspoken discussion of fundamental principles.

It was even less possible to talk to Ole about anything as profound and complicated as religious ideas. His approach was simplicity itself and took the form of the most naïve piety. From his effeminate manner and pseudo-English accent you would think that ritualism and incense and silks and satins would appeal to him. They did not. He seemed as completely unaware of the sensual allures of the Church as he was of the intellectual enticements. He just loved Our Lady and Our Lord, and accompanied this love with an increasing sense of ecstacy. It was interesting to watch. I was to lose track of him in the period in which he finally became a Roman Catholic, and then a member of the first Catholic Worker group. It was at this time, however, around Buck Ellis' and around my place, that he met Dorothy Day, who had been a girl friend of Lionel Moise's and was still far from being a Catholic—to any outside observer, anyway.

CHAPTER 26

About this time, at the Church of the Ascension, Ole and I met Kenneth Thorpe. He was a long, thin, pale young man with a long, thin, pale mustache. He dressed like a slightly modified Southern colonel, an unreconstructed reb from about 1890. He spoke to us after the service and introduced himself as a poet, too. He had gone to Vanderbilt and had come under the influence of the then forming Fugitives' Group. They were all very young men in those days, and most of them were still at Vanderbilt. He was the first principled reactionary I ever encountered. He had all the attitudes of John Crowe Ransom's circle, all the sentimental opinions derived from reading *Red Rock, The Clansman*, and other Southern imitations of Sir Walter Scott, and his taste in poetry was rigorously English.

Just at this time the Fugitives' Group had distinguished themselves from the Modernists and yet given themselves a slight flavor of eccentricity. They had taken up the doggerel of Skelton and the metrics of the Middle English breakdown—the prosody that evolved with the loss of the mute "e" and the general French pronunciation of English —in other words, poets like Occleve and Lydgate. The bumpy, irregular metric of John Crowe Ransom's "Captain Carpenter" is probably their best expression of this interest: eccentricity reduced to a system.

Thorpe explained this to me and I sat down to read all of Lydgate and Occleve in the Early English Text Society. Such books do not circulate from libraries and I had to read them at the Newberry Library on Bughouse Square. I sat and read volume after volume of Middle English verse and copied out a huge longhand anthology. I don't know of any poetry, including French verse since Baudelaire, which has meant so much to me as this—except medieval Latin. Not the Post Chaucerians, who are dull fellows, but the Scots Chaucerians and Middle English lyricists. It was wonderful to have it all come at me in one blast when I was most receptive to it. I would go over every day and read for hours. The librarian gave me a cubicle where I could read alone.

Through medieval English verse I discovered medieval Latin. It knocked me off my feet and picked me up and whirled me around. In those days there were few good books on medieval Latin. There were textbooks in the Latin of the Vulgate Bible and Missal and Breviary used in Catholic schools, and a couple of things in French (German I couldn't read) and H. O. Taylor's book *The Medieval Mind*. About this time Allen, at the University of Chicago, wrote a book on Carolinean verse and one on later medieval poetry. He had become a fad at the University of Chicago, but I didn't know this. Eventually I met graduate students who were taking his courses. I audited one of them. He was far from friendly and didn't welcome an auditor and so I went away. I didn't need any course—I saturated myself with medieval Latin and got it wherever it could be found. Once I mastered the strange simplicity of the Latin I could use the scholarly German publications and ignore the German. I read the *Carmina Burana* in the old edition so full of mistakes. I read all the poetry of Abelard and Thomas Aquinas and the Victorines and Venantius Fortunatus in Migne. I read all of the *Analecta Hymnica*. The only English was John Addington Symonds' *Wine, Women and Song*, which bore little resemblance to the Latin. Helen Waddell's book was not out yet. I was alone on Darien. To this day I still love to read medieval Latin and I still hope someday to publish a translation of the *Planctus* of Abelard, the finest poetry of the Middle Ages still untranslated.

Along with medieval Latin verse I started to read St. Thomas Aquinas and Abelard and St. Bonaventura and Duns Scotus in Migne. I guess Scotus appealed to my adolescent snobbishness. I had never heard of anyone who considered himself a follower of Duns Scotus. He was practically incomprehensible, so I took to him like a duck to water. I began to meet Neo-Thomists and followers of *L'Action Française* and churchy Anglo-Catholic homosexuals. Characters of this sort were just putting in an appearance around American bohemia. I read all the medieval Doctors of the Church who were at all interesting reading. Rickaby's translation of the *Summa Contra Gentiles* had always been one of my favorites in all philosophy, because of its mathematical elegance, the cocksureness of its demonstrations—all those dubious conclusions presented with the aplomb of Euclid.

I went on to read the early Fathers of the Church. I bought cheaply the two sets of the *Ante-Nicene and Post-Nicene Fathers* and the *Ante-Nicene Library*, products of the Tractarian movement, edited by Pusey or Keble or both, and sat down to read it all, from Lactantius to Clement of Alexandria. I must say I found most of it weary reading. But Clement, Augustine, Origen, and Dionysius the Areopagite were different. I discovered that all religious people were not fools. I must say

I found Hippolytus' *Philosophumena* on the early heretics the most fun to read—better than Flaubert.

Reading the Alexandrians I studied Dean Inge on Plotinus and Neoplatonism and in this strange way, through Dean Inge, of all people, I became acquainted with the learned apologists for Anglo-Catholicism. I have never been able to read Newman with any pleasure—I think it was Carlyle who said he had the mind of a rabbit. He seemed to me to be a mushy and sentimental writer and his famous prose, I found, was as bad as his poetry. Anyone with any taste can recognize that *The Dream of Gerontius* is flaccid and dull doggerel. Taste in prose is not so easily come by. Newman has always had the reputation of being a great *prosateur*. I found him dreadful. However, I dutifully read him because I was anxious to follow the evolution of modern Neo-Catholicism. The religious utilitarianism of *L'Action Française*, T. S. Eliot, Maritain, religion as reaction, I was never able to take seriously—either Roman or Anglican, least of all as a revival of the old thing. I am quite sure that St. Thomas Aquinas would not have the faintest idea of what Jacques Maritain was talking about and would have ordered him summarily burned as a heretic. Somewhere in Bishop Gore or Ronald Knox or Father Thornton I saw a footnote quoting Von Hügel, and I immediately read all of him that I could lay hands on. My fondness for him has never left me.

I feel that the neoreligiosity, as distinguished from religion *simplicitas*, of my time has been pernicious, not only socially pernicious, as the handmaiden of fascism, but pernicious for the people themselves, personally. I have watched a good many atheists who were harmless, inoffensive people. They committed a few adulteries or a little quiet pederasty and they were not to be trusted with unattended typewriters or valuable books, but, by and large, they were inoffensive. Then they would start going to church and listening to the clink of thuribles and inhaling incense and suddenly they would acquire all those wonderful Christian virtues—bigotry, pride, intolerance, chronic anger, sexual dishonesty.

It didn't take me long to learn to avoid converts. I greatly prefer birthright, as the Quakers say, Catholics. I think it's a mistake on the part of the Catholic Church to welcome to its bosom all these people who flirt with strangers in front of its doors. Here in Cornwall, where now I'm dictating this, I have a friend across the street who's a birthright Catholic and an artist, and we've been discussing Simone Weil. Simone Weil has virtues but they are none of them Catholic and many vices and they are all those of the neoreligious. I never found the world of modern neoreligiosity attractive, although from this time on for a few years I was to be around it quite a bit. I did find Baron von Hügel

extremely enjoyable reading, a beautiful writer, a wise man, and a
man who as a Catholic considered himself almost as powerful as the
Pope, and who set out to redeem the Church from within. He was quite
a bit different from the ex-atheist ex-Socialist who becomes an intolerant and snobbish Neo-Thomist. When Von Hügel says that a pervading
sweetness of temper and a sense of joy are one of the signs of sanctity,
I think this is far more important than all the quotations from the
Summa that can be marshaled by French literary dilettantes at cock-
tail parties.

Through Von Hügel I read all the liberal Catholics, Father Tyrrell
and Monsigneur Duchesne and Loisy and other people whose names
I've forgotten, all of Monsigneur Duchesne's works on liturgics, on the
history and evolution of the Church, and similar books that might be
called Catholic anthropology and archeology. Lord Acton, I realized,
was the soundest of the lot but Father Tyrrell also made a great impression on me. He is never mentioned today. He was expelled from
the Church and condemned. It's not to anybody else's interest to read
him, but I have discovered among liberal Roman Catholics of my acquaintance that he is still secretly read. The Church presents itself
nowadays in terms of papal infallibility, the Assumption, the Miracle
of Fatima, intellectual rigor, and anti-birth control—an apologetic taken
from Tertullian. You are asked to believe things because they are absurd. Whatever the faults of the Catholic Modernists, they did try to
crown modern thought with Catholicism as its fullest flowering. I realized then that it is better to be a humane, sensitive, and concerned
Catholic Modernist than to be an unprincipled Anti-Modernist, to use
the term that Maritain used for one of his first books. At this time I
read Maritain and I started reading the other Neo-Thomists, always
with a haunting sense of moral dissatisfaction—I just didn't like these
people. I know of few writers in contemporary society whom I dislike
as much as Maritain. It seems to me that he is a showy, chic, unscrupulous journalist. Even when his ideas are sound and his judgments correct out of his context, as he uses them they all seem a bag of tricks,
just as on a more vulgar journalistic level the tedious paradoxes of Gilbert K. Chesterton are persistently dishonest.

Coming from generations of Liberal-Radical Orthodoxy, I discovered that St. Thomas Aquinas and St. Augustine and St. Clement of
Alexandria, St. Bonaventura, Abelard, and Hugh of St. Victor were
quite as intelligent men as Eugene Victor Debs or Clarence Darrow or
Herbert Spencer or Thomas Huxley, and much prettier writers. Reading medieval philosophy, I came to the conclusion that philosophy as
such had ended with William of Occam and the breakdown of the
medieval synthesis. It seemed to me that bourgeois philosophy, the

philosophy of the capitalist epoch, didn't mean anything. Nobody in the world takes it seriously. It's just something that's taught in universities.

With the beginning of the epistemological battle, it seemed to me that philosophy was emptied of all meaning. I am inclined to think that philosophical speculation, at best, is a form of artistic activity, and that philosophy has no real purpose whatsoever in society—considerably less than music does. It's a minor play activity. Many people believe that the arts are play, and trace artistic impulse back to the play of puppies and bees. I don't think this is altogether true; I think that a special role of considerable significance can be attributed to the fine arts. But I think that philosophy, by and large, is just play. In the Middle Ages, this was not altogether true. It was an excess activity of the social order, a surplus activity, but it did reflect society and it did influence it. This sense of being a part of the world is what gives medieval philosophy its great appeal. Too, it had not lost ethical content. Encountering the medieval and patristic philosophers, I was meeting a world which was totally unlike anything I had known before; an intellectual world which purported at least to be at grips with the real world.

Anglo-Catholicism is full of all sorts of interesting things, people, and events. Years later I was to know one of America's best poets, a more or less manic individual who talked constantly. Once he was talking away a blue streak at me and all of a sudden he drew breath and looked at me and said, "You know, I never lack for conversation. I've always got something to talk about, some gossip, some dirt to dish, because I have been a member of the three most gossipy organizations in modern life, the Anglo-Catholics, the Trotskyites, and the homosexuals." It is perfectly true that the history of the Anglican Church from its beginning is full of interesting detail, both in the lives of its members and in its liturgical and doctrinal changes and chances and evolutions. This made for interesting doings, not just something to read about. I met people who were all excited about how Father So-and-so had just put six candles on the altar instead of two, or about a translation of the prayer book of Bishop Challoner which had just come out, or what did I think of the latest pronouncement of some Broad Bishop on reunion with the Baptists.

I was never able to identify myself with such concerns—I always remained just a little an outside observer, but I found it a great deal of fun and I started going to church regularly. At first for the major ceremonies I would go to the Roman Cathedral, but in those days things were still pretty bad liturgically and musically, and I would always go away frustrated, so that more and more I came to go entirely to the Ascension, which was the most developed Anglo-Catholic church in Chicago at that time.

I read Huysmans' *En Route* and *L'Oblat;* looking back I realize he was a lot of blather, but then it was intrinsically interesting and rather wonderful. In little time I uncovered the wrong information and errors in judgment and taste and sickened of the lush style. Then it was all new to me and gave me a springboard which I could use to move on to better and sounder writers. In the year-round liturgical life of the Church I encountered something I had never known before—a social organization which, whatever its great evils, devotes its best energies to ennobling life. Any Catholic will tell you that above all other things what holds him to the Church in spite of doubts and manifest evils is the sacramental system. In the rites of passage—the fundamental activities and relationships of life—birth, death, sexual intercourse, eating, drinking, choosing a vocation, adolescence, mortal illness—life at its important moments is ennobled by the ceremonious introduction of transcendence; the universe is focused on the event in a Mass or ceremony that is itself a kind of dance and a work of art. This is the real significance of religion. We think of religion today as something to believe, the Westminster Confession, the Athanasian Creed. The virtue of Catholicism is that it has never lost the anthropological religion which it shares with the Northwest Indians or the Bushmen or the Eskimos—it is something you *do.*

I don't think Kenneth Thorpe was the best guide for this process of discovery of mine, and certainly Ole Olson was no guide at all. Ole didn't verbalize—he just loved Our Lady. Thorpe was full of information, he could tell me where to go and who to meet; but Ole's piety gave me a silent rudder in this new sea that I was exploring, a control I didn't even realize was there.

CHAPTER 27

I met through Thorpe a new group of college kids. He had a girl who had gone to the University of Illinois, whom he later married, and she had a bunch of friends who were the intellectuals, the *révoltés,* writers, and poets of that institution. They were much more provincial than the young people I had met around Chicago. They knew nothing about modern verse. They had been taught poetry, most of them, by a teacher down there by the name of Bruce Wyrick, and their heads were full, not even of Carl Sandburg or Vachel Lindsay, but of Beardsley and Dowson and Symonds and Wilde, and they wrote villanelles and triolets and rondeaux and went in heavily for Flaming Youth. These are the only people that I met in anything resembling intellectual circles who were the F. Scott Fitzgerald, John Held, Jr. type of the Twenties. They were all more or less nonpolitical—they didn't know anything about politics and were uninterested in it. Certainly none of them were revolutionaries; their tastes were conditioned entirely by the revolt against Middle Western puritanism. These youngsters came from narrow, savage homes in the small towns in the Middle West, and they went to Champaign to school and discovered gin and sexual intercourse and art for art's sake. The literary set of the University of Illinois founded a magazine called *College Humor,* which was originally published over in Iowa someplace and was edited and written by Flaming Youth from the corn-belt universities. This was really the foundation of the legend of the Twenties, and it is remarkable how few people there were of this sort about.

About the same time Willy McCauley fell in love with a girl at the University of Chicago. She came from a scholarly and radical Jewish family. Her father was a skilled craftsman and her uncle a rabbi. Her brother became a famous revolutionary leader. She was beautiful and intelligent. She somewhat resembled Masha—another athletic young Jewess who looked like a Gauguin girl. She had a large group of friends, the radical, highbrow girls of the University.

It was curious to compare these two groups of students, both of them

typical of the Twenties. The University of Illinois set became canon-
ized in the Twenties legend. The University of Chicago girls did not
flame. They were liberated sexually. They were intense and full of
agony and struggle, but there wasn't anything very flaming about
them. They didn't consider spectacularly immoral the intervisitation
of male and female dormitories in the middle of the night, even though
one of them got thrown out of school for being found in somebody's
room in the medical students' dormitory. They were principled and
learned. Their heads were full of, precisely, to my joy, medieval Latin
and Provençal—courses in early Romance literature were popular just
then. They knew no one who ever went to football games. They were
all left-wing Socialists or Anarchists, although they talked very little
about it, and they read *Ulysses* as it came out in *The Little Review*.
They had already heard about Wittgenstein, and their tastes in French
literature went to Aragon and Eluard, who were just coming up in the
magazines, then, or Valéry or Cocteau. Those who read German read
Rilke, and Yiddish modernist poets like Yehoash. They were practically
all Jewish. I can't think of a Gentile among them, and they were not
in revolt against their Jewish background. Indeed, they were trying
to assimilate it and reorganize and restate it in modern terms. They
were the exact antithesis of the antipuritans of the University of Illinois. I have two daughters whom in a few years I will be sending to
college. What a fatal mistake I could make by putting them in a corn-
belt college where they would acquire the 1960s equivalent of a *College Humor* culture! At the best, the people from the University of
Illinois became successful but unhappy newspapermen and advertising executives, whereas this circle of people from the University of
Chicago became unsuccessful and happy people on the fringes of literature. One of the girls is the power behind the throne on a leading
magazine, another is married to the world's leading Sumerologist, and
so on down the line. Their lives have been far richer and more significant than those of the kids from the provincial school downstate.

To me, and to Willy McCauley, they were all just a lot of new girls
who had showed up on the Near North Side looking for Life, and immediately we became interested. I met a girl, the closest friend of
Willy McCauley's girl, who was, as a gypsy fortuneteller told her as we
were walking down Halstead Street one day, a beauty of a rare type.
She was an extreme Armenoid Jew. She had a large hooked nose and
large eyes, a deep, delicate jaw, a peaches-and-cream complexion, and
walked with a slight stoop. Verbal description cannot convey the fact
that she was a raving beauty—one of the most beautiful girls I have
ever known in my life—and had a personality which went with her
appearance: a solemn, brooding sensitivity of a kind I had never seen

before, and which I supposed peculiarly Jewish. I certainly have never known any Gentile like her. She was not at all an unhappy person, but the plastic feeling, so to speak, was of *Schwärmerei* and incurable melancholy.

I was getting nowhere with the girl I wanted to marry, so I fell in love again, and until I married and left Chicago I was very attached to Ruth. Once again, this was a relationship that never seemed to get anywhere. She was afraid, I think, of what promised to be a doomed life, at least economically. It didn't look as though I was ever going to make any money or ever be in a position to have any children or a good home or a respectable position in society. I was an aberrant type, although I was not particularly poor. I usually had more money in my pocket than anybody else I knew around the North Side, because I had a regular income, and was always wandering off and getting a temporary but skilled job someplace as a fry cook or reporter or whatnot, and usually got a fair amount of money. Nevertheless the girls all seemed to think me a bad risk. They mostly made unsuccessful marriages to Babbitts of one sort or another, who immediately folded up and demanded that they be kept, and as it turned out I was one of the better economic risks, but this nobody was able to judge when I was sixteen or seventeen years old. I had various lovely love affairs, but none of them took.

Ruth was a mathematics graduate student and knew a great deal more than most girls I had met up to that time, so it was possible for us to talk as equals about the philosophy of mathematics and symbolic logic and the philosophical revolution which has since matured into logical positivism and established itself precisely at the University of Chicago. This thing was all very new then and it made an exciting substance of communion. It was possible for her to talk about something else besides the Nineties literature that thrilled the people from the University of Illinois or Shirley's precious Bloomsbury universe of discourse. Whether under my influence or independently, she, too, was drawn toward Catholicism. I imagine it was for the same reason I was: that in her family and surroundings and in her education she had never known anything like it. It was completely strange and yet obviously satisfactory to an immense mass of people and full of graces and amenities. Carnap was unheard of in those days, but there is one thing about logical positivism—it does not have any Gregorian chant or incense accompanying it.

There were never any conflicts over politics. She was at least as sophisticated politically as I was, so I never had the problem of having to adjust myself to a conventional political or social attitude. I suppose of all the girls I knew in this period, she was the person most like myself, except Meta Laninger. Between the two banal personalities of Meta was one exactly like myself, but it was deeply hidden and my acquaintance with her lasted such a short time. Ruth and I sat about and talked about *Principia Mathematica* or St. Thomas Aquinas or Jean Cocteau or *Ulysses,* but Meta played Bartók and Vaughn Williams and Stravinsky. And now that I'm getting old it seems that maybe there was more in the few nights spent listening to the *Gymnopédies* or the *School of Ragtime* than in all that passionate, solemn intellectual discussion.

But anyway, Ruth was there and she was beautiful and had a kind of gentle loyalty. I always felt this girl was gently and kindly disposed toward me. I was anxious to marry her and never a week went by that I didn't propose.

It was becoming apparent to me that in painting I was expressing myself, more completely than in poetry. I felt that literature in English had lagged behind the development of painting, which had an international language and had achieved a new idiom. French poetry, which seemed to me to speak words of the world in which I lived, nevertheless was not what I wanted, but I couldn't find anything that was. And, of course, all this time I was the victim of my adolescent sentiments, so that I was writing, in spite of myself, sentimental love poetry. I began to try to put into practice various things that I had learned from medieval Latin and from Old and Middle English and from reading and discussion of philosophy and what knowledge of human beings I had gained. From the beginning I had a strong antiliterary bias. The antiliterary movement which begins with Apollinaire —it does not begin with Rimbaud, who was essentially a literary figure —and comes to its first flower with Dada, the movement against literature with a capital L which has been led for so many years in America by William Carlos Williams, was in germination in those days. There must be some way in which I could break out into a style that would be especially my own, free of literature and with some relationship to what I was able to do in painting. I wrote a series of poems which in a month or so I was able to start reorganizing as a long poem. It was just recently published as *The Homestead Called Damascus.* I kept it for many years and never tried to publish it. I worked on it off and on for at least three years, and finished it about the time I left Chicago. It's odd that when I have published it now, past the middle of the century, everybody seems to think it is wonderful, and the person who printed it, Ted Weiss, the editor of *Quarterly Review of Literature,* neglected to say that I wrote it when I was sixteen, seventeen, eighteen, and nineteen, so everybody thought I had written it just recently. Harriet Monroe heard about it—everybody around the North Side had heard about it—borrowed a copy from Mark Turbyfill, said, "It's just a lot of talky-talk," and advised me to go and write about machinery.

About this time *The Waste Land* came out. Just prior to its appearance Ruth had been taking a course from Edward Sapir, and we were full of *The Golden Bough* and Jessie Weston and Jane Harrison and Cornford and Gilbert Murray and all the rest of them. One day I stopped in at Marshall Field's and bought a copy of *The Dial* and met Ruth at Washington Park and we walked across to the Midway and over to the University. We stopped off in the park near a bed of tulips —I can still see them very clearly, yellow tulips with red stripes—and we sat down on the grass and I opened *The Dial*, and there was *The Waste Land*. For the rest of the trip across the park we were only half-conscious. It is hard to convey to anyone today the impact of that poem on someone young and full of ideas when it came out. Everyone reads it today prepared for it—it's *The Waste Land*, you've heard about it in grammar school and even once in a while in the newspapers—but this was just another issue of *The Dial*. There was no preparation for it whatsoever. Now, the remarkable thing about *The Waste Land* is that we all thought it was a revolutionary poem. Either in *The Dial* or in the notes that came out a couple of years later, Eliot speaks of the moral collapse of civilization in Eastern Europe. We thought this was a typographical error for Western Europe. The dissociative style, borrowed from Apollinaire, seemed to us revolutionary, and the picture of decay—of course it *was* Western civilization—was so overpowering that it seemed to be a revolutionary rather than a reactionary indictment. Another thing about T. S. Eliot, whatever his manifold faults, he had the authentic accent of current idiom. English writers who take up most space in a book of quotations are Shakespeare and Pope, and they do this because, irrespective of their merits as poets, they say numerous things with the exact accents of veracity so that people say, "It sounds just as though I'd said it!" or, "I wish I could have said that!" People who try to do this, like Oscar Wilde, by and large do not succeed. But Eliot sounded like "us" speaking—it sounded as though you had written that very line yourself. I would say that the influence of *The Waste Land* on myself was entirely for the bad. I was writing my long poem, and a lot of Frazer and Jane Harrison and Jessie Weston crept into it and didn't do it any good. Eliot's tone of weary, disillusioned withdrawal crept in as well. This came from Remy de Gourmont to Eliot, but in Remy's prose it's tinctured with irony. By the time I'd got it at second- or thirdhand it had become extremely infectious and the irony had evaporated. I am afraid that *The Waste Land* temper was a serious disease of young writers of my time. We all wrote things like it, from Nancy Cunard to Sam Beckett to Louis Zukofsky. I think that most of us, particularly people like Zukofsky and me, were able fairly rapidly to write ourselves out of Eliot's idiom, possibly due to the fact that we had more wholesome examples in French verse.

CHAPTER 28

Then as now, most advance-guard writing was in fact amateurish corn.
The tradition of the Nineties in England, and of characters like
Lafcadio Hearne, was still strong in America. For us in Chicago, New
Orleans and the University of Illinois and the *College Humor* set were
centers of English decadence, transmitted and transmuted by the
children of farmers. In New York there was a literary movement built
on Emma Goldman's noisy free love, which found voice in Joe Kling's
Pagan magazine, where lonely women in Greenwich Village house-
keeping rooms published poems about imaginary love affairs with the
Italian truck drivers they watched out the window. Ben Hecht wrote
with Maxwell Bodenheim a comical play, a favorite with the Little
Theater in those days, *The Master Poisoner*. He wrote a novel with
the same character, *Fantasius Malaire,* and another called *The Kingdom of Evil*. He thought these were real art and things like *Eric Dorn*
were just hack work, but they were shocking productions. I played in
The Master Poisoner and I worked briefly in Covici-McGee's bookshop
when they published the novels. It didn't help that my mother's favorite writers were Mrs. Voynich, Henry James, Michael Field, Renée
Vivien, Remy, and the *Chansons de Bilitis*.

Maxwell Bodenheim, who was very much about the Gray Cottage,
was a perfect example of this taste. All of his ideas about poetry were
totally wrong. He had achieved the remarkable distinction of accu-
rately defining poetry by negative example. He was from Natchez,
Mississippi, where his father was a clothing merchant, originally a ped-
dler who traveled through the South and sold to Negroes on the farms.
He married a girl who was secretary to the IWW, to whom he wrote
his best-known book of poems, *Minna and Myself*. This one book did
contain a few sincere and moving utterances. Minna herself was one
of the most lovable people I have ever met and she was devoted to
Max, who was dirty and drunken and incompetent, even in those days.
When I first started to hang out in the Gray Cottage, her baby was
just born, and Minna was staying in the back rooms.

The Gray Cottage was in fact a little gray cottage sitting back on a lot, with a long yard in front and next door a bookshop, run by an old friend of Herman Gorter's, a man by the name of Grenzenbach, who had recently come from Holland, where he had been one of the leaders of the Rotterdam Commune. Grenzenbach was the man around the Near North Side with the best education and the greatest sophistication, except possibly for his comrade Steen Heindriksen, and a man who, unbeknown to anyone, had played a small significant role in modern history. Above the bookshop was a flat which later I was to rent. There were two gray cottages, one the bookshop and the flat, and the other the tearoom, and in the back of the tearoom lived Minna.

The proprietresses were Ruth Norlander, a Cézannesque painter, and Eve Adams, who wore men's clothes and for years traveled about the country selling *Mother Earth, The Masses,* and other radical literary magazines. Eve and Ruth didn't serve meals. They started serving coffee and cake and pie and setups along about nine o'clock at night. When the first customer would come in the gate we would all run around and pull down the strings, take down the baby's diapers, fold them up and put them in the folding bed, fold the bed up and push it in the closet, and take the crib and push it, baby and all, out beyond the pantry into what had originally been a coalbin. Then the place was open for business. The windows had blue and white tied-and-dyed curtains, which Minna said looked like bed sheets from a Martian abortion. The tables and chairs were flimsy secondhand dining-nook furniture painted in bar-mirror Cubism. The place was always short of food and always running out of coffee and it was much the most bohemian of the bohemian tearooms of the Chicago North Side. It was about two doors down Chestnut Street from State Street, and the Dill Pickle was on the other side of State Street through a narrow slot between two buildings.

The Gray Cottage was a great deal more intellectual and radical than the Green Mask. Both Ruth and Eve were convinced libertarians and part of the movement. They attracted few customers from show business and almost no one from the world of carnival, cheap vaudeville, and burlesque, the people who had been June's closest friends, and none of the tough homosexuals who came into the Green Mask. Ruth and Eve were very principled young women and they objected to such people. Their friends were cast more on the pattern of Edward Carpenter or Inez Mulholland than lady prizefighters and drag queens and cheap burlesque girls. The transfer of Chicago's equivalent of a *café terrasse* from the Green Mask to the Cottage was a decided loss in color.

In those days there were no proletarian poets; on the contrary, they mostly worked for a living—as proletarians. The IWW poet Charley Ashleigh, who lived at Jake Loeb's, had been directly involved in the organization of the lumber mills of the Northwest and almost killed in the Everett massacre. Even Mike Gold was in those days much closer to the working class, and Morrie Pas was a tramp sign writer, IWW organizer, harvest hand, and fry cook. Hays Jones was a seaman and eventually got an engineer's ticket. Eddie Gilbert was a structural steel worker. John Loughman was a competent house painter. Rickey Lewis was a printer and typographer and had been an official in the printers' union before he quit for the IWW. Caleb Harrison was several kinds of skilled mechanic. They were working men as well as intellectuals. They didn't go to the working class to write about them or agitate them; they were workers.

The girl I knew in Amherst—the wife of the sociology professor—I had met while I was playing in a couple of plays and making stage sets in a Little Theater over on the West Side, a garage back of the house of a Jewish family. They had a very odd son who called himself Ivan Sokolov. He wrote plays that were like something in the *Follies*. They were hilarious parodies of one-act Russian tragedies. He didn't know it. He took them perfectly seriously and preached in them a muggy gospel derived from Soloviev. He used his family as actors and stagehands, and he used their garage as a theater. He married a pretty and passionate poetess who worshiped him. She was one of his female leads and my friend Billie was the other. Billie was a beautiful blonde who looked like a Russian heroine and fitted her parts exactly, especially Grushenka. She lived down on the South Side and was going to the University, and I used to take her home and we'd have long discussions about the Revolution. We decided that we should join the Young Workers' (Communist) League—that it was wrong to be independent and that you couldn't really be a Communist unless you were a Party member, an argument which I was to hear for many years. One day, hand in hand, we went over to Ukrainian Comrades' Hall on North Avenue and said that we wanted to join up and were invited to a meeting.

This was an unforgettable experience. I have never seen greater inefficiency and folly. "Where are the dues stamps?" "The dues secretary didn't come." "So, where is she?" "I don't know. I think she had a date." "How about the leaflets? Tonight we got to have the leaflets calling the masses of Milwaukee Avenue to rise against the conditions on the bosses' streetcars. It's an assignment from the City Central Committee. Where are the leaflets?" "The leaflets aren't here?" "So, what's the matter with the Agitprop?" "The mimeograph isn't in his kitchenette." "Where is the mimeograph?" "I don't know where it is. I think some stool pigeon stole it." Finally the meeting was over and the group broke up. I don't mean to imply that we were middle class and shocked by the workers, nor is it true that all radical girls are fat and plain, but these people were peculiarly ugly—a squalid and foolish generation. We walked away wondering, "What in the name of God was that, and what monster will it produce? Is this the leading organization for the overthrow of capitalism?" We never went back.

Sometime earlier the post office had been bombed, and the police arrested a man named Louie Mellis, who had been expelled from the IWW. He'd been quietly kicked out—nobody knew why. He used to hang around Bughouse Square and when we'd get down off the box we'd give him two bits from the collection. He had a chow dog which always accompanied him. He was in rags, and wore a torn Army overcoat, winter and summer. He ran a roominghouse for the most impoverished fellow workers. Everybody who was down on his luck used to live there—it was particularly cheap. There were about twenty rooms in it, which his wife took care of—he just bummed around. The police arrested him for the post-office bombing, and then they were informed that they had arrested the wrong man and that he really *had* set off the bomb. The Anarchist clap doctor who had given me the injection in the Bandhouse hired Sloppy Liz and Angela d'Amore to come down to his office after midnight and retype all of his records. They had to be moved around on certain days, to place Louie Mellis in his office at a certain hour taking treatment for clap. So he was provided with a flimsy alibi. Flimsy or not, it stuck and Mellis was released. This was conclusive evidence to me. Angela worshiped me and was always trying to get me to sleep with her and offering to support me if I would live with her. She told me about it and I put a considerable amount of pressure on her to expose the doctor. The other girl had been tricked; she'd understood the thing backward and thought she was saving a stalwart revolutionary. I persuaded Angela and she persuaded Liz and I took the two girls to a meeting of the Italian Anarchist Circle over in Smoky Hollow or Goose Island.

These were the leaders of proletarian Anarchism in Chicago (some I think are still alive)—two or three Jewish people and most of them Italians—and I presented them my evidence. Angela got up and made a little speech and Liz made a little speech. They had purloined some of the documents and they had the letters to the doctor from the police. When they finished—there was no chairman, we were all sitting around a table in a kitchen—one of the older Italians got up and said, "Comrade Rex is a very fine comrade and we admire work like this and we think he's done a very fine thing, but the thing Comrade Rex doesn't understand is that we've all known this for a great many years. We know all about this doctor, and what Comrade Rex doesn't understand, since he's more of a Syndicalist than he is a real Anarchist, is that if he wants to be a stool pigeon he has a perfect right to as long as he doesn't endanger anybody's life directly and nobody has any right to interfere with him." This took the wind out of my sails. I had thought of myself as a revolutionary Sherlock Holmes. I disliked the doctor intensely, and I thought I had found an opportunity to expose the Azef of American radicalism. I left in a very crestfallen state, but I left illuminated as to the nature of real libertarianism. I never forgot. It didn't give me any more tolerance for stool pigeons but it gave me an unqualified respect for that kind of incorruptible Italian working-class Anarchist.

Willy McCauley and Harold Mann and I used to help a fellow by the name of Dick Vail, an old-time Wobbly who later became a successful bootlegger, who ran a handy-man shop. He had been prominent in the organization of the Northwest and of the construction workers in France during the war and though still a young man had retired from the movement to work as a handy-man electrician. I worked with Dick wiring old houses. Many of the houses on the North Side were still gaslit. We'd take out the gas fixtures and string up electric ones, and fish B X cables through the walls and ceilings and rewire the house. Sometimes we did new jobs, too, but mainly it was converting gas to electricity, and we made a lot of money. We didn't belong to the union. One time Dick was up, standing on the ladder, dipping the ends of the wire into a ladle of hot solder, and a tough business agent showed up and said, "What's the matter with you guys? You think you can get away with scabbin' a job like this? Don't you know the union'd come around? Thought you'd get away with this, didn't you?" Dick said, "Fellow worker, take the card out of my clothes down there." I took the Wobbly card out and handed it to the business agent, and Dick said, "Now read that. And look, scissorbill, stay away unless you want to wind up with a pineapple in your hip pocket." That's all the trouble we ever had with the electricians' union.

One day a girl came in when I was alone in the office. She said, "Do you do locksmithing?" and I said, "Sure." She said, "Licensed locksmiths?" and I said, "Yes, sure." "Could you change a lot of locks for us? Could you change them so that they all have different keys?" "Yes. Simplest thing in the world." And she said, "You'd have to do this at night. It's a big office building and we want all the keys in the office building changed." I said, "Fine." Dick came in and I told him what the girl wanted and he asked what was the building, and I said, "U. S. Five." He said, "Fellow worker, what have we got?" I looked puzzled and he said, "You know what it is, don't you?" "It's a group of insurance companies." "Yeah, I know, but they're big in this so-called industrial insurance business. They hire stool pigeons. One of the companies made a fortune off the Great Steel Strike. It is that industrial insurance outfit in that building which hired all the stool pigeons within the leadership of the Great Steel Strike, besides all the goons and plug-uglies, and right now they are hiring people on all sides for the coal war down at Centralia."

We went over with our kit that night, and the same girl, who was the secretary of the manager of the building, let us in and left. The first thing we did was to go to the files of this one company, and there was the dope all right. It didn't take us long to find it. Later, Dick, who was handsome, always had a bottle of liquor in his hip, and was full of blarney, was able to find out from the girl why the locks were being changed. The place was being prowled by another detective agency and by the Department of Justice, which had apparently been unable to get its own trustworthy agents inside. Here was a file of both private and Federal stool pigeons, provocateurs, police agents, labor spies, the whole business. We got the same two girls, Angela and Liz, and we copied it all night for a week.

However, we were pretty naïve in those days. The evidence we uncovered had a good deal to do with the split in the IWW at that time. Several people were quietly forced out of the IWW because of the evidence we uncovered. There were dossiers on agents in Bill Foster's Trade Union Educational League, which had been the ginger group of the Great Steel Strike, and on confidants of Fitzpatrick, the leader of that strike and of the Chicago Labor Council—an incorruptible individual and one of the finest men in the American labor movement. There were dossiers on agents in the United Mine Workers, the West Virginia Federation of Miners, the Progressive Miners' Union, and the old Western Federation of Miners, intimate friends of Bill Dunne, the newspaperman from Butte, Montana, and leader of the Silver Bow Miners' Federation, who became a prominent Communist journalist and was eventually expelled with Browder. The ordinary trade unions and every conceivable radical sect had their stool pigeons—they were all there. Besides the documents on the employees of the insurance company there was material on every other kind of labor spy. They had to keep track: you couldn't have people going around shooting one another who were on the same side, although that is precisely what happened at Centralia that next year—possibly because parties unknown fouled up the records. They had dossiers on all the Department of Justice people and Pinkerton Detectives and Burns Detectives and all their competitors' employees. It was all there in a battery of filing cases. We could take care of our own and we gave the information to the regular Anarchist groups and to the Socialist Party and to the trade unions. But what to do about the Workers' (Communist) Party? Finally Dick said, "Well, I guess it's a workers' party. We'll go and see General Goosey. This was the Ukrainian Red Army general who had succeeded Pepper. He wouldn't see us, so we got hold of William Bross Lloyd, the millionaire who was under indictment, having been arrested in the Michigan raids, and his lawyer, and we arranged an interview with Lloyd, the lawyer and General Goosey. Lloyd accused us of being police agents and stormed and raged at us and threw the stuff at us and threw us out of the place. The General sat, fat and impassive, and said nothing. We decided that they must all be employees of the Department of Justice. A few days later a woman at whose home I had met the General called me up and said, "Come over. I want to talk to you." She said, "You don't understand the position of the Party. The General can't talk to you about this directly, but we know all these people and we tolerate them. Many of them are double agents, the rest of them we keep track of and use for our own ends." Since the list included a sizable percentage of the leadership of the Communist Party, it was just a little difficult to see who was watching whom.

CHAPTER 29

Bob Crenshaw was one of the few Negroes in the IWW. He was around the Pickle a great deal of the time and was one of my closest friends. He was either a cousin or a brother of the pianist Bess Crenshaw. He was adopted by a German chemist and his African wife and taken to Germany as a boy and trained as a biological chemist. They came back to America early in 1914, before the war started. April 1917, they were hurrying to Washington to do something about their status as aliens. The train was wrecked and they were both killed. Bob Crenshaw was thrown out on the right-of-way, a young man with a nice, fresh biological chemist's degree from a German university, an "American nigger." The effect on him was what might be expected. He was extremely embittered and unhappy. He disliked American Negroes, especially Negro intellectuals. He was an IWW, but he called himself an Anarchist, and he was totally hostile to American white civilization. This was the first encounter that I ever had with this kind of hostility. The average Negro I had met had worked out a method of outwitting white society, like Louis Armstrong, or avoided the issue altogether, like Lil Hardin, who was perfectly confident of her own abilities and kept out of the way, or went over on a celebrity level, like Alberta Hunter, or made their own world as Negro intellectuals, like Alain Locke or Fenton Johnson. One way or another they had figured out a way of coping with white society, but Bob Crenshaw had not.

He translated the first volume of Spengler's *The Decline of the West* and sent it to a publisher. He got a friendly letter saying that unfortunately they had long since commissioned someone else to do it and the book was going to press the next year. Bob's delusions took over; he was convinced that they had never heard of Spengler, and when they received the manuscript they had said, "Don't let this nigger do it," and turned it over to a white man.

He'd worked on it for years and all of his conversation was taken up with Spengler. Not a Syndicalist or a Communist—he was an Anarchist but a Stirnerite individual Anarchist, and his head was filled with German romantic storm and stress. To me it sounded quite bombastic, but since he was a Negro and so impassioned and so much more learned than the average person that I knew around the IWW, I was able to accept it, even if I did think it was a little lurid. Not having read Spengler I thought this was just the effects of race. I thought perhaps there was something to the legend that Negroes were given to colorful and melodramatic language, jungle drums, and missionary soup. It's amusing that although I never felt this about Negro music, when Spengler was presented to me perfectly straight by an educated young man, who was actually, of course, a German biological chemist and just happened to have been born an American Negro, I responded with the Negro stereotype.

Bob had a long face with a prognathous carriage to his head, and a nose very much like Akhnaton's, the same full lips and heavy-lidded, large eyes, the same lean body with a low-slung paunch, and beautiful, long hands with very long, spatulate fingers—physically he bore little resemblance to a Negro.

He believed that the Negro race was going to take over after the next and lethal war that white civilization was going to fight. From this vantage point, 1959, he was apparently one war off. He became an intellectual adviser to Garvey's personal circle. He interested me in Garvey and took me to meet him, and he also interested several IWWs. It was only the group around the Chicago IWW office and the independents, my soapboxer friends, in all American radicalism who had any sympathy for Garvey. All the Socialist and radical and progressive groups condemned him to a man, especially the radical Negroes. DuBois never tired of attacking him. Many years later DuBois was to admit rather sadly that Garvey, fundamentally, was right.

I used to soapbox quite a bit in association with Garveyites and later with the African Blood Brotherhood, of which I was a sort of honorary member. This was the first that I had ever penetrated to the Negro working-class South Side so different from the world of jazz or the Talented Tenth. An old man named White who had been a high school teacher in the South and I used to pitch together. I would recite some poetry and give a little talk—I used to recite my friend Fenton Johnson and the other poets of the Negro renaissance. Gene Toomer would once have been pleased to know that when he was still caviar to the general in the pages of *The Little Review* and *Broom* I was reciting him to the workingmen on South State Street. White always opened his talk by saying, "My name is White, and that's the only thing about me that is, except my teeth and a few hairs that I can't do anything about," and he would take off his hat and show his gray hair. Then he would go on with a long speech about the wonders of the Sudanese kingdoms and the ruins of the Mines of Ophir and the glories of African sculpture and its influence on Cubism. The first time he ever cut loose with this on the soapbox I almost fell over, because I had no idea he had any such knowledge. Like many educated Negroes he was a very cultivated man behind a mask of "country" talk.

Bob used to talk with us and I always felt that he was much more interested in the Night of the Long Knives, that he hoped the day would come when the South Side would rise up and run through the streets of Chicago and cut the white population in half in a night. Most of his talk was a long harangue, unbeknown to us, adapted from Spengler. He demonstrated in windy Teutonic rhetoric the inevitability of the collapse of white civilization, the inevitability of the rise of black civilization. This young, virile race, still in its childhood, historically speaking, was the only uncorrupted one left, and it was surely destined to produce an Athens and Rome and Chartres and Paris within the next few hundred years. The South Side just loved this triumvirate of Bob and White and me.

Crenshaw couldn't get along with Negroes emotionally, and disliked Negro girls intensely. The last time I saw Naomi Fitzgerald, I made a date for her with Bob and another colored girl for myself—I thought Naomi just the girl for Bob—but he didn't like her at all and they quarreled most of the time and I finally took both girls home. Naomi liked him less than he liked her. She said he had white fever, which was perfectly true, and that the white fever would kill him.

He took up with a girl from New York who had hitchhiked to Chicago. As I look back on her I realize what a perfect beatnik she was, although this was 1924. She had torn blue jeans and a very plump bottom which more than filled them, and sandals, and a dirty, sleazy sateen blouse and no brassiere, and sort of chewed hair. It was thirty years before Audrey Hepburn. She just whacked it off herself, I guess, with pinking shears. She also had heavily made-up eyes and no other make-up. It never occurred to me until this moment that she must have been the first of this type, perhaps landed from the fourth dimension. She was otherwise typical of the slatterns who hung around the Pickle, seeking what they might devour, and on Saturday nights waited tables in the Pickle coffee shop.

Bob went to live with her. Now there were plenty of white girls he could have lived with, but you felt that, like ex-Communist she-intellectuals who pick up Negro pimps, he was crossing the racial line to degrade himself. He couldn't get along with Naomi Fitzgerald —he was extremely nasty and obscene to her, and she was a person very like him in attainments and appearance. Instead he picked up with this bum.

One morning I went over to the Pickle to paint some stage-sets and Jack Jones came down from his machine shop and made some coffee and we were sitting around talking when Bob's girl, Minnie, showed up. It was January and very cold and she was bundled up in a surplus Army overcoat and Army cap with earmuffs, like someone out of the Siberian campaign, for once without bare feet. She came in stomping off the snow and said, "Jesus Christ, give me some coffee." I said, "What's the matter?" and she said, "I spent a hell of a night with that mother fucker, Bob." I said, "What was the matter?" She said, "He was raving around all night and I never got any sleep. He was talking about how he was just a nigger and nobody had any use for him and how his own race hated him and the white race hated him and the only person who would associate with him was a tramp like myself. He'd storm around and beat on me and then he'd fuck me, and this went on all night and I didn't get any sleep at all. And then he'd say he was going to kill himself and that he had a pistol hidden away and that he had veronal that he was going to take." I said, "Where is he now?" She said, "I left him. I tried to cook breakfast for him but he threw the dishes and knocked me around, and I told him he was right, he was just a goddamned nigger and that I might be just a Jewish whore but I was too good for him and he could go ahead and kill himself for all I cared." "How long ago was this?" "It was real early. About eight o'clock in the morning. We never slept. I was fixing breakfast."

I had spent the day before with Bob and he was in an extremely bad mood and had been taking some chemical stimulant—I don't know if they had Benzedrine yet—to keep himself going during the day. Then he had taken veronal to sleep. He hardly drank at all and didn't take any kind of hard dope, but he was always full of pharmaceuticals, and the lashback was severe. I had told him, "You know what's the matter with you? It's not psychological or political or sociological or radical or economic or anything else like that; it's just chemical. If you keep on you're going to sink into a psychotic depression and you're going to do damage to yourself or somebody else."

That night he had been very low and he'd gone home to Minnie to find surcease which he obviously had been unable to get, due, of course, to himself. She was, like most fallen women if given a chance, very loving; although, again, she was a shrew and a virago because of her own guilt. Like all the later draggletail beatnik girls she was guilt-crazy.

The situation sounded terrifying and I'm afraid my sixth sense came into operation, because I said, "You know, it may sound like superstition but I have an overwhelming feeling that Bob has already killed himself—that he really did it—and I think it's worth a taxicab. However,

I don't have that much money. Have you any dough?" She said, "I haven't got a penny. I had some money that he'd given me but I threw it in his face when I went out." So Jack, who was certainly not superstitious, cocked his cross-eyes at me and said, "I've got the money. I think I'll go along."

We piled into the cab and went out to Sixteenth and State Street to a dreadful hotel, the only place that Bob claimed—falsely—he could get into with a white girl. The plumbing stank and there was no heat and the place was gaslit and the beds looked like bathtubs and the linen was filthy and full of bedbugs and cockroaches. You could rent a two-room suite with a gas plate for five dollars a week. The gas plate was all covered with grease, the windows were cracked and patched with tape and had dirty, torn lace curtains and broken blinds. The carpets were filthy with an indistinguishable pattern, with coal soot and grease ground into them. It was, I guess, the dirtiest hotel I have ever seen. I have seen such places that bohemians got dirty, but I've never seen anything that came that dirty.

There was no one around downstairs but a very old Negro lady staring off into space, who said she hadn't seen Mr. Crenshaw. There were two or three toilets, like privies, at the back of the hall, and a water tap out in the hall itself. I tried the door to one of the toilets and it opened and Bob was sitting there with the top of his head blown off. And that was the end of one of the handsomest and most sensitive and most cultivated men I knew in those days, a European who suddenly discovered in his youth that he was an American Negro.

The girl disappeared immediately after. Considering the degree of her guilt she, too, may well have killed herself, and we worried about her for a little while, but she vanished without a trace. I had always felt close to Bob; probably, really, because he demanded it, but in many ways I think we had the same kind of mind. I was very buoyant, happy, really extremely well adjusted to the special society I was in, and he was just as maladjusted and unhappy as he could conceivably be; nevertheless I felt there was a good deal of similarity between us. We often talked of the responsibilities and the nature of friendship, and I had looked forward to having all my life a devoted friend.

I had started in the Dill Pickle and other Little Theaters about town playing the part of a clown. Wherever there was a part that could be turned into slapstick I developed it, and since most of these parts were short it also gave me a chance to assist the director and do the make-up and costumes and sets. I believed that the clown was the highest form of dramatic art open to anyone in the American theater. The vulgarity of the American theater, of the Barrymore brothers and their kind, made it impossible to be a serious dramatic actor, but there were still plenty of openings for clowning.

Bob Cody had published *Soil* and Gilbert Seldes was in the process of writing his *Seven Lively Arts* as a series of magazine articles. We believed that the fine arts had been so saturated with commercialism that it invalidated them, but that in the commercial arts, the comic strips, vaudeville, Charlie Chaplin, and burlesque, commercialization had proceeded to such a degree that the capitalist class was so self-confident that art slipped by. We believed that George Ade or Ring Lardner or Harriman of Krazy Kat, an artist whom I never liked, or burlesque comics gave expression to judgments of society that wouldn't be accepted in *The Dial* or the Stieglitz Gallery or the Provincetown Theater.

So I decided that I was going to be a clown. I took all the parts that I could. In the legitimate theater it was impossible for me to get even any regular walk-ons. I do not wish to give the impression that I was a successful bit actor. I was nothing of the sort. I would just do fill-ins, emergency calls, understudies, and those only for walk-ons and spear-carriers. First, still in school, I was in extravaganzas, like *Chu Chin Chow* and *Mecca* and *Aphrodite*. I'd work only a night or two out of a week. I had such jobs in *East Is West* and *Irene* and *Hitchy-Coo*, Raymond Hitchcock's attempt at a revue. Even jobs backstage were always fill-ins. I never had a regular job. I did gain an inconspicuous entrance to the theater at all levels. I learned a lot about what makes theatricality and I could persuade myself that I met, however slightly I knew them, a wide range of people—from Eva Le Gallienne to Bert Williams and Bert Savoy.

Shortly before I left Chicago, Alla Nazimova opened there a production of *Salome* with the stage-sets and the actors both painted to look like Aubrey Beardsley illustrations. It must have been sublimely ridiculous, but for a couple of nights I even had a speaking part. I opened the show. I stood with a spear and said, "The moon is like a dead woman," and I may have been the only heterosexual on the stage, or probably in the audience, including the electricians. It was just about the queerest thing I ever got mixed up in and a great deal of fun.

Alla Nazimova, as has been remarked by others, was one of those individuals like D. H. Lawrence and Gertrude Stein's bell ringers—a person who gave off an unbelievable charge of radar. If you were sitting in a room and Alla Nazimova came in behind you, the whole place reverberated as if enormous dynamo poles had been put against either wall. I worshiped her. She could have flayed me alive and toasted me for marshmallows and I would have loved it. She took quite an interest in me, and one day she took me out after a rehearsal. She said,

"Would you like to take me to lunch?" She was quite the most fascinating woman in the American theater and I was not much more than a little boy, and I went along swooning. She told me, "Rex, the Tay-at-tra ees not for you. The Tay-at-tra has been torture to me. When I lef' Europe, George Brandes say I was greatest Ibsen actress in world and I have spen' my time making a fortune as a harem beauty in the cinema, and the Tay-at-tra ees not for intelligent people. I am sorry I ever went in eet."

I put up a little argument. At that time there was a play called *Lightnin'* which had a run like *Abie's Irish Rose* or *Tobacco Road*, maybe even longer. It was one of the record breakers of the American theater. It was an abominable play, but it had a very smart man in it whom we both knew. Nazimova said to me, "How would you like to be Frank Bacon and repeat the lines of *Lightnin'* three hundred times a year?" The vista was so horrifying that I think she effectively stopped, then and there, my theatrical ambitions. I went on with *Salome* until it left Chicago and went to New York, I think, but that was the last experience I had with the theater.

The Radical Bookshop was in Northside Turner Hall next to Charlie Appel's Northside Turner Restaurant. At the time I was eating in Turner Hall with Nancy, I was also hanging around the Radical Bookshop and acting in the tiny Little Theater in the back in all the plays of pre-War I revolt. Emma Goldman, by endless speechmaking, had sold large sections of the radical movement in the United States the idea that the theater might be a good medium, not exactly for propaganda but for something much more fundamental than that—for changing the attitudes and manners of society. This led, not to the Maurice Browne sort of thing, based on Adolphe Appia and Gordon Craig, which we looked on as bourgeois, but to a revolutionary Little Theater. So, in these days, there blossomed all over America—in bigger communities at least—in barns, in unrentable shops, and in back of bookstores—pathetic, earnest Little Theaters devoted to Wedekind, Chekhov, Strindberg, Schnitzler, Sudermann, Gerhart Hauptmann, and Shaw. I played in it all. I must have appeared in all the plays that Shaw had written prior to *Back to Methuselah* and I used to know most of the parts in Hauptmann's *The Weavers*. There's hardly a play by Strindberg or Ibsen in which I didn't take part. All I had to do was have a good memory, and even that wasn't essential: lots of people never rehearsed their parts at all and simply read them. These productions were pretty absurd, but I learned something about drama and my own attitudes on society were reinforced.

I became very fond of Geraldine Udell, who ran the Radical Bookshop Little Theater and acted in all the plays. She was a quiet girl, sure of herself, more secure in her position as a *révoltée* than other girls I knew. She'd come from at least two generations of secession from middle-class society and standards and she was perfectly confident. With her I had long discussions about that Revolution which then seemed so near and about Anarchism, Bolshevism, Syndicalism versus Socialism, Federalist Anarchism versus Syndicalism, Alexander Berkman versus Lenin and Trotsky, and Herman Gorter versus all of them. It may seem academic now and very far away, but it was not then; it was life and death to us in those days.

Bertrand Russell had visited Russia prepared to accept Bolshevism, and had written, "The present holders of power, Lenin and Trotsky, are evil men, and there is no depth of cruelty, perfidy, and brutality from which they will shrink when they feel themselves threatened." These words, printed in red block letters, still survive in one of my notebooks for the year 1924.

All day long the bookshop was a hotbed of argument. I think that it was there, in discussions with Geraldine and others, that I straightened out my attitudes toward the pressing problems of the revolutionary movement. I don't think the straightening out was due to Geraldine's brains, I think it was due to her calm. Nothing was said that was decisive but the atmosphere was decisive. I look back on the period and place and discussions as a determinative moment. I remember standing there and arguing with Charlie Ashleigh, Jim Larkin's lawyer (whose name I've forgotten), Caleb Harrison, and Geraldine. Geraldine spoke little but to the point. We were discussing the Kropotkin letter.

I realize now the Kropotkin letter was a fake, but we were hotly debating it then in good faith. In a letter circulated by the Bolsheviks, Kropotkin had said, "This is not our revolution. We were unable to make a revolution. The Bolsheviks did. We should never take part with the bourgeoisie, let along the Czarists, against them. We should cooperate with them in trade unions and mass organizations and defense and let them take care of their own politics." This is the definition of fellow traveling. I think it's highly unlikely Kropotkin ever wrote this letter. He was deliberately starved to death by the Bolsheviks in a little cottage in the country and he died about this time, and this was supposed to be his testament. It hit America along with Alexander Berkman's revelations, Trotsky's apology for terror, and news of the suppression of the Kronstadt rebellion, and the betrayal of Makhno by Trotsky.

I made, pretty deliberately, the decision that I would avoid the political issues. I had no use for the Socialist Party or any of its works. It was obvious that the IWW had reached the end of its tether; something had gone wrong with it. I decided that the thing to work with rather than the IWW was the ordinary trade-union movement, which, of course, we all despised. Lenin was mild in his criticism of lieutenants and agents of the bosses in the ranks of labor in comparison with us. But I was coming to the conclusion that my job was to find what the Bolsheviks called "the masses," and to avoid the factional fighting which surrounded any Bolshevik incursion into the labor movement. The most effective tactic seemed to be to bow before the storm and keep out of the way, to try to work on a mass level and avoid pie cards of any kind, to try to work with the rank and file, to constantly increase rank-and-file initiative and democratization, and to assist any measure that led to greater control on the part of the workers, but to keep quiet about my personal program and never get myself drawn into a factional position. By and large, I was able to stick to this decision.

CHAPTER 30

That spring Morris Pas and Masha and her new husband showed up in Chicago, and Scoop Phillips came from Seattle. Eve Adams had gone off to New York and Ruth had opened a place at 19 West Pearson Street in an old barn. We all moved in. All the talk about the Pacific Northwest decided me to cut loose and go out to the Coast. Turning this decision over in my mind, I took a trip up into Wisconsin to do a little fishing and camping. Along a side road by a couple of wooded lakes came a man in an old Ford touring car. He was lost and looking for the road to Duluth. I directed him to the road and he gave me a ride. He said, "Where are you going?" and I said, "I'm not going anywhere—just camping around here." "I'm going to Seattle." I counted over my money and didn't say anything. After we'd ridden awhile he said, "Would you like to go to Seattle with me? I need company and somebody to help me drive the car." I said yes.

He was a watchmaker who had worked in factories in Massachusetts and Connecticut and then had a shop in Michigan, which he had sold out. He was going to open what they call a retirement business—a quiet little shop—in Seattle, and settle down to an old age of peace. He was an old-fashioned German-Swiss left-wing Socialist, once again one of those people who crop up in jail and give me rides when I'm hitch-hiking. We drove across the country and stopped along the way for a day or two to investigate things in Fargo, Bismarck, Billings, and Missoula while I picked up some money soapboxing. All across the country we looked things over—a very leisurely trip. It was early in the year, and the roads were deep in mud.

In western North Dakota we came in for the night to the town tourist camp—a little knoll with a pump in the middle and a few brick fireplaces. Nearby was a white wooden Protestant church sticking up into the sky like an American Scene painting. A little way off was a gravel pit with a steep cut and a place where trucks went through under a loading platform; behind that the gravel had been dug out in a shallow cave. Several people came in and camped for the night.

It was late May and early in the evening. After supper was over it began to look very much like a cyclone. The other tourists didn't do anything about it. Although some of them were North Dakota farmers, they didn't seem worried. Finally the watchmaker said, "You know, I don't know much about cyclones but it sure as hell looks to me like one's coming. Let's get out of here." I said, "We can't. Where we going to go?" He said, "Let's drive down into the gravel pit. At least we'll be a little better sheltered there, unless the wind tears right through it like a tunnel." So we drove down into the gravel pit, and when we got there we found that there was room enough to drive the car under the loading platform and back into the cave, and so we did. Just before dark she hit with the most tremendous noise. I guess it's the only time I've ever been near the eye of a cyclone. We may have been in the very pupil, because although the superstructure of the loading platform was swept away, we were undamaged—the soft top of the car was not even blown away. The other cars were all damaged, the church was blown completely away, and two children just above us were killed. Well, thought I, here I am, out West.

We stopped one night on the Crow Indian reservation. I don't know how we got down there—I think there was a detour down the south side of the Yellowstone. They were just starting the spring drive into the high country and this looked very interesting to me. We camped for the night with a bunch of white and Indian cowpunchers, and I thought "I'll come back here someday." Missoula, Montana, looked inviting—I marked it down as another place worth investigating. When we got to Wenatchee, in the Columbia Valley, we got jobs spring spraying in the apple trees for a few days. Then we went on to Seattle.

Seattle was declining from its heroic period. The drastic improvement in working conditions in lumbering, hard-rock mining, and wheat harvesting, which was due to the Wobblies, nonetheless had led to their sudden decline. They were still the ginger group in Seattle, culturally, politically, and economically, and gave the city a character unique in America. The Seattle general strike was only a few years back. The atmosphere was like San Francisco in the heyday of the Maritime Federation, after the '34 and '36 strikes, and before the Second War. Bill Dunne was out there then, and Harrison George, Verne Smith, Red Dog Haines, and his brother Blue Dog. Hays Jones and his sister Zenith were back from New York. There was a sizable Red bohemia around the Wobbly paper all engaged in a deadly undercover fight—pro- and anti-Bolshevik. In the background was the Comintern man who later ran the C.P. in California, busy corrupting journalistic fellow workers with unlimited Moscow gold. The theoretician was a brilliant young philosophy student, married to the daughter of a former Russian prime minister, who years later became Harry Hopkins' private one-man brain trust. The most popular soapboxer was a redheaded, derby-hatted Irishman with a wooden leg who talked down at the Totem Pole near the market. Sometime before, he had taken off his wooden leg and had crowned a cop with it. He had been arrested for assault with a dangerous weapon and had been forbidden to talk with his wooden leg on, so before he got on the soapbox he always unstrapped the leg and handed it to the cop assigned to watch the meeting.

He introduced me and I gave a little speech and recited inflammatory poetry. The fellow workers in Seattle had already heard plenty of soapbox poetry from Charlie Ashleigh, and I recited his "Song on his lips he came/Song on his lips he went/This be the burden of his re-frain/Soldier of discontent." It was greeted with noisy enthusiasm. Everybody was wonderful to me but I didn't like Seattle very much. It seemed to me to have a narrow life, consisting of the circle around the Wobbly paper and another around the University, which shared a con-siderable number of fellow travelers, all of them bigoted and not very civilized, characterized by the militant know-nothingism Hemingway was soon to make fashionable. I was offered a racket teaching rich girls at a place called the Cornish School. I went to a party to meet the fac-ulty and students. I turned down the job. Compared with that of Chi-cago, the Wobbly leadership was not just provincial but sectarian and rigid. I had never before encountered this kind of IWW-ism. Actually, the behind-the-scenes bitter struggle was not for principle, but for pie cards. The jobs were what were important. The Bolshevik issue was just a convenient banner, like the Shiboleths of Guelph or Ghibelline.

After being around for a little and writing a couple of stories for *The Industrial Worker,* I decided to pull out. I hitchhiked up north, through Bellingham and Sedro Woolley, looking for work. I discovered nearby the largest white spot on the map, the largest spot without a road, that was not a desert in the United States. I hitchhiked up the Skagit River to Marblemount, where, in those days, the road ended. From there on, around the headwaters of Lake Chelan and down to the Columbia River, was a roadless wilderness—the heart of the highest Cascades.

At Marblemount was a ranger station, where I got a job. Almost forty years later I was to meet Gary Snyder, who had worked for the same district ranger just before his retirement. At this time the ranger was just starting. He was what they call a local man in the Forest Service—he was not a forestry college graduate. His name was Tommy Thomp-son and he was a wonderful fellow. He eventually became Chief Ranger of the Baker National Forest.

I came in the evening with a rucksack on my back and asked for a job. He said, "Come on in and have supper. Maybe I've got a job." I didn't know anything about work in the woods. He said, "Before we eat—can you set a saw?" I didn't know anything about setting saws, but I said, "Oh yes, nothing to it." He gave me a kind of funny look and said, "Well, I'll show you." Before supper there arrived a forestry student from the University of Washington, and Thompson said, "We got two jacks [or whatever you call the thing you put a saw into to set it] and setting tools out there in the barn. Why don't the two of you go out there and work on them?" They were actually in two different buildings, so that we didn't see each other, and we had to get the saws ready for the next day. I took a big crosscut saw which looked monstrous to me, did exactly what he told me, set the teeth and sharpened them to the best of my ability, and came in to supper. Thompson came out and looked quizzically at the saw and said it would do, and then he said, "Did you ever do this before?" and I said, "Well, as a matter of fact, no." And he said, "I guess it will work. It's all right—not very sharp." He showed me how to hold the file. We went around the other side of the barn to the tack room, where the forestry major was sharpening his saw and setting it. He had sharpened the rakers—that is, the teeth on the saw that scrape the sawdust out. They are supposed to be perfectly blunt. He'd had the enormous labor of sharpening them—though fortunately he'd only sharpened a few of them, quite an operation—and he said, "This saw is dull. What could have been done to it? It looks like it had been sawing stone." Tommy said nothing and I thought, "Gee, maybe I did it wrong."

They didn't have fire lookouts yet in that country. It was difficult to get stock through, and the Forest Service didn't have enough stock to go around, so this boy and I were sent out on different trails as patrolmen. I think the office of patrolman has practically disappeared from the Forest Service, and if it exists it's mounted, but we set out on foot to open up the country in the spring. He went up the Skagit and up, I think, Richardson Creek, and I went up Cascade Creek and over Cascade Pass and down in the Chelan National Forest to Stehekin at the head of Lake Chelan and came back over Agnes Glacier and down the Suiattle River to Marblemount again. This was some of the wildest country in America and I had never been in real mountains, except as a child sightseeing in the Alps. Thompson gave me a short crosscut saw. I said "Oh, are we going together?" He said no. I said, "Who's going to pull the other end of this? It hasn't got any handle on it." He said, "There isn't going to be anybody to pull the other end of it. You'll do it alone." Off I went with a rucksack on my back with a week's supply of food and a couple of light tools and a crosscut saw and ax. The distance was not great, but between Marblemount and Stehekin I did the work which later would be assigned to a CCC crew of twelve boys. I had no pack horse and nobody to give me any advice. I did what seemed to need doing. I sawed open the trail. In one of our tool caches I found some dynamite and an auger. At that cabin I camped with an old hardrock miner who said I was wasting my energy. He showed me a little of elementary powder-man technique. After that I blew open the windfalls. I bored a hole in the log, put in a little powder and a cap, and blew it to pieces. On the way back on the other trail, which was extremely rough and steep—in those days it was impossible to get stock over the Suiattle River trail—I blew my way out of the country, but going in I sawed my way. There were plenty of tool caches. You don't camp out in that country, it's too wet, particularly on the Sound slope. All through the country there were cabins to stay in where there were supposed to be tools for Forest Service use. A saw and an ax would not keep very well over the winter, so those two things I carried, but there were bars, peevees, mauls, picks, hammers, wedges, and dynamite cached all over the country. I tipped rocks into mudholes and pulled rocks out of the rocky spots and leveled off the trail, and was a one-man trail crew and thought nothing of it, because I'd never seen such things before. I got back probably the happiest boy who ever lived.

The trip took a little less than two weeks. I got another week's supply at Stehekin at the head of Lake Chelan for the return trip. My job was not actually to repair the trail going in but to open the country up after the winter so the trail crew with stock could get through behind me. In those two weeks or so I discovered the whole world of the Western mountains. I camped with Basque sheepherders, insane prospectors, and cattle outfits, and climbed all the most interesting peaks along the way in the early morning or in the evening after I was through work.

One weekend I was above Lake Chelan with Glacier Peak far off across a steep canyon to the west. It didn't look particularly near. I was not deluded by the distance, but I was deluded by the apparent ease of access. I started off Friday night down the canyon with no experience of the dense understory of the Puget Sound rain forest. In a short time I found myself hopelessly entangled in a jungle of down timber, vine maple, devil's club, and blackberry bushes, all growing on a surface at the steepest possible angle. Sometimes I would descend for a hundred feet scrambling in and out of branches like a monkey without ever touching ground. My shirt got torn and my knuckles barked, my eyes smarted with lashing branches. I kept on because after I had gone a little way it was impossible to get back up. I reached the river at the bottom of the canyon after about three hours. The climb up the other side, although steeper, was not so difficult and I got to the broad meadows on the western side of Glacier Peak the afternoon of the next day.

It had taken me several hours to cover an airline distance of little over a mile.

I built a fire and made some tea and sat eating hardtack and cheese. All round me like a herd of domestic sheep were Rocky Mountain goats. As the sun set, just like domestic kids and lambs, the young ones played over the grass, up and down the hummocks and protruding rocks and down timber at follow-the-leader and king-of-the-mountain. To the southwest the great mountain rose up covered with walls of ice. There was no one near me for many miles in any direction. I realized then with complete certainty that this was the place for me. This was the kind of life I liked best. I resolved to live it as much as I could from then on. By and large I've kept that resolve and from that day much of my time and for some years most of my time was spent in the Western mountains.

Early next morning I climbed the peak and spent a long time on the mountaintop. Going back, I stopped to fish in the river in the canyon, which, at that point in those days, was far from a trail and absolutely unfished. There wasn't much sport in the fishing because the first cast I caught a two-and-a-half-pound cutthroat and could have gone on catching one every half minute for the rest of the day. I put my fish in my pack and started up the west side of the canyon. It took me all Sunday until late at night climbing over the tangled timber by flashlight to reach the pass where there was a trail. Monday morning I started out for Marblemount, blowing open down timber and heaving rocks along the northward-heading trail on the lip of the same gorge that it had taken me a day to climb out of.

The extremely rough nature of the country and the luxuriant vegetation and rapid weathering can be judged by the fact that at the beginning of the century one of the last Indian battles had been fought at the head of Lake Chelan and the Army had built a road and moved fieldpieces in over the route of the trail I was working. There was no trace whatever of this road—not a cut, not a fill, not a log bridge. In twenty-five years it had vanished completely.

On the way out I camped for a night with a man who was driving horses over the Cascades to sell in the cities along Puget Sound. He had two boys as helpers and nobody in the party could cook. They made a miserable supper of scorched canned beans, bacon, and doughy bannock. In the morning I made breakfast for all of us and they offered me a job as third assistant horse wrangler and cook. I took his address and promised that next year I would meet him in Yakima. A couple of years later I did work for him gathering wild horses in the appropriately named Horse Heaven country.

When I got back to Marblemount I took a one-week trip up to the headwaters of Skagit River along the Canadian border in an even wilder and steeper country of sharp granite peaks. I tried to arrange my itinerary so that I'd have a peak to climb every evening after work. This was along the Richardson Creek—Fraser River watershed and official first ascents were not to be made in this country until ten to twenty years later. I knew nothing about such matters as mountaineering records and still less about mountaineering techniques and nothing about the unsportsmanlike evils of solo climbing. I scrambled up everything that looked difficult and steep and watched the sunset and came down. I suppose I could have been killed many times over because some of the peaks involved long passages as difficult as the climbs around Chamonix. I had never read about laybacks or kneeing up a crack. I just did it. I didn't have sense enough to know how dangerous it was. In fact, the only place where I ever feared for my life was the climb over the jackstraw tangle up and down the east wall of the Suiattle River on the way to Glacier Peak. When I got back to Marblemount the second time, I discovered I was bumped by a forestry student from the University of Washington who had first call on the job and was waiting to take over.

That Sunday I went fishing with Tommy Thompson and he gave me a lot of advice about living and working in the mountains and sold me a horse. This was the first horse I ever owned and one of the best. I went out Monday night and fed him a handful of oats and curried him and put my arms around his neck and rubbed his nose and ears. It's impossible to convey the intense excitement of an adolescent boy from a great city rubbing noses with his first horse deep in the Western mountains the night before he starts off on a typical wandering, horseback, Western-story quest for range and mountain work. The horse's name was Bob. He was about five years old—a small zebra dun, yellowish buckskin in color shading to dove gray on the belly with a dark gray cross stripe down his spine and across his shoulders like a donkey—dark faced and light around the eyes, with stripes on the hocks like a zebra. Many people consider this the natural horse marking and the sign of a horse most perfectly adapted to wild country. Certainly he was the best horse I've ever had—as intelligent and affectionate as the canniest burro, and, like a donkey, with practically no nerves at all. I must confess that although I have been around horses all my life there are few of them—perhaps only this one—that I ever completely trusted. You can raise a beast from a colt and spend a lifetime on his back and one day he'll kill you at the sight of a piece of newspaper in a hedge along the road. Bob could well have been a cavalry horse and thirty years old for all he was bothered by waving objects and sudden loud noises. He could walk the top of an adzed log bridge with you on his back. He could ford rocky streams with hardly a stumble and when they got deep, swim without a tremor with me holding his tail. Like a donkey or a mule he seemed to be able to sound snow on the passes—anyway he never fell through, although he would take mysterious detours over snow fields that I never interfered with. Not only that, he had the trick of kicking his feet into steep snow like a man and he could handle himself in that most difficult of all ground for stock—steep mountain marsh filled with granite rockslide—without ever a serious stumble. He didn't have to be picketed or hobbled or even whistled for, but always showed up in the morning for a pancake. He cost me twenty-five dollars and an old McClellan saddle and a Spanish ear bridle thrown in for free. Anyone who has ever ridden a McClellan saddle can understand why it was free.

I rode back over the pass to the head of the lake, a fine ride as far as Bob was concerned and a miserable one as far as I on the McClellan saddle was concerned, and got a job with a pack outfit hauling building materials for a lookout on the summit of Mt. McGregor. The boss's name was Old Dan and he looked just like a boss packer named Old Dan. The first thing he said was, "I'll give you five dollars extra a week if you promise not to smoke them damn cigareets."

Old Dan weighed about ninety-five pounds and had a hunchback, the result not of disease but of toting mining machinery and six months' supply of grub, slung from a tumpline around his forehead, on snowshoes over thousands of miles of Alaska trail. He was the son of a French trader from the Nez Percé country in Idaho and he spent his youth as a horse wrangler and trick rider and roper. He had been in Alaska at the time of the Gold Rush and had spent twenty years there driving stages in the summer and dog teams in the winter. His lifetime bridged the history of the Wild West from the mountain men to Anaconda Copper. Now he was retired and just worked as a government packer packing freight for the Forest Service. The ranger at Stehekin who introduced me to him said, "This is the man who can really teach you how to pack. There's no load, no hitch, and no saddle he can't handle. He could pack a kitchen stove on a wet seal and make it stay put, drive it thirty miles, and never sweat the seal."

Considering the short, steep nature of the job, we had a big outfit: about forty head of stock. We carried long, light girders, big panes of glass, corrugated roofing, and prefabricated walls in six-foot-square sections over a trail we made ourselves up a steep mountain gorge, over huge boulders and sand, onto a high rocky plateau, and then up the very steep, but still the least steep, southeast face of the mountain. The western face overlooked Lake Chelan and was a sheer drop of two thousand feet. Three times up the switchback to the summit we had to unpack the girders, which were slung on two mules like the poles of a litter, turn the mules around, back up, and go off the other way.

All this took the latter part of July and we spent the month of August packing in trail crews around other parts of the country and keeping the carpenters and other workers on the summit supplied. Since then I have worked with many other pack outfits but I was never to handle such recalcitrant freight over such difficult terrain. Once the summer was well advanced, the gorge dried out and we toiled up switchbacks over round boulders as big as automobiles through impenetrable clouds of glacier dust. Above the moraine the rocks to the summit were slippery and splintery—the stock was always stumbling, but not one of them ever had a serious fall and we never lost a pack, let alone an animal. Later when I was to go to California and work with the slipshod mountain men of that state, everyone marveled at the efficiency of my packing.

I didn't do much packing. I was horse wrangler and cookee—the job they always give the kid—and like all other horse wranglers and cookees, I was called Kid; Chicago Kid, in fact. After the first week the cook left and I was promoted to cook at a very substantial pay raise. I got up about half an hour before daylight, built up the fire, put the sourdough biscuits in the sheet-iron oven, and went down to gather up the cavy, which were fortunately held in a more or less fenced meadow. After I had gathered them in the corral near camp I finished breakfast and woke up the men. While the men were eating I laid out the tack and Dan and I went over the cargoes, which had been laid out the night before and covered with tarps.

There was every kind of pack—Spanish *alforjas* and kyacks, cavalry pack saddles and McClellan saddles, even Dolger saddles from Idaho from which you slung the load in a special hitch. All we needed were a couple of Irish donkeys with willow basket panniers. We usually made two trips a day and sometimes three. I loaded up two or three animals and rode along with the string part of the day. But I couldn't spend too much time handling the stock while it was working because I also had to cook dinner at noon and supper about nine at night. I got thirty dollars a week when I started but the second week my wages were raised to a dollar fifty an hour and all found, plus rent and feed for my horse and a new Pendleton saddle—fantastic wages for those days. At the end of summer I had learned everything I was going to learn about packing mules and handling horses. Doubtless there is a good deal more to be learned, but I never found anyone as skilled and knowledgeable and ready to teach as Old Dan. When I was paid off

I had quite a roll because I had spent absolutely nothing. Old Dan had even bought me some blue jeans and boots when my own wore out.

I went down to the town of Chelan at the foot of the lake on a picnic with the daughter of the district ranger. She was only about fourteen and somebody got her drunk while I wasn't looking and she became very red, very sweaty, and aggressively amorous. This looked like plenty of trouble so I unloaded her on an aunt and uncle who were there and spent the rest of the day by myself. This turned out to be a lucky break.

I met a fellow named Blackie Edwards who traveled up and down the whole West Coast from Alaska to Mexico painting pictures on bar mirrors—what are called buckeyes. They were painted very rapidly with house painter's edging brushes, the sort of thing that used to be painted in shop windows before admiring throngs in American small towns and sold for a couple of dollars. Blackie had been a tramp storewindow buckeye painter but he discovered that there was much more to be made painting in showcard colors on bar mirrors. He could dash off views of every major peak from Mt. McKinley to San Pedro Mártir at any time of day under any light, with assorted fauna, fishermen, hunters, or redskins in the foreground. He had a whole repertory of light effects for each subject, rather like Monet's haystacks and water lilies. In the side mirrors he painted fish and game. He said, "Those cowpunchers and hard rockers are expert art critics—you can't get a scale on a fish or a snow patch on a mountain wrong but somebody will spot it." I had learned a certain amount of this trick fast brushwork used by tramp painters from Morris Pas, and Blackie offered to take me on as an assistant when I got through with the packing job. A couple of years later I was to take him up on his offer.

In the afternoon Blackie went off on some appointment and he had no sooner left than I got in a conversation with a man who turned out to be the head of the Moses Coulee Apple Growers Cooperative. I believe Moses Coulee is now a lake, but in those days it was a new applegrowing region in competition with the Wenatchee area which has since come to monopolize most of the apple marketing of the middle Columbia. This fellow explained to me that they were anxious to start a publicity campaign in competition with the Wenatchee growers' Skookum label, which had a little Indian head as a trademark, and that he was going down to Seattle the next day, Monday, to see an advertising agency. When he found out that I was a writer and artist, he offered their job to me. I made a copy of the head of the Moses of Michelangelo, like a gold wax seal impression and wrote a whole batch of advertising copy like "Moses was found in the bullrushes. Golden delicious apples are found in Moses Coulee," and sketched a label for the end of the apple boxes and made some newspaper and magazine rough layouts, sitting in the park and drinking home-brew while my employer got stinking drunk. He gave me two twenty-dollar bills, which he said was an advance. I assumed this was the last I would ever hear of it, but about two weeks later I got a check for two hundred dollars, so I made as much money in an afternoon drinking beer as I did in a month packing in the mountains. This, however, did not have the effect on me that it did on Jack London. On the whole I preferred working as a packer to working as a commercial artist or advertising copywriter.

While this was going on there was a bunch of hard-rock miners behind us at the next long picnic table, eating roast chicken and drinking moonshine and swapping lies. It has been proved that the Paul Bunyan legend is largely the invention of a couple of Seattle newspaper people. Tall stories spring up spontaneously amongst lumberjacks and hard rockers and seldom become fixed as enduring legends. These fellows were talking about the aspirin tunnel. One started it and one by one they added outrageous details. It seems there was an old Nevada prospector up north of the Pyramid Lake country who was going along behind his burro in the hot sun with a terrible headache and he saw a dyke of powdery white rock sticking up ahead of him. As he went up to look at it, a rattlesnake scared the burro and it kicked him through the air and he landed face down in the white stuff. When he got up his headache was gone. Thus was discovered the great Aspirin Reef that ran clear through the Rocky Mountains from Reno to Denver. The best stuff lay straight down under the Continental Divide where she took a twenty-thousand-foot dip. When they got the shaft down to that depth they couldn't find anybody who could stand the heat. Finally they got a bunch of stevedores from Natchez, Mississippi, and asphalt workers from Trinidad—colored guys who were used to such conditions. You see, the aspirin was of the highest quality at that point because there it was molten like lava and they mined it in buckets. There were some poor strata of the stuff at a higher level and a bunch of Southern hillbillies came in there and squatted on a claim. They got in a row with the colored guys one time and threw the stove full of burning firewood down the shaft. But it melted before it reached bottom. In a month or so the heat was too much for anybody and after a while they began to run out of men. Then a Scotchman named McGregor and a fellow from Brooklyn named Cohen introduced a new system, all mechanized. The stuff was sucked in hoses and blown out at the other end like Puffed Rice out of cannons and shot up the shaft through a series of screens like an upside-down shot tower. As it came out at the top it blew out through a long fishtail vent and alongside this vent they had two rows of Mexican girls in white uniforms, each one with a little hammer on the head of which was printed in reverse "Bayer-Bayer," and as these little pellets of molten aspirin, weighing exactly five grains each, would come shooting up, two girls would sock it, one from each side, with their little hammers, and it would fall on a traveling belt and go off to be packed in dozens, fifties, and hundreds, untouched by human hands.

This is all I remember of the story but it went on all afternoon while I was making drawings and writing slogans. Nobody ever told the story of the aspirin tunnel before or since. In years of association with lumberjacks and cowpunchers and hard-rock miners and prospectors, I never ran into any evidence of the formation of permanent, extensive legends of the Paul Bunyan type, although all the standard short anecdotes, like the mosquitoes that flew away with the iron kettle, are told all over the West.

As the years have gone by vulgarized folklorism has spread to all classes of society, but the original folk culture has practically disappeared from the Eastern slums and the Western ranges and hardly hangs on in the Southern mountains. In the early Twenties it was still living at its sources, and I feel that the contact with folk culture through my grandparents and the old men I met working in the West and the South has been one of the most important factors in the shaping not only of my speech and literary style but of practically all my fundamental life attitudes. One of the greatest shocks of my life, intellectually speaking, occurred years later when I was traveling through the mountains with a girl and we stopped at a corral and I passed the time of day with an old packer, swapping lies and information. After we went on she accused me of being affected and I realized suddenly the tremendous gulf which had opened up in American life in only twenty years, so that the language and attitudes of the only America which has ever seemed very real to me would appear as affectation to a person twenty years younger. Of course, as with Fourth of July oratory and all other expressions of that patriotism which is the last refuge of the scoundrel, the Burl Ives and Woodie Guthries and Pete Seegers and B. A. Bodkins have made the folk culture of America an integral part of its total opposite, the organized Social Lie. Fortunately my youth was passed in the days before Eleanor Roosevelt had ever invited a dulcimoor singer to the White House, or Earl Browder had announced that "Daniel Boone Belongs to Us."

After this weekend in town I went back up to the head of the lake for a week or so, looking for some work to turn up and meantime cooking for the trail crew which was based on our old camp. About this time a prospector—a tall thin man with a very small head, young but with a deeply wizened face—showed up one day while I was cooking lunch. He invited himself for lunch and then invited himself to go fishing with me. He was a member of some pentecostal sect. The first words he said when he came into the trail cabin where I was cooking were "Are you saved?" And he never let up. His intense religiosity did not prevent him from catching one hundred cutthroat trout, for which he apologized by saying he was going to keep them in snow in back of his cabin. In the evening he went on up to his claim about twenty miles away in Horseshoe Basin on the crest of the range.

About 1 A.M. the phone rang and the ranger down on the lake asked if Jacobson had gone on up to his claim or if he was staying with me. When I said he'd left, he said, "That's too bad because there are three fellows here on their way from Chicago to Seattle who stopped off to look at his property and talked as though they might buy it." I wasn't very enthusiastic but I said, "I'll go on up and bring him down." When I hung up I realized that the trail crew had taken all the stock from the corral and that I'd have to walk. I hiked up during the night and got there just at dawn and was greeted with another barrage of evangelism and a poor breakfast.

On the way back we got into some kind of argument. He boasted about dynamiting fish and I told him that I'd had about all of his religious oratory that I could take and that if I caught him violating any more game laws I'd run him in. At this point I was standing at a steep cliff above the river and without warning he leaped on me foaming with rage and tried to push me in. After I had forcibly calmed him down I left him and went back up the trail while he stood shouting threats and Biblical curses. Although the experience was a shaking one, in the course of time I forgot about it. But in the next year he was to make a considerable amount of trouble. Fortunately for me, because he was quite insane and a dangerous enemy, I left the country at the end of that week.

In Billings, Montana, I got a ride from a boss of a cattle outfit who was working on the fall gathering on the Crow Indian reservation. The work was about all done that fall, but when he found out that I could cook and pack he insisted on taking me down to the reservation and showing me around. He promised me a job on the spring drive-in or on the fall gathering or both for next year. The Crow Indian range was one of the finest in the northern mountain country and the tribe had grown rich both from their own beef and from rentals. I believe it was the largest unfenced good range left and the last stand of the old ways and the old men. The outfits were made up about half and half of very old-timers who had come north on the drives from Kansas in the last century and young fellows who heard that it was the last place (outside of the big Texas ranges, which nobody but Texans liked) where you could get the experience of a genuine old-fashioned cowboy just like in the movies. The country is spectacularly beautiful —high uplands, plateaus, rimrock, rising in steps southward to the mountains in Yellowstone Park. Things were drawing to a close—most of the cattle had been separated and driven out to the railroad. I was anxious to get back to Chicago but I resolved to come back the next year. The boss, a man named Williams who figures in several cowboy memoirs, drove me back to Billings and set me on the highway.

Just out of town I got a ride from a handsome, buxom woman of about thirty-five, driving a Model T, with the back seat heaped with luggage and camping goods. She was on her way to Wisconsin to enter a convent. Now a Model T didn't make very good time along the roads of the northern prairie states in those days and the trip must have taken us at least a week. The convent she was entering had originally been an Anglican sisterhood but the sisters had got in a row over the misplaced Gloria or taking ablutions in the right place with Grafton, the Anglo-Catholic bishop of Fond-du-Lac, and had all swum the Tiber some years ago. The woman who had given me the ride was named Emer O'Neill and she looked it every bit. She was an intellectual Irish Catholic revolutionary from Belfast. Her brother was a friend of Jim Larkin's and had been shot in the streets of Belfast during the Easter days. She was full of Yeats and A. E. Waite and even, at that early date, James Joyce, and had been the Western manager for Mrs. Sheehy Skeffington, the widow of the Irish martyr, when she toured America after her husband had been murdered. Furthermore, another brother, a priest, had been a disciple of the great liberal Catholic Father Tyrrell, and had been expelled from the Church for Modernism. He had become an Anglican priest, very spiky, but with a wife and four children. Emer O'Neill's hatred of the English was immeasurable. Her fund of literary and political quotations in Gaelic and English was inexhaustible, as was her reservoir of gossip—the fascinating gossip of Irish left-wing Socialism, Communism, Anarchosyndicalism, the IWW, the Western Federation of Miners, Anglo-Catholicism, Catholic Modernism, and all the lunatic sects on its fringe from the Old Catholics from Dollinger to Archbishop Leadbeater of the Catholic Theosophists and the "American Catholic Church." In addition she had a sister who was a "liberal Catholic" (Theosophist) nun who read A. E. Waite and the Marquis de Sade, Sar Péladan and Eliphas Levi, had taken part in black Masses, and had theories about Gilles de Rais and Joan of Arc.

She was a very hot chauffeur indeed and probably at that moment, for my interests, the most fascinating conversationalist I could have met up with if I had searched the salons and conspiratorial cellars of six continents. I hadn't been in the car five minutes when, I suppose to discourage me from making a pass at her, she told me she was on her way to enter a convent, and within the next hour all the rest of these basic vital statistics that I have just given came out. In the course of explaining herself, she said that she was deliberately entering this convent of English nuns to cure herself of Anglophobia, and a little later when I said, apropos of some remark about hell, that the Catholic religion as well as any other system of thought should be completely justifiable morally and intellectually without appeal to the actual facts of the existence of God, the historical Christ, or any future life of rewards and punishments, she said, "If I didn't believe in hell, I would have lived a lot different life and done a lot of things I haven't done, and I wouldn't be here today." I suppose this was really a pass at me, but instead of following it up with the natural response, I was young and idealistic and started a theological and ethical argument that lasted clear across the middle of the country. Every night we camped out on the high plains and fried steaks over the campfire and sat around drinking tea and arguing until midnight.

Late the second evening while we were looking for a campsite in the dusk we were flagged down by two little girls, about thirteen and fifteen. They were dressed perfectly in the oncoming international hip costume of the middle of the century—skin-tight torn jeans, dirty gray sweat shirts, no socks, tennis shoes full of holes. They had no baggage whatsoever, not even a purse. They were the daughters of a tramp acrobat whom they worshiped. Although they carried nothing else—not even handkerchiefs—each of them carried a picture of her which they showed us as soon as we made camp. "That's our mom" —as though she were the Virgin Mary, Joan of Arc, and the Queen of England. The picture was of one of the most beat-up-looking trollops I have ever seen, and from their story they seemed to have been unaware that she had abandoned them in Calgary to go off with a pimp from Chicago who now had her hustling in Detroit. Penniless and practically unclothed, they were hitchhiking home to join the family. We discovered they were acrobats when we stopped the car to make camp. The big one plunged out of the car head first, did a somersault in the air, and landed on her feet, caught the little one's flying hands and held her over her head, and they went bouncing around the campsite like a couple of rubber bear cubs. They were at least as hot as Miss O'Neill but they were too young to have got it fouled up with theology and politics. Every time our prospective nun wasn't looking and sometimes when she was and I was in reach, they were making grabs at me, making obscene faces, or assuming compromising postures.

Amid all this sex, juvenile and acrobatic or devout and middle-aged, I preserved the singleness of purpose of St. Thomas just after he had received the cincture from the angel to save him from the sin of impure touch. Ideas are a wonderful thing, especially if you're young. It's hard to believe now, looking back, that they could have saved me from the orgy that hung over my head like the blade of a guillotine for over a week. But they did. Instead of keeping my mouth shut and simply acting in a convivial spirit, I argued myself into the Catholic Church. When we parted and I turned south outside of Duluth on the road to Eau Claire, Miss Emer O'Neill—soon to become Sister Juliana (for the *English* St. Julian of Norwich)—kissed me and told me she felt that I had been sent from God. The two little girls got a ride to Chicago without me from a very debauched-looking traveling salesman before the second one had got out of the Ford. It looks as though some kind of .providence kept sending me the same kind of people. Who else ever met a revolutionary screw in prison or an Anarchosyndicalist Modernist Catholic nun bumming home from a summer spent as a migratory worker?

The next ride I got took me through Eau Claire, Wisconsin, and let me out a little south of town. At the crossroads where I got out, there was an old man over in the field cutting corn by hand. I should explain that corn does not ripen that far north but is cut late in the year for silage. He came over to the fence and asked me if I was looking for a job. "What do you want done?" I said. "Well, you see it's this way, there's been so damn much rain I can't get the cutter into the field for the mud and I'm cutting the stuff by hand. If you can help me do that till it dries up, and then work with the silage crew, you'd get me out of a tough spot."

I agreed to stay after a little discussion. It didn't look like very much work. It wasn't very much pay either. It didn't take long for me to discover that although the place was over two hundred acres in good crops and dairy pasture, it was just as much a marginal farm as though it had been on a side hill among the laurel bushes in the Cumberland. The old man worked shaking down engines in the railroad yards all night and tried to farm during the day. There was no market for anything. I waded around in the mud and cut corn and fed it to the pigs and cows. I milked the cows and fed the milk to the pigs and calves. We could sell the butterfat but not for much money, and it was the only cash coming into the place. They'd had a good truck-garden business supplying merchants in Eau Claire. But the bottom dropped out of that, and there were several fields of rotting vegetables. That far north it was the height of the tomato season, and we ate tomatoes at every meal, in every form. The staple of the diet was floury spaghetti with stewed tomatoes every night. It was a little like being in jail.

The wife resembled my paternal grandmother. The stairs were stacked with *Country Gentleman*. The back room was full of *The Saturday Evening Post*. The cellar was full of antiquated Mason jars of graying peas, corn, and lima beans. Since these formed the only quasi-protein in the diet, and I had a healthy fear of botulin poisoning, I took over the cooking. I suppose I made a healthy diet: there was plenty of milk, homemade cottage cheese, fresh sweet corn, and millions of tomatoes. There was hardly any work because the rain didn't let up, and I read whole years together of *The Saturday Evening Post*.

This was another of those jobs where pretty soon I was doing most of the work. It was all right with me because it relieved the monotony, except for the milking. If you don't milk cows regularly it's extremely hard on your hands. I got a mild multiple bursitis in both hands and had to turn the cows back to the boss. A good deal of time I spent trudging around in the rain looking over the country, and fishing for pike to supplement our peculiar diet. I forgot to mention that I'd picked up a small half-breed black and white collie on the Crow Indian reservation, and spent a lot of time teaching her to handle the cows and fulfill the other duties of a farm dog. This was the only companion I had for a couple of weeks, and then the daughter-in-law of the family showed up. She had just been fired as a schoolmarm over in the next county. I soon discovered why. Although she was large and pink and plump she had the sexual habits of a tireless and very delinquent small child. There was nothing to do but fish, and it was too wet to fish, so I spent a good deal of my time hiding from her in various odd nooks, recuperating my strength, and studying the prose of Clarence Buddington Kelland.

Eventually it dried off. The silage crew showed up, we cut the corn and got it into the silos. I didn't know much about this activity so I was put into the silo to spread the stuff as it rained down around me. After about three hours of this, I passed out and was almost buried before they discovered what had happened. Since then I've learned a silage cutter gives off an immense amount of carbon monoxide, but at the time I was completely unaware that I had narrowly escaped death.

The next day, after an argument over my wages, I went on my way. I've never had any appetite for Eastern farm work since. I'm sure all farms of this kind are not the scene of so grubby and hopeless a life. But once was enough.

CHAPTER 31

I no sooner got back to Chicago than Harold Mann persuaded me to start off on a trip around the world. We planned to hitchhike through the Southwest, ship out from San Pedro, work our way through the Orient, up to Europe, and back to New York. We expected to be gone about five years. We got a lot of pitchman's supplies from one of the places on Wells Street that specialize in such stuff: indestructible artificial pearls, rhinestone cuff links, five-cent perfume, razor-strop ointment. We hit the cotton harvest in Arkansas in the midst of three weeks' steady rain. It turned out that nobody in Arkansas wore a shirt with cuff links. No matter how much we stomped on the pearls nobody bought them. Climbing onto a truck, we broke all the perfume in Harold's rucksack, so we just panhandled.

In Mineral Wells, Texas, we saw a fellow going from door to door with a little satchel. Harold yelled across the street, "Hey, Realsilk." The fellow came over, "How's it going?" said Harold. "Terrible," the guy said. "These weed monkeys don't even wear stockings except for a pair of darned cotton ones to church." Harold said, "I used to be St. Louis manager. You want to lend me the kit for a couple of days and I'll split with you." So for the next two days while I pitched razor-strop ointment, Harold peddled Realsilk.

The second day he met me down at the courthouse square for lunch. He had a frightened look on his face. "What's the matter?" I said. "I've had an awful shock," he said. "I just discovered that the human race has passed through one of the great climacterics of history without anybody noticing. When I worked in St. Louis the sales meetings were run on the principle that you were all fellow grifters together. We used to coach the fish—the sucker opens the door, you put your foot in the door, the sucker says she doesn't want any, you say this, she says that, you break out the kit . . ." This was all in a lot of house-to-house man's slang that I don't remember. "Now, these poor bastards report to work at seven thirty in the morning and spend an hour and a half on their own time singing Realsilk songs to the tunes of 'The Battle Hymn of the

Republic' and 'Dixie.' You've not only got to eat your own horseshit, you've got to believe it tastes good before you go to work. A fundamental change is sweeping over the human psyche, this is more important than the World War, the Industrial Revolution, or the Fall of Rome."

El Paso was as far as we got. Harold was in love and had started off around the world to get over it. While waving our arms at lonely crossroads in the Texas desert he would moan continuously and plaintively, "Helen, thy beauty is to me . . ." or, "Wad I were where Helen lies,/ Day and night on me she cries," and all the rest of the surprisingly large number of poems written to Helen down the ages. Finally he couldn't take it any more and we headed for home. The slum and the razor-strop ointment were too much trouble, so we threw them away and relied on panhandling and backdoor handouts.

As we got into the Ozarks panhandling didn't work very well. Neither did hitchhiking, for that matter. This was before there was any regular highway from Texarkana to Hot Springs. There was only a narrow, partially graveled turnpike wandering through the hills. As a matter of fact, the new highway was at that moment being built off to the north of us. We got almost no rides, and those only from farm to farm. But it was all right; it was very pleasant walking through the late-autumn mountains. The only trouble was that we could neither beg nor buy anything to eat. The barefoot natives leaned in the passage-ways of their dog-run shanties and either didn't speak or told us to git when asked for food. We didn't try to beg; maybe we should have. The most distraught pleas to buy even a piece of bread met with the standard response, "We feeds all our cold bread to the hogs, and we just ain't got none hot." Every few miles there'd be a country store. These were long, dark, shedlike structures with no windows whatsoever, each with a group of men leaning upright or in tilted chairs on the high porch, motionless except when somebody spit. Around their feet there was always a passel of drowsy hounds. Inside the store there were barrels and bins, shelves of denim, gingham, and calico, hams and bacons hanging from the rafters, and no prepared food of any kind, not even crackers. One day for lunch we bought a pound of sugar and walked along the highway eating it out of our cupped hands.

That evening we were pretty hungry. We came down the road into a little valley and there was a genuine house, the first dwelling we had seen all day that wasn't a dog-run shanty. It was freshly painted bright yellow with scrolls of white millwork in the gables and around the windows, and a beautiful flower garden behind the white picket fence. "Hum," said Harold, "I guess we get some supper." Alongside the house tending to some straw skeps of bees was a young, rangy, redheaded man in new waist overalls with shoes on his feet. We offered to buy some food or do some chores. "Oh, that's OK," he said. "Come in and make yourself at home. I never turned down a man yet." He talked to us while he was tending the bees—he was cleaning the hive of something like foul brood but not so prurient, and with this we couldn't help him. We did help him swill the pigs and rode out bareback with him to chase in the cows. I guess he was pretty lonesome because he talked a steady stream. Just like my grandfather in Elkhart, he had come into the Ozarks "driving twenty of the sorriest-looking jackasses you've ever seen, and with nothing in his pocket but five bucks and a broken knife." That was just after he was discharged from the Army. Six or seven years had gone by and he owned about two thousand acres, most of it in separate farms scattered over three counties. He was beginning to swap these properties off and consolidate them. A couple of years later he was to set out what was then the largest peach orchard in America. I think it's still flourishing. He himself went on to Congress and a small measure of fame.

We had a fine dinner of venison, sowbelly, blackeyed peas, hominy, cornbread, potatoes with lots of flour gravy, cobbler, and one of the few pots of real coffee in the state of Arkansas. We sat up late talking about everything under the sun, and then he escorted us with a lantern down the road through the moonlight a quarter of a mile to an empty shanty on his property.

"Make yourselves to home," he said. "You can stay here as long as you want. There's a fireplace out in back and a pile of wood. Don't use the well. The neighbors throw a couple of cats in it every week or so. It's taking a little time for the folks around here to get used to me." Just before he left he said, "I don't want to embarrass you but you boys fixed for money?" "Oh, sure," we said. "We've got a hundred bucks waiting for us in the post office in Hot Springs. We'll be there tomorrow." "That ain't going to do you no good," he said. "Tomorrow's Sunday. Let me lend you five dollars."

After a good deal of urging we took it and sent it back the minute we cashed our money order in Hot Springs. He was one of the few nice Texans I've ever met. Like most nice white Texans, he was a descendant of one of the German pietist families who had set up Mennonite and Dunkard colonies in the state three generations before. Furthermore, he subscribed to Oscar Ameringer's paper, and in spite of the fact he was a big land operator, was a passionate Socialist. He was full of stories about the Green Corn Rebellion, of which I had never even heard. Once again my fate followed me—scoutmasters, prison screws, would-be nuns, these people follow me around.

We went to sleep on a bough bed in the open passage of the shanty, the full moonlight streaming in our faces and packs of hounds baying off in the hills in all directions.

In the morning I woke with a start. "Harold, Harold!" I yelled. "The joint's on fire!"

We sat up and looked out. Three men were frying eggs and sowbelly over the dooryard fireplace. "Y'all better git up," one of them said. "Yo breakfas reddy." We staggered out, rubbing our eyes, and sat down to a regular banquet: hot bread in a Dutch oven, sowbelly and eggs, persimmon jam, and Ozark coffee made out of burned corn and molasses. When we finished eating, one of the fellows, who had been sitting on a jug which I thought was full of water, pulled it from under him and said, "Let's perk up the coffee a mite." It was the purest mountain dew, five years old, aged in the wood, and uncolored. It tasted as if it were about 180 proof. These were the fellows who had been sitting on the porch and glowered at us and spat while we begged the storekeeper to sell us something we could eat. Our host of the night before had let the word go round that we were OK.

As the morning wore along, more and more fellows dropped in. Most of them just appeared suddenly out of the brush. But some of them arrived crashing and banging in ancient cars held together with baling wire, most of them with broken, disused acetylene lamps and hard rubber tires or no tires at all. The local blacksmith shrank wrought-iron bands on the wheels just as though they were wagons. Every third or fourth man brought a jug. The first one was the only glass jug; all the rest were local stoneware. We played cards, chewed tobacco, and talked all day. They were tireless in their demands for information about the outside world. One of the fellows had been to St. Louis and backed us up when we described skyscrapers and elevators. It being Sunday, the womenfolk were all off to church, but the men were free thinkers every one. Furthermore, they were all sorts of illiterate peasant Socialists. Technically, I suppose, their ideas would be classed with those of the Russian Socialist Revolutionaries, a kind of Populist Anarchism. The biggest piece of machinery they'd ever seen was a locomotive. The nearest thing to a capitalist they knew was the country storekeep, and the only financial documents they knew were mortgages and IOUs marked with a cross. But they had very pronounced ideas about the evils of Wall Street, the trusts, and the system. This was a little too far South for the Green Corn Rebellion, but they were the same kind of men. They were also extraordinarily bawdy and seemed to spend most of their time screwing each other's wives and daughters. A local character who wasn't present, an old man with long white whiskers, was quite a line-breeder, as they call it. He'd just had a child by his granddaughter, who was his daughter by his daughter. As they said, "She sho bred true, had cross eyes jist like her maw and grand-maw."

People kept showing up with food all day. But as it drew toward evening we had a feast: wild-pig meat, coon, deer; and although the women hadn't come, they sent the men along with pies and cakes. By dark there were about fifteen of us sitting around the fire, five or six jugs of liquor, an indefinite number of dogs, and little groups of kids that came and went. Finally the picnic broke up, but they all promised to be back shortly before midnight and take us on a fox hunt.

About eleven o'clock four or five of the old cars returned with troops of dogs running alongside. We piled in amongst shotguns, Civil War muskets, jugs, and more dogs. We drove down the pike for a couple of miles, up a dirt road, and then across country through the open oak forest. At a big clearing, white as a sheet in the moonlight, we stopped. Everybody got out and all the dogs took off through the woods. Harold and I started after them. "Where y'all goin?" somebody said. "Why, we're going to follow the dogs," I said. "Come on back here," somebody said. "Them hounds don't need no help. They'll take care of theyselves." There was a fire already going, and a couple of decks of cards were being dealt out on the ground. They played some antique forgotten game a little like euchre, and passed around the jugs of mountain dew. Away in the woods, the hounds had turned up a hot trail. Each man knew the voice of his own dogs, and the betting for pennies on what the dogs were doing was inextricably mixed up with the card game. We sat silent and dumfounded. After about two hours of running, the dogs treed a fox (the Southern gray fox can climb a tree if the trunk has any tilt at all). We all trooped through the woods with lanterns and the men fed the dogs cold cornbread and scraps of pig rind, and clubbed and kicked them away from the tree. "Ain't you going to shoot the fox?" I said. Everybody looked at us in amazement. "Hell, no!" they said. "You can't eat the critters, and if we started shootin them, pretty soon there wouldn't be no foxes around."

When we got back to Chicago we entertained parties for a winter with a story of the Ozark fox hunt. In our audience now and again was a young intellectual, then a mildly modernistic and unsuccessful poet. At that date, I doubt if he knew as much about the Southern mountains as he knew about the North Pole, but he put it all down in his little notebook and next fall he went on a trip to the Ozarks. He wrote a story which I think has been in the movies three separate times, and made a pot of money.

In Texarkana we used our press cards to get a handout from a combination country newspaper and print shop. We made friends with some of the people and when we left they presented us with a hundred business cards printed:

REXROTH & MANN, Inc.
POEMS
AROUND THE WORLD

They thought it was quite a joke, but as we got back up into civilization, the cards proved to be a good deal more profitable than indestructible pearls and Realsilk Hosiery. We used them every time we hit up a housewife for a handout. At night we presented them to the cops and got shakedowns, not in a crummy cell but on a davenport in the chief's office. We decided to say that we were on the last leg of an extremely successful trip around the world, and in every town made up new stories about hand-to-hand combats on the wharves at Celebes, beautiful maidens in Madagascar, and adventures with Dadaist poetesses in Paris. In each town we went first to the newspaper offices and left instructions to have clips mailed ahead. By the time we got to Cape Girardeau, Missouri, we had accumulated an epic, three times as interesting as the real trip could possibly have been. Our adventures were a special feature with pictures in the Thanksgiving edition of the Cape Girardeau paper. As we left our free hotel room and started out through the suburbs to the highway, eager citizens rushed out and invited us to breakfast. We decided to make a Thanksgiving Day of it, and devote ourselves to a scientific experiment to discover just exactly how much the young healthy human male organism could eat. By the time we had eaten two full-dress Southern breakfasts, it was getting along toward noon and the beginning of holiday dinnertime. In about six hours we consumed four Thanksgiving dinners each and two breakfasts. It had not been necessary to rap on a single door. As we staggered up the street eager housewives in love with literature ran after us and implored us to share the family bounty. Fortunately, most Missourians stop eating Thanksgiving dinner along about five o'clock, so we were able to escape. The first ride took us to St. Louis and directly to the home of Harold's parents. They were extremely happy that we'd arrived just in time for Thanksgiving dinner.

CHAPTER 32

When we got back to Chicago we rented the top story of an old apartment house on the corner of Ontario Street and Michigan. This was not a loft, but a completely unfinished attic with loose rough board floors that we had to nail down. The entire area was about an eighth of a Chicago block. It wasn't just big enough for a bowling alley, it was big enough for a golf course. Off in one corner a forty-foot square had been walled off with beaver board and turned into a studio apartment. We didn't even notice it was there until we'd been in the place for a couple of days.

A big nonjuried show of Chicago modernists had broken up in some kind of wrangle and all the pictures were stored with us. Most of them were large, violent, and abstract. We hung them around on the bare studding and still had lots of space left.

I forgot to mention that the year before we had met an elderly Alaskan prospector, an imitator of Robert W. Service and an amateur of the romantic tenor saxophone. He had decided to leave his wife, retire from a contracting business, move to bohemia, and devote himself to his two arts. He rented the little flat in the Gray Cottage over Grenzenbach's bookshop and encouraged me to decorate it in true bohemian style. This was his idea, not mine, and he had very strong ideas of interior decoration which were certainly bohemian enough. We boarded up the windows in the main room, and draped the entire room in yard-wide strips of tied-and-dyed muslins, each one a different Diamond Dye. This, said the old man, was a bohemian-style Arab tent.

It was sure bohemian. The small room next to it he completely covered with his own version of Arabic decorations, and here he sat alternately smoking a water pipe, playing "Dardanella" on the saxophone, and waiting for us to bring him models. No models showed up, and one day his wife came and took him home. He had payed three months' rent on the place, and turned it over to us.

Those three months were historic. The place was a continuous brawl

—full of revolutionary girls from the University of Chicago, Little Theater actresses, models, waitresses, whores, expressionist dancers, and all my drunken IWW friends. There was seldom a time when there wasn't somebody passed out in one of the bedrooms. We hadn't been there many days before McGonigle and Putz pinched the joint. We were turned loose next morning. John Loughman and his girl, and my girl and I, and another couple went back to the place for breakfast. The others never left, so finally we did.

To return to Ontario Street, and our attic, when we ran out of paintings we reluctantly draped the raw walls with the tied-and-dyed which had survived from the tent. This place became a hangout for a whole new set of people. Three very beautiful girls came into the coffee shop of the Dill Pickle one night, looking for Poets and Life. They sat down alongside Harold and me and the most spectacular one said, "Oh, I'm so thrilled at meeting a genuine poet. What do you think of Baudelay?" This was the beginning of a spectacular series of relationships. They were ballet girls from the Chicago Opera Ballet. The Baudelay one was just a little too spectacular and ungrammatical for my taste. One had very serious literary ambitions, and in addition, was a pious Catholic, subject to violent qualms of conscience after an hour in bed. I finally decided on the third girl, who was really the most beautiful and most talented as a dancer, and the least possessive.

Since there was so much space, the attic made a fine practice studio. The building was in litigation and half the places downstairs were vacant. One had been a dress shop, walled with mirrors. We unscrewed the mirrors, carried them up, took down the horrible tied-anddyed, ran a sander over a piece of the floor, screwed the mirrors to the beams, and put a *barre* in front of them. About ten o'clock every morning we would be awakened by four or five girls in leotards bounding about over in the opposite corner from our beds—half a block away.

The little apartment in the corner turned out to be occupied by two stenographers from Milwaukee who had come to Chicago for art's sake. Our place was filling up with ballet girls, Little Theater tragediennes, quarreling painters, and music lovers. From somewhere we acquired the best Victrola of the day, a large collection of classical music —mostly imported—and a dozen apple boxes of what were then called race records, Cow Cow Davenport and Chippie Hill and all that noise. The stenographers were afraid of us and never came near. One unseasonably warm December night we were all alone for a change. There came a gentle rapping on the communicating door. There stood a very shy, tall, blonde stenographer and an even shyer, short, dark one.

"I hope we're not disturbing you," the blonde said. "We thought you were alone and might like to receive a call."

"Fine," I said. "Come on in. We're listening to records."

They sat and listened for a while to "The Firebird" and "The Afternoon of a Faun." Even for shy girls from the provinces they seemed unusually ill at ease. At last, while I was changing a record, the blonde braced herself, cleared her throat, and spoke.

"We have a terrible problem," she said.

"Yes?" Harold said.

"Well," said the blonde. "You see, we're virgins."

"Yes," said Harold, "I see."

"That isn't all," she said. "It's worse than that. You see, we're afraid."

"Yes," Harold said, "I see."

"No, you don't see," she said. "It's even worse than that. We thought once we got out of Milwaukee Downer and came here to the Near North Side, we'd get over it. But we never met any nice men, or if we did, we were afraid of them. Tonight we decided to do something about it. We decided to go all around bohemia and see if somebody real nice wouldn't pick us up. But before we did, to give ourselves nerve, Margot went down to the druggist and got him to sell us an aphrodisiac. After supper we each took four pills and now we're scared to go outdoors."

And with this they both started to cry. Neither of them was exactly our dish, but we did the best we could in a gentlemanly way. In the course of the next week we introduced them around. Fortunately, since they lived right there in the middle of our attic, once they had been inducted they lost interest in us. As the years rolled away, the blonde became a famous bohemian strumpet and died of booze in Paris. The plump one is now one of Chicago's semisocial grandmothers.

Ballet moved in on us more effectually than the virgins. Doris stayed with me most nights. Harold started taking classes from Pavley and Oukrainski, and since he was normal, in almost no time at all was on the stage in Aïda, an adagio boy. As Doris said, "You don't know what a relief it is not to have one of those bitches touching you."

Doris was a perfect ballet girl with knee-length brown hair and a heart-shaped face like, as they used to say in those days, a Benda mask. I've never gone to the ballet anywhere in the world without seeing four or five Dorises in the company. She was that special kind of completely conventional girl who was the product of three generations of show business. She looked like the girl who broke the man who broke the bank at Monte Carlo. She could have been a fabulously rich courtesan. But she was interested only in marriage, home, children, getting out of show business. She worked like a dog: practice all morning, rehearsal all afternoon, on stage until midnight. In those days a ballet girl was considerably lower than a porter. Not only did they have no real dressing rooms, they didn't even have a place to wash up. I used to pick her up after the show. When I'd lean over in the cab to kiss her, behind her ear her neck would glitter with encrusted salt like an overworked horse. Since ballet paid practically nothing, she worked on her off nights in cabarets, mostly Marigold Gardens and Ike Bloom's Midnight Frolics. Through her I met Gilda Gray and her bitter rival, the only genuine original shimmy queen, Bee Palmer, and through Bee Palmer, Jack Dempsey.

Doris had self-dramatizing but fetching little ways. One night she got out of bed and danced naked in and out of the shaft of winter moonlight coming in through the dormer window. When she got back in bed she said, "You've never seen me dance that way before. When I was going to college I took modern dancing." I was a little startled. "I didn't know you had gone to college," I said. "Where did you go?" "Oh," she said, "I have a B.Sc. from Chicago." "Really," I said. "In what subject?" I was a little afraid I might be holding a heavily disguised nuclear physicist in my arms. "Domestic science," she said. "That's a funny major," I said. "What moved you to take that?" "Well," she said, "I thought it would make me a better wife and mother when I got married."

The next day she was off on a brutally punishing tour with that old salt mine the San Carlo Opera Company. I've always regretted that we didn't get married, but it so happened that we both were out of town so much—she most of the winter, and I all of the summer—that we were never together long enough to do what automobile salesmen called "firm up" the relationship. A couple of years later, anxious to escape from the world of ballet, she married a very respectable young businessman who immediately folded up in drink and pederasty. She spent several years unsuccessfully trying to redeem him. Today I believe she still runs a ballet school. As sheer beauty goes, I suppose she's the most beautiful girl I knew. Her pictures were all over *Vogue* and *Harper's Bazaar* of those days. Like many beautiful girls, even though she had a degree in it, she had a wonderful talent for domesticity.

About this time Lawrence Lipton, Sam Putnam, and I organized Chicago's deliberately abortive Dadaist movement which we called the Escalator. We wrote freely associated poetry, gave lectures in which we read antiphonally from *The Critique of Pure Reason* and the telephone book, while shills in the audience set off alarm clocks and shot at us with blank cartridges. We made collages out of rubbish and filled the attic with an audience for a dance recital in which Doris starred. Everybody was masked and in leotards, did handsprings and flip-flops, and all killed each other with rolls of folded newspapers and bladders, struggling over a broken bicycle. The music was Bach's "Air on a G String" and "Cohen on the Telephone," both accompanied by two trombones which made them completely inaudible, except, as they say nowadays, at "random" instances. We put Roger Vitrac's *The Painter* on the Dill Pickle stage, with a pathetic imitation of a Meierhold automated decor designed by me and built by Jack Jones. All the participants in the movement were known as Escalator and were numbered. Escalator No. I was a little schizophrenic who swept the floors at the Dill Pickle. Not only were the people numbered, but the pictures and poems and demonstrations were numbered, too. The works of art were on an equal footing with human beings.

We inaugurated the movement with a parade up and down the escalators in The Fair, a Chicago department store; all of us wearing rented evening clothes, Halloween false faces, plug hats, and carrying open black umbrellas. The trouble with all this was that it became a great social success just as we began to realize that we were being silly and dated. So after one last all-night party in the attic we buried the Escalator movement for good.

While the movement was at its height we were invited to give one of our lectures at a sort of South Side branch of the Dill Pickle called the Shadows. This was a Little Theater, art gallery, open forum, and coffee shop run by the Negro actor Gerald Holmes, who had been an understudy for *The Emperor Jones,* and with whom I had played in many a chestnut by Lord Dunsany. His vice-president was a wryly knowledgeable, portly young man from Texas named Libby. A couple of years before Libby had been riding on a boxcar through Texas. All the other fellows on the car had been colored. While the train was in motion a crew of railroad dicks had ordered them all at pistol point to jump off, and Libby had fallen under the wheels. Under the impression that he was a Negro, the dicks had just let him lie along the right of way until a work crew found him in the morning, so he had a wooden leg. This accidental Bessie Smith case made Libby a voluntary Negro, even if he was one of the Texas Libbys.

Lipton and I put on one of our standard performances, which, as I realized even while we were doing it, was, considering the audience, a little degrading to us, not them. After we got through, a beautiful young girl got up and gave a long speech about how we were a perfect example of the bankruptcy of Western civilization. She said the future belonged to a world view that was just then aborning—on the South Side, for instance.

So I met Madia. Except for Bob Crenshaw, she was the first well-educated black nationalist I knew. After all, there weren't very many of them in those days. She had worked out a personal philosophy of history which was an ingenious combination of Marx, Spengler, and Du Bois, and I must say she had taken, if not the best from each of them, their most cogent arguments. She was in a sense even more intransigent than Bob, because she was incomparably more at home in the world and able to do something about it. She was a successful dancer and had played all the big joints on State Street. This was in the days before the modern striptease routine, let alone the highbrow stripteaser like Gypsy or Lili St. Cyr. For all I know, Madia may have invented strip-teasing. Since, like Gypsy and Lili, she could really dance, and took off her clothes with a contemptuous and very intellectual expression on her face, she was a great success. She was a kind of heroine on the South Side, at least among the few people who weren't scared to death of her. Through her I got back into the swing of things in the "community." Life with her became a weird mixture of tedious waits for her to get through her act in shoddy cabarets, or to get through lectures—some by me, some by her—at Lincoln Center on anthropology, African history, and the Negro renaissance. It occurs to me now that in those days this sort of activity was an exclusively male prerogative. In fact, she is still the only girl I have ever known who was an active black nationalist until Abby Lincoln.

It turned out not only that she was a member of the Communist Party but that she was the mistress of the General. She was as cynical about the rank and file of the Communist Party as Lenin ever was, and had nothing but hilarious contempt for their agitation on the South Side. This was in the days of the decline and fall of the African Blood Brotherhood, and they were casting about for a new line. For the General, she had more than contempt.

"You know," she said, "I can never get that fat swine to treat me as anything but a cannibal princess out of Rider Haggard. He just doesn't know I'm there at all. When I try to explain to him that the people I introduce him to look on themselves as members of the First Families of Virginia and as more American than most other Americans, he thinks I'm kidding. It's impossible to stop him from treating them like natives and talking about what the Bolsheviks have done for the Mongolians. Of course this makes everybody mad, but he never knows it."

For years after he went back to Russia, and until he vanished toward the end of the Great Purge, the General was one of Stalin's most trusted lieutenants and his expert on America. During the twenty years that the Party line was "Self-Determination for the Black Belt" and "For a Negro Soviet Republic," I often used to think of Madia's graphic descriptions of the genesis of that profound bit of political wisdom in a comic and pitifully perverted ritual, a boots-and-saddles act, straight out of *Sexy Adventure Stories* which she carried on with the General.

One day Madia announced, "I've just been accepted for the lead contralto in Rossini's *Stabat Mater*." At first I thought she was kidding and was about to make some wisecrack about how she could take up the collection when I looked at her face and saw she was in deadly earnest. "You never told me you were a singer," I said. "I've been keeping it to myself," she said. "I don't understand," I said. "Why don't you sing in these joints? It's lots easier work." "I'd rather not," she said. It was becoming a tight-lipped conversation.

So she sang on Good Friday in St. James Church and got written up in the newspapers. From then on it was Verdi's *Requiem* and the *Saint Matthew Passion* and Mozart and soon she was making enough money to live on it. Within a year she left Chicago for New York, and as soon as she could she went to Europe. In 1949 I met her in a Chinese restaurant near the Sorbonne. She was with Kenneth Spencer, whose voice I recognized booming behind my back. She was a stately, middle-aged woman. She had just come back to Paris from Edinburgh or Salzburg. She had never returned to the United States. With her party was Alberta Hunter and everybody sat around and talked about the old days as if they had taken place on another planet.

CHAPTER 33

This seems to have been a less eventful winter than most. It wasn't really; probably the opposite. Perhaps I was just getting used to my forced adulthood. My love life was more relaxed and less romantic. Girls like Doris are a good deal more sensible, possibly more intelligent, than revolutionary young intellectuals full of principles. Although Madia played a tempestuous enough role in her charades with the General, with me she was quiet and comfortable. Even the lectures and discussion groups she got me into on the South Side we both took calmly. About all they did for me was to teach me how to get along with a special kind of middle-class people, and start me off on years of anthropological reading.

Field anthropology or ethnology, especially of Africa, was still in those days a limited literature. I read it all. Little of it contained anything on art or spoken literature. What texts of African songs existed I copied out. I went on to the oral literature of other peoples and eventually formed a collection which filled many notebooks. Most of this, however, was a couple of years in the future after I'd come to San Francisco. There were no records of this stuff available commercially in those days, but individual anthropologists had collections of old-time cylinders made on primitive field apparatus. Wherever I could turn them up, I listened to them all. In the course of these researches I discovered Frances Densmore's series, which was just beginning, of texts and music of American Indian songs. These were a most important influence on the development of my own poetry. Another, possibly even more important influence was the collection of Bushman texts published by the Bleek family. These were in a literal translation of Bushman syntax, and resembled nothing so much as Gertrude Stein.

At this time I first read and shortly after met Edward Sapir. He was not just an anthropologist who could teach me a great deal, but a poet of some attainment and even greater insight. He stimulated an interest in language that several years later led to a protracted and intense study of linguistics and philology. More than this, he *is*, I am almost

afraid to say, the only person I have ever met who thoroughly understood what I dreamed of doing with poetry. Out of anthropology,
psychology, and linguistics he had developed a kind of philosophy of
interpersonal communion and communication. Fragments of this philosophy turned up later in Ruesch, Sullivan, and Whorf. It appears
only between the lines of his published work. On principle, he transmitted it only by personal contact. Unfortunately, I never spent as
much time with him as I would have liked. Still, his influence on me
was very great indeed.

I painted a lot that winter—certainly I had an ideal studio—doing
several large paintings which rather resembled the Cubist work of Marcel Duchamp or the canvases that Wyndham Lewis was painting at
that time. Music seems to have been more important that year than
ever before. Possibly this was due to the large collection of foreign
records and the good phonograph that someone had left with us. Then,
too, both Doris and Madia liked to dance. So I spent many hours
watching one or the other bound about to everything from Bach to
Erik Satie. It is hard to believe that in those days there was practically
no music of the kind which has since become so fashionable available
on American records. The only Renaissance and baroque music was
on the old Victor educational series which was listed in a separate cata-
logue and had to be ordered specially.

Through Madia I met a couple of fellows who ran a record business
on State Street. I suppose their records would be extremely expensive
today. I have never understood just what these records were. This was
the year in which electrical recordings first became common. In jazz
discographies you seldom see any mechanical recordings; in fact, few
records before 1927. I don't know what these things were, but they
were all race records and they were all mechanical. That spring they
had begun to bore me and I gave them all away.

This seems to be a recurrent phenomenon. I can take just so much
jazz. Every few years it goes through one of its minor revolutions and
I get interested in it again, I listen for a year or so, then it begins to
bore me and finally exasperates me. I forget about it for a while and
then go back and catch up.

During this winter I met an awful lot of people who were making
jazz history on the South Side. While they were performing I guess I
was so interested in Madia that I didn't pay much attention. The only
two I remember clearly were Cow Cow Davenport, I suppose because
of his fantastic name, and Isobel Ducasse—I suppose because she became so famous later. Also, she got a terrific crush on, of all people,
Ole Olson, and used to stand behind his chair in the Fiume, rub her
boobies against the back of his neck, and sing, "Redheaded man made

a fool out of this here redheaded woman," while he dissolved in embarrassment.

This year, Bard Major showed up. He was one of the historic eccentrics of American bohemia. He is still around today, an influential, if not very successful, science-fiction writer. His parents were even more eccentric than he was, but his grandmother was the leading modiste of Canada and matriarch straight out of G. B. Stern. On her massive shoulders she supported an acrobatic pyramid of oddballs. Bard had been put in the best prep school in America which admitted Jews. In his fifteenth year he read Lenin, Trotsky, and Shaw, and ran away. He went to work in the Allis-Chalmers plant outside of Milwaukee, married, begat two children, and became a member of the State Central Committee of the Communist Party. One day he walked out of all that and showed up on the Near North Side with a large stack of what would someday be called "Socialist-Realist" manuscripts. The night he got in town he came to call. Although he was six months younger than I, he had a long, bright red beard and a fine collection of excited mannerisms which foreshadowed a thoroughly eccentric old age. We sat around drinking wine, and after everybody had left, except Madia, he became confidential and told me all the details of his already remarkable life.

I asked him why he had broken with the Party. He launched on a long technical Marxist explanation of his disagreement with the Politburo. He believed that the NEP was driving the proletarian dictatorship into the arms of a rising bourgeoisie and the rich peasants. He believed that the revolutionary impulse would flag and die if it was not kept at its highest pitch. He believed that the Bolsheviks should liquidate the NEP and undertake a program of planned, forced industrialization. He believed that all private property in land in Russia should be collectivized as soon as possible, and great agricultural factory towns should be substituted for the peasant villages. He had a few ideas about the American working class, too, but he didn't seem to think they were very important. As he talked Madia and I exchanged glances. Finally I said, "Where did you get all these ideas?" "Oh," he said, "I thought them up myself. I drew up a document of twenty theses and sent it to Moscow. When the Center heard about it, they called me up before the Control Commission and accused me of petty bourgeois adventurism, so I quit. I think I have more to give the working class as a novelist anyway."

This was all pretty hard to believe, but after considerable questioning we had no doubt but what it was true. He really had thought it up himself, and his impertinent document had created quite a commotion in the North American leadership of the Comintern. He had received a couple of cautious letters, one from Maurice Spector, the head of the Canadian Party, and one from Moissaye Olgin, but he couldn't make head or tail out of them, they were so cautious. Nor could he understand why they of all people had written to him. "Don't you know that these ideas are practically identical with those of a powerful group in Russia?" No, he didn't know. "Don't you know whose program this is?" "It's my program," he said. "It may be," Madia said, "but it also happens to be Leon Trotsky's."

Besides being a self-made Trotskyite, two years before there were any Trotskyites in America, he was also a devoted Shavian, a vegetarian, and was in the process of converting himself into an Orthodox Jew. His family were from Vienna and I imagine had been atheists for a thousand years. I think he became an Orthodox Jew out of sheer annoyance. Around the Near North Side in those days there was a whole covey of decayed young intellectuals, mostly from Jewish Socialist families, who were busy reading Huysmans and St. Thomas Aquinas and becoming Neo-Catholics—the last device left to them by which to scandalize their parents. I think Bard decided that he would do something even more outrageous, so he started peeing with his hat on, making a nuisance of himself at mealtime, and painfully trying to learn Hebrew. He didn't just scandalize his grandmother; she showed up in Chicago, and called on me, distraught and in a state of pale blue shock. It's a wonder it didn't kill her.

Mostly that winter stays in my memory as a period of work, of calm, a sort of ingathering of my resources. The memory is comparatively uneventful, but it is extremely vivid. I can remember the warm, dusty air of the attic—all the heat in the place rose up the elevator shafts and accumulated around us—and the sickening smell of the restaurant on the ground floor, which we could never get used to, even for a minute. I can see again every one of the huge gaudy abstractions of my contemporaries looming up in the brown dimness. I can see the girls practicing in front of the cracked mirrors. The tied-and-dyed couch covers, the two matching antique green vanity tables somebody left us, which as long as Harold stayed there must have done our reputations no good. And very sentimentally I can see a naked girl dancing in the moonlight to the first scratchy record of *Le Sacre du Printemps*.

During this winter some unknown distant relative died and left me a little money, which almost doubled my small income. I sold a couple of pictures and I got a job doing some interior decorating. This was not a tied-and-dyed tent for a demented prospector. In fact, it was a coffee shop for a church. I made it very chic with dull plum-colored curtains, umber-brushed antique green tables and chairs, faded orange linen, and a deep crimson jug for flowers on each table. There have probably been a hundred thousand teashops exactly like that since, but this must have been one of the first, because it created a sensation and made me a bit of money. I don't know where I got all those chic ideas; maybe from Madia, because my mind has never normally functioned that way. Anyway, I went around and collected out of pawnshops and junkshops all the good antique jewelry I could find, especially jet, garnets, seals, and Wedgwood-type cameos. In those days there was still a lot of this stuff lying around, and most of it could be bought for under a dollar. I waited until I had a suitcase full of it, and then sold it to a couple of the first *boutiques* to open around the Drake Hotel. On this deal I made what for me was a large sum of money. That's all the work I did that winter.

Toward spring I took a trip to New York. Ruth was there but she was in love and not very accessible. 201 West Thirteenth was being torn down and most of the people were in Chicago or Seattle. The painter Teall Messer was going to Europe and he sublet me his room on West Fourteenth Street. When he left he warned me that he was himself subletting it and his landlady might show up from Paris any time. I lived there for a couple of weeks. There was all sorts of artists' equipment and I painted every day. One bitter cold March night I was snuggled down in the big antique bed under a stack of patchwork quilts. There was no heat except the fireplace, and no electricity. The door opened and somebody pulled the chain on the gaslight. I woke up as the pale green light of the Welsbach mantel shone down on a remarkable sight. There stood a woman in a black velvet cape, a high black taffeta-swathed turban with a black veil wrapped around her neck. Her long, flat face was powdered dead white. Her eyebrows were plucked off and painted back on in thin black arches. Her lips were painted purple. She looked like something out of a bad expressionist play.

"Who the hell are you?" she said. She was quite drunk.

"My name's Kenneth Rexroth," I said politely.

"Where the hell's Teall?" she said.

"He's gone to Paris," I said, "and sublet the place to me."

"Oh, he did, did he!" she said. "Why, the dirty son of a bitch. How much rent did you give him?"

"I just gave him twenty dollars," I said, "and the landlady's due back any day now."

"Oh, she is, is she?" she said. "Well, you just move your pretty little butt over, because I'm the landlady."

It was the commencement of a memorable night. She was a famous poet, painter, and short-story writer; but far more famous for her insatiable and peculiar erotic appetites. I stood two nights of it and moved out.

Frances Midner was setting up a co-op down below the Village in that wonderful lost section which was once the outer edge of eighteenth-century New York. It was a beautiful house of bright red, white-pointed bricks, a hand-wrought iron fence, a white marble stoop, and, at the doorway, slender Ionic columns, and a shell portico—certainly one of the handsomest Georgian houses in New York. I moved in along with Frances, Minna Green, Masha and her new husband, Hays Jones, Bill Gropper, and a musician who played the piano all day and all night, mostly Bartók. The ceilings were a perfect American version of the finest Adam ceilings to be found in London, done by the office the Adamses opened in America. The floors were of six-inch planks of pale hardwood, possibly chestnut, and the woodwork, even the window frames, was black walnut. We hadn't been there very long when the city started to tear down the entire neighborhood. Our house was supposed to be left, but as the excavation for the vehicular tunnel grew larger and larger, the walls began to groan, and the floors tipped. We stayed on until the police evicted us. The last week the house could be reached only by a narrow plank catwalk. Two days after we left it toppled over. This was on Dominic Street—today a wasteland of freeways and warehouses.

Just before the Dominic Street house tumbled over, Jarvis Fairfax showed up with a new girl friend. She looked like a moderately depraved, very expensive French model—sleek head, long neck, narrow shoulders, a shape a little like a ninepin, protruberant, heavy-lidded eyes, mobile mouth, and an ivory skin. They moved into the Dominic house and I discovered a new type, the avid, churchy, purple sinner. She was at least as religious as her lover, but she had obviously embraced Catholicism only because it provided a strong erotic seasoning to an already overly rich diet. She hadn't been in New York more than a week before she discovered a tribe of stinkards who I had always assumed existed only in the imagination of the sillier French novelists.

Scattered all through the Village, even to this day, there are tourist teashops for visiting schoolmarms from the hinterland. They do most of their business in the afternoon and serve bridge-party cuisine, and the waitresses read tea leaves or make charcoal portraits. One of them was called Mrs. Smith's Tea Leaf Shop, where at one time a kindly white-haired lady had cut silhouette portraits with nail scissors and told fortunes while her babbling customers consumed the petits fours. She had sold the place to two forceful, tiger-eyed women. Silhouettes were still snipped in the afternoon, but at dinnertime the place began to fill up with a very odd crew indeed. The two women always called each other "sister" and I had assumed that so they were. They were not; they were escaped nuns. The elder had been named Sister Mary Alicoque and always made a great thing of it. The customers were characters of a wide assortment of sexes in similar or analogous situations. There were Manichaeans, Albigensians, Theosophical and Anthroposophical Liberal Catholics, vicars of obscure Levantine heretical churches—every outfit in the second volume of Harnack has a church somewhere in New York—and a liberal sprinkling of incense-soaked Anglo-Catholics who hung on to respectability, lending choirboys "The Priest and the Acolyte," puzzling their congregations, and giving the Bishop sleepless nights. Every evening the mistress of ceremonies, so to speak, was a six-foot-two, three-hundred-pound Norman-Frenchman with pop eyes and a vast expanse of pink cheek like the traditional portraits of St. Thomas Aquinas. During the day he went by the name of Tom LeMoine; evenings in the Silhouette Shop he was known as Mother Aquinas. He was considerably campier than Bert Savoy. He always wore a pectoral cross, a bishop's ring, and used a penitential stole for a scarf. Although most of the men had been defrocked from at least one "Communion," considerably fewer of the women had inside experience of the religious life. Many of the more rugged torpedo dykes, true, had first flowered in a convent garden, but most of their fluffs were pickups from around the Village who had been attracted like flies to the strong meat of mortal sin signed with Imprimatur and Omnis Obstat. The majority of the girls were merely highly ecclesiasticized nymphomaniacs.

The Fairfaxes spent almost every night in the Tea Leaf Shop and even took their meals there. Jarvis said his interest was pure objective curiosity, and it's true that he never seemed to get involved with the gang-bangs which took place after closing time in studios lit with racks of vigil lamps, thuribles hanging from the ceilings, and statues of the BVM which looked like underfed, Aubrey Beardsley Salomes. Madeleine, on the other hand, dived in with enthusiasm. She became inseparable from Tom LeMoine, and always referred to him as her confessor. Maybe she did go to confession to him, because she began to scandalize the highly principled free lovers in the Dominic Street soviet.

Pretty soon we began to hear about black Masses celebrated every Friday midnight in a barn in the Bronx. Finally one Sunday Tom LeMoine showed up with a little band of followers and a suitcase with alb and chasuble. He vested in the bathroom. Madeleine took off her clothes and fired up the incense, and they started a black Mass in the Fairfaxes' bedroom. We had a little meeting in the kitchen, and finally, led by Bill Gropper, who was fully as husky as Mother Aquinas, the Comintern burst open the door and expelled the Devil and all his minions into the hard, cruel light of a downtown Sunday morning, vestments and all. Madeleine had a hysterical fit—a very convincing imitation of possession—and next week got herself up in a plain gray dress with a bit of white at the throat, hung a crucifix around her neck, and went to a two-hour confession at St. Luke's.

Such was my only experience with diabolism. I've heard rumors of such people in Paris and London, but I've never been able to run them down. I've often wondered if William Butler Yeats ever actually found any. I think he made them up, because he took them so seriously. As a cathedral of Satan, the Tea Leaf Shop bore a distinct resemblance to an act in the *Ziegfeld Follies*.

After the Dominic Street soviet was toppled into the abyss—it occurs to me possibly for its involvement in this Village Gomorrah—I went back to Chicago.

The year before I had walked up and down a windy, wintry afternoon in Lincoln Park, quarreling with Shirley. I'd had a bad cold for about three weeks and in true social-worker fashion she was badgering me to get a chest X ray. The more she convinced me, the less I wished to tempt fate. When I returned to Chicago this year, she had moved out of her apartment. It took me several days to locate her. She was in a tuberculosis sanitarium, where she had been confined to bed for three months, seriously ill. She had also had an operation for hyperthyroidism. Three months on bed rest and a high-caloric regimen, coupled with the surgically altered metabolism, had produced an entirely different person. I showed up with an armful of flowers, some books, candy, and fruit, and walked past her bed on the sleeping porch without recognizing her.

I can never forget that visit. This had been not just the great love of my adolescence; I still look back on it as the most profound emotional involvement of my life. But the other person had gone. As a matter of fact, she had been replaced by an in every way more desirable person but a person with whom I could make no intimate contact whatsoever. We sat and talked and looked out at the May weather in the Forest Reserve, and behaved to each other as though we were friendly business associates of years' standing. Possibly I might have fallen even more in love with this different girl, but she was already finally bespoken. As soon as her cure was completed she was to marry the young doctor who had courted her for so many years. Before the visiting hour was over he showed up, with his own load of candy, flowers, and books. I went back to the city, and for a long time I felt not sorry or puzzled but certainly empty, as though I myself had just got out of the hospital without a leg. If I think about it, even today, the old emptiness comes back.

CHAPTER 34

My trip around the world with Harold had aroused my curiosity about the Southwest, which we had never reached. So I only stayed in Chicago a couple of weeks, and then took off through Kansas and southern Colorado to Taos and Santa Fe. On the way down I visited Haldeman-Julius in Girard, Kansas. He had a large stock of a Little Blue Book on diet which he couldn't get rid of. I bought the lot at two cents a copy and had them shipped ahead. On West Madison Street and Bughouse Square, Eddie Miller once made a good thing pitching a similar book from the Lindlahr Naturopathic Sanitarium. If the stiffs in Chicago bought them, I could envisage an even hotter pitch that would sell them to the weed monkeys.

Taos was under the bitter cloud of the presence of D. H. Lawrence, a miasma which has only recently begun to die away. Lawrence may have been an apostle of love, but his immediate followers hated each other like poison. They spent their time quarreling and organizing the innocent bystanders into their several factions. I went to a couple of parties at Mabel's where everybody shuffled around full of sugar moon while tame Indians hammered on tom-toms—a weary orgy of skinny or overweight millionairesses, hitchhiking hobohemians, disordered anthropologists, lady imagists from the Middle West, and a select number of very mercenary Indians. During these brawls the Master periodically stormed out of the room in white-faced, red-whiskered rage whenever anybody used a dirty word. However, he magnanimously ignored the considerable amount of gumming-up that went on in the inglenooks of Mabel's stately home. I won't say I was disillusioned—every genius to his insanity—but I didn't cotton to it either.

The only people in the Lawrence set with whom I could make friends were "Clarence"; the Danes; Knut Merrild, still one of the finest human beings I've met in my life; Meta Lehman, who seems to have fallen out of all the memoirs and who was much the nicest woman in Taos, being very similar in personality and appearance to Shirley before her TB cure; Jaime de Angulo; and Witter Bynner, who didn't get along any too well with Lawrence anyway. Most of them I met at the first parties at Mabel's, but from then on I visited them in their own homes.

Much more interesting were the painters who had their own well-organized world, carried on much less, and seldom mixed with the Lawrence set. The majority of the first generation of Taos painters had lived in Chicago. They had already achieved a distinctive style, a kind of virile Impressionism, and were painting some of the more interesting pictures of the day. They knew the country thoroughly, and had traveled all over its mountains on horseback. And they knew the Indians a good deal better than the professional Indian worshipers, although they, too, were corrupted by the same sort of Theosophical nonsense which was a blind, bigoted religion with the others.

Two of the second generation of Taos painters were very good indeed—Willard Nash and Andrew Dasburg—and with them I formed fast friendships. I believe that Dasburg is one of America's better painters. His style is temporarily out of fashion, but I think his pictures are still popular on an invisible market, uninfluenced by dealer-promoted fads. Willard gave me the run of his studio, and I painted several pictures alongside of him with great benefit to myself. I left all the pictures behind me, and thought no more of them. Over twenty years later I discovered one of them in New York on the wall of a poetess who was visiting in Taos for the summer and had picked up some paintings in a junkshop.

The local Indianism began to infect me. The first Indian painters were just becoming known in those days. There was one at Taos who wasn't very good, and another at Santa Domingo who was the best of the lot. The others, who have since become famous, were not nearby, but off in the Zuni or the Hopi pueblos. I did my best to make friends and they were friendly enough in their turn but we didn't communicate much. I'd come to call and we'd sit and talk very little and, when we did, just pass the time of day. It was all very Indian.

The poet Hal Somers had a handsome secretary, a young Navaho girl whose father was the richest man in the tribe. She had been East, not to an Indian "college," but to one of the better girls' schools, and was a great deal more communicative. Since she didn't fit the local stereotype, she wasn't popular around Taos. We became good friends.

Much the solidest writers and the ones incidentally who knew the most about Indians were Mary Austin, Witter Bynner, and Alice Corbin Henderson. They may not have been quite as advanced as the Lawrence set, and any one of them would have been horrified at the suggestion that they were Biblical prophets. But they were far more civilized people. Witter Bynner was just beginning to translate Chinese poetry. He was the first person I had met with whom I could share my own interest. He had a very sensible Chinese informant, and had never fallen victim to the outrageous ideographic theories of Ezra Pound and Amy Lowell. He introduced me to the major Sinologists in French and English, in those days still a rather limited study, and recommended a Chinese student at the University of Chicago who was a great help to me the next winter. He also helped me to shift my focus of interest from the poetry of Li Tai Po, in those days considered by most Westerners China's greatest poet, to Tu Fu. For this—an hour's conversation in a sun-baked patio—I have reason to be eternally grateful to Witter Bynner. Tu Fu has been without question the major influence on my own poetry, and I consider him the greatest nonepic, nondramatic poet who ever lived. In some ways he is a better poet than either Shakespeare or Homer. At least he is more natural and intimate.

Tu Fu comes from a saner, older, more secular culture than Homer and it is not a new discovery with him that the gods, the abstractions and forces of nature are frivolous, lewd, vicious, quarrelsome, and cruel, and only men's steadfastness, love, magnanimity, calm, and compassion redeem the nightbound world. It is not a discovery, culturally or historically, but it is the essence of his being as a poet. If Isaiah is the greatest religious poet, Tu Fu is not religious at all. But for me his response to the human situation is the only kind of religion likely to outlast this century. "Reverence of life" it has been called. I have saturated myself with his poetry for thirty years. I am sure he has made me a better man, as a moral agent and as a perceiving organism. I say this because I feel that, above a certain level of attainment, the greatest poetry answers out of hand the problems of the critics and the esthetician. Poetry like Tu Fu's is the answer to the question "What is the purpose of art?"

Alice Corbin's role in the development of American poetry has been almost forgotten. She was unfortunate in being survived by more ambitious people. Actually it was she, not Harriet Monroe, who made *Poetry* magazine available to the best modern verse. And it was she who was responsible for what little modernist poetry there was in the early editions of the Monroe-Henderson anthology. She was a more civilized woman than Harriet Monroe, both in her literary taste and in her human contacts. Harriet lived and died a provincial suffragette with the manners and tastes of a crank. She was convinced that a glorious future awaited young American poets who would write bad sonnets about dynamos, and confident that time would vindicate her judgment that George Dillon was a better poet than T. S. Eliot. I found it impossible to sit in the same room with her for five minutes without losing my temper. Alice Corbin, on the other hand, sought me out, invited me to dinner, tactfully suggested that I bring her some of my work the next time I came, and devoted hours of conversation and several long letters to discussing it with me on my terms—she certainly belonged to a different school of poetry—and in the sanest and most helpful manner possible.

Mary Austin was a type I had never known well before, a thoroughly professionalized and successful woman writer. We didn't have much in common in a literary way, but talking about life and letters she helped me to realize that it was possible to adopt literature as a profession with the same dignity that you adopt medicine, and in turn demand the same respect from society. In addition, Mary Austin knew more about Indians, and more about Indian song especially, than anybody else in the country, except Frances Densmore and Natalie Curtis Burlin, whom I never met. She understood my interest in the, so to speak, non-Aristotelian syntax of Indian and African languages a generation before Whorf. She played cylinder records of Indian songs for me, and gave me a list of books to read when I got back to Chicago. She knew people all over the Southwest, especially off the main lines of travel; people in remote valleys in central Nevada and east of the mountains on the California line, around the Four Corners, on the Tonto Rim, and tucked away in box canyons in Utah, like the one in *Riders of the Purple Sage*. She gave me all sorts of addresses, both Indian and white, and many of them I used. All these people, as a matter of fact, gave me names and wrote letters for me all over the intermountain country. In addition, I had a list of names of more or less political Indians given me by Chief Little Bear, who was a friend of Kep Thorpe's and a most effective one-man lobby in Washington for all the Indians in the country. He was himself, I think, a member of the Sac and Fox tribe.

There is one thing wrong with this narrative: I can't keep straight who lived in Taos and who in Santa Fe, back in those days. It seems to me that Bynner, Alice Corbin, Mary Austin, and Andrew Dasburg all lived in Santa Fe. I know they did a few years later. On this trip I did a considerable amount of shuttling back and forth, and it's become confused. Certainly Santa Fe was much the better place. Not only did Taos have all the fakery of an art colony, but in addition, the people lived in mud huts with little or no plumbing and were all badly infected with the absurd theosophy of highbrow Indianism. To this day they circulate petitions to protect the sacred rights of the pueblo to get its drinking water out of polluted irrigation ditches.

It wasn't long before the scene began to pall on me. The painter Hal Somer's secretary was going back to Window Rock and then north to the San Juan on a visit with her parents. I went along. In those days the Navahos were a good deal less embittered and ethnocentric. Nobody in the family inquired about my intentions toward their beautiful daughter. I was made completely at home, as though I had been born and raised in a hogan. Maybe, but I drew the line at sleeping in one. My girl and I slept outside under a pile of quilts and sheepskins. Except for Nanda Devi, she was the most accomplished lover I have ever known, and she was at least as beautiful. She wore the Navaho fashion of those days—hair in two big wheels, black velvet blouse with little silver conchas, silver belt, full black satin skirt with rainbow stripes above the hem, and bright red moccasins. Underneath all this she wore nothing. Whenever she came near me, the thought of her body made me a little dizzy. She had three perfectly ravishing younger sisters. They were even more beautiful. On the trip to the San Juan, which took a good many days on horseback, they let me know they were quite available. However, they had not been to Smith College. They had not only never learned the use of modern plumbing, but had grown up in a world in which water in any form was not abundant. They dressed in exactly the same way as my girl, and whenever they came near, the thought of their bodies made me dizzy, but in a different sense. Evenings around the fire of roots of mesquite and greasewood, I always sat upwind.

However, I learned that this blemish was situational. After several days' riding we entered a rocky arroyo, and the horses caught the smell of the far-off muddy San Juan. The whole party broke into a furious run. Horses loaded with women and babies, pack animals with coffeepots and Dutch ovens clattering and banging, off they went at the long rocking run of Indian horses, leaping over boulders and whinnying like birds. I tried to draw in my horse, and had expected the Indians to do the same. On the contrary, they were all shouting, kicking with their spurs, and whipping on the pack animals with their quirts. My animal jumped over five-ton boulders like a jackrabbit, oblivious to what might lie on the other side. After about an hour's run, still mounted, still running, people began to undress on horseback. When we hit the river, saddles were thrown off, packs dumped, and panting, sweating stock, men, women, and children plunged into the brown swirling water. There we all stayed till nightfall.

We camped for a week in a little box canyon near the Bends, where there were peach trees planted by the Indians but left untended and only visited at harvest. Scattered amongst them were a few cherry trees, already loaded with ripe fruit. My girl and I lay around nude in the flickering shade of this orchard, made love, gorged ourselves on cherries, and read *The Canterbury Tales,* which she had brought along.

I imagine this was the strangest brief love affair that savage orchard had ever seen. At last the group headed on up the river and we parted when they turned back south up the Chacos. I went on with a pack horse and another zebra dun. In the pack was the box of health books. Carefully cradled in one of the saddlebags was a tame Gila monster which I had bought from one of my girl's little brothers.

In the first little town, maybe Durango, I set up shop. I didn't have a regular keister, so I put the box of books on a folding camp chair which I got at the general store. On it I put a candle and a big bright navel orange. It was getting along toward dark. I stood there for a while fondling the Gila monster stretched across my chest with his nose nuzzling my ear. After I had collected a small crowd I lit the candle which burned steadily in the hot, windless twilight. Then I slowly peeled the orange in one continuous spiral. Then I broke off a piece of peeling, held it close to the candle, skin side toward the fire, and snapped it back between my fingers. When the oil of the orange hit the flame there was a little explosion of blue fire. I put the Gila monster down on the stand and got him to mumble at my fingers, and began my pitch.

"Ladies and gentlemen," said I, "would you all stand just a little closer? It will serve to shelter the candle from any vagrant breeze of the evening that might spring up and I would under no circumstances wish to block traffic and cause any embarrassment to the local guardian of law and order, otherwise known as the town clown. However, ladies and gentlemen, do not stand too close. Do not, in sudden moments of interest and passion, belly up, so to speak, against the stand and irritate or annoy the little animal. As you know, having grown up in this country, although the Gila monster is one of the most lethargic of all living reptiles, he is nevertheless subject to fits and starts of sudden wrath, and, as you further undoubtedly know, the bite of the Gila monster is more venomous than that of the cobra of India, the tiny jewellike but deadly coral snake, or the instantly fatal fer-de-lance of the jungles of the tropics. Compared with that of the Gila monster the bite of the largest diamond-back rattler is but a scratch. Furthermore, these notorious snakes strike like lightning and instantaneously release their victim, unless, as sometimes happens, their fangs become embedded in a bone and they have to be pulled off by main force. The Gila monster, on the other hand, hangs on and gnaws and chews with a bite far more tenacious than any bulldog. Once he has seized hold he is more difficult to remove than the treacherous abalones of the Pacific which often trap the Japanese and Mexican divers and condemn them to a watery grave. Now, the most interesting thing about the Gila monster is that, unlike all other venomous reptiles and all other poisonous animals, he is not equipped with any poison sacs whatsoever. In addition, his alimentary passage is not provided in its upper reaches with any digestive juices. His stomach and upper gut are extraordinarily resistant to all toxins. You could feed this little animal a half ounce of pure prussic acid and it would have no effect on him whatsoever. His digestive processes are unique in the entire animal kingdom. After he has ingested a rodent or other reptile, he retires to his burrow, usually an abandoned gopher hole, and lies in a somnolent position while the food slowly rots. After it has become an amorphous, putrid mass, it passes on into his middle gut where it is absorbed by a peculiar chemistry of his cold reptilian blood stream. Now the venomous effect of the bite of the Gila monster is due entirely to the fact that he regurgitates a small part of this appalling mess into the open wound of his victim. There is no poison more deadly, and it is composed exclusively of food which had decayed in the beast's alimentary passage. Ladies and gentlemen, I know, just by looking at you, at your lackluster eyes, at the pimples on your foreheads, at your pale hanging lips and thinning hair, that you, too, like most of the inhabitants of the United States, suffer from exactly the same conditions as are beneficial to the Gila monster but which cause you untold harm—rheumatism, nausea, habitual colds, hot and cold flashes, back pain, swelling feet, bad breath, acne—conditions which not only afflict you with these minor diseases and discomforts but which weaken your resistance and leave you the prey of fatal diseases and epidemics.

"Like the Gila monster, ladies and gentlemen, you are full of shit. Your innards are a compacted mass of decaying food which moves slowly out of you like glaciers move down the valleys of the mountains of Greenland. Cathartics are of no help. They only blast a narrow passage like a tiny tunnel through the surrounding abomination."

At this moment I squeezed another orange peel into the candle flame. By that time it was dark, and the spurt and the flame were very impressive.

"However, ladies and gentlemen, just as poison kills poison and thieves catch thieves, food, properly used, can cure the conditions which are the result of its abuse. In the most ordinary foods are hidden tremendous powers of which the average person knows nothing. You have seen the fireworks display which resulted from a gentle squeeze of an orange peel. In the skin of an orange is a small quantity of oil of orange, mixed with water and other substances. Oil of orange is potentially more explosive than nitroglycerine. The only reason that it is not used to blow open safes is that it cannot be extracted. It must be used fresh, and its power starts to decay the minute it leaves the skin of the living orange. Now I do not advise you to go about munching orange peels, they will only make you sick. In fact, as you might have noticed, if you've ever left an orange peel along the trail, they are so violent in their effect that every animal, no matter how wild, instinctively knows better than to eat them. However, there are many perfectly normal foods which, if properly prepared and eaten in balanced meals, will cure you, in a matter of a couple of weeks, of the constipation which has made all your life miserable. Not only that, but there is no part of the United States so remote or in such wild or desert country that some of these foods cannot be obtained. Many of them are things you eat every day; they only have to be properly prepared. Furthermore, they are far more delicious than soggy, hot bread, flour gravy, and meat fried till it is like leather, which, as I know, having grown up in this country, is what most of you eat three times a day.

"On a visit to Colorado I was employed by the Foundation for Natural Health, a nonprofit organization financed by one of the world's most famous philanthropists. I am traveling through the Southwest, distributing a little book of healthful recipes and menus which will teach you the proper way to eat. There is nothing freakish or cranky about these foods. They are all perfectly ordinary American vittles, but this book will teach you the proper way to prepare and serve them. And after two weeks of following their menus, planned by one of the greatest living dieticians, all your constipation will pass away in more senses than one; your petty, nagging illnesses will leave you and you will discover the world of radiant, robust health. Now the Natural Health Foundation could easily afford to pay my salary, and for livery for my stock, and in addition, give these little books away. If we did that, you would have no respect for them. In a couple of days they would be out hanging on a hook alongside last year's Monkey Ward catalog and Dr. Miles's Almanac. So we are charging a small pittance, only a fraction of the cost of printing alone—two bits, twenty-five cents, a quarter of a dollar."

The only trouble with this pitch was that after I'd made three or four towns I ran out of books. In the course of the summer I managed to connect with a couple more shipments here and there in the intermountain country. Each time I sold them out in a few days. I imagine I did a lot of good.

I spent the rest of the summer drifting up and down the west side of the Rockies, from the San Juan to Jackson Hole. For several years I was to work here every summer. It was still pretty undeveloped country with thousands of square miles of unfenced range. I picked up jobs for a week or two, mostly as relief cookee and wrangler. This is an easy job to get if you're trustworthy. The regular fellow seldom gets a chance to go to town. I suppose in many ways this is the best of all cowboy jobs. It isn't anywhere near as hard as driving or gathering cattle and there are short periods in the day when you don't have to work. Furthermore, you're up before anybody else, and it's wonderful to start the fire and go out and chase the cavy in the early dawn. Sitting on a horse in the midst of illimitable miles of sagebrush and rock under the paling stars is an experience like those described by the mystics—the smell of greasewood and juniper smoke, the strong smell of horses as you come on them in the chill air, the stringent smells of the land itself, the sound of thrashers and wrens waking up the country, the sharp aseptic smell of mountain streams in the night.

There's only one trouble with this work—most cowboys are not interesting people. From Nebraska to the Sierra Nevada they tell the same jokes, and respond to all of life's situations with the same limited number of reactions. Still, the particular part of the country I had chosen did in those days offer the widest variety of people and customs in the West.

In many ways the nicest people to work for were the Mormons. Southern and eastern Utah were in those days still strongholds of practically unreconstructed Saints. Big stone ranch houses surrounded with their "wife houses," great barns, neat outbuildings, and barnyards that were raked every morning, all set under a clump of Lombardy poplars in the midst of an irrigated meadow. It's not just the neatness and efficiency of the Mormons; they have built a genuine culture in the anthropological sense, one of the most integrated in the world. Mormonism is a farmers' version of the radicalism of the pre-Civil War America, in which it was born, an Oneida Community held together by religious sanctions. Certainly it is very unlike the puritan tradition of the rest of rural America. Possibly the long struggle over polygamy gave the Mormons a more wholesome attitude toward sex. Most gentiles think that this has resulted in clandestine promiscuity. It hasn't, but it has produced an American community which takes sex as a natural determinant in human relations. And it's permissive enough. Drinking coffee and smoking cigarettes are considered more harmful sins than a few premarital and extramarital relationships. Every Mormon church has weekly socials which are among the most enjoyable get-togethers of any kind in America, and in spite of the anti-Mormon literature about the Mormon debasement of women, the spontaneous and easy relationship between girls and boys can be compared only with the French Auberge Jeunesse Laïque or similar activities in modern Scandinavia—there just are no symptoms of the American sex war. Whatever the demerits of polygamy, it should not be forgotten that thousands of women, alone and voluntarily, crossed thousands of miles of desert, in very inconvenient conveyances, to take part in it.

I made the most of my introductions and spent as much time as I could with Indians. Nowadays, wandering hitchhikers are hardly made welcome. In those days it was still possible to "live on the mesa," as they say, and I spent a week at Oraibi treated like one of the family by an Indian artist on whom I simply walked in. I had looked forward to a week or more at Zuni, but it was too much for me. There are limits to togetherness. I would say that within an hour anyone of the slightest sensitivity would begin to feel the oppression suffocating. It's like being in the midst of a boxcar stuffed with pillows. I discovered in talking about this to the Hopi and Navahos and Apaches that they are well aware of Zuni group dynamics, and joke about it. Today I believe it is quite impossible for a white man to live in any of the pueblos. Nowadays, of course, in their bitter struggle to preserve every jot and tittle of their way of life, Zuni is far worse than it was then. Every cholera vibrio in the water is as important as the most important kachina.

I'm not opposed to togetherness as such. Some of the most socially happy hours I have ever spent were with the tiny Havasupai tribe deep in their canyon amongst their peach trees. The Havasupai were at least as well integrated as the Zuni, but they were not so damn compulsive about it. In fact, they weren't compulsive at all. They just seemed to thoroughly enjoy being with one another, securely locked away from all the world. In those days the trail to the bottom of the canyon constituted a minor mountaineering feat.

Toward the end of the summer I worked my way up to White Rocks, the Ute reservation in the southeast foothills of the Unitas. I don't want to sound prejudiced, but, although they treated me royally, I believe the Northern Ute in those days were the most disagreeable people outside the island of Manhattan in the Western hemisphere. They were pretty savage. Many men were still alive who had taken scalps, but they were in the first shock of reservation demoralization and withdrawal. They were dirty, cruel, drunken, and promiscuous is too nice a word for their sexual habits. The moral atmosphere, I imagine, was something like that of a Puerto Rican gang of delinquent kids in New York today—for obviously much the same reasons. The Anglican missionary at White Rocks was a friend of many Anglo-Catholic clergy whom I knew in the East, and I went to Mass and Sunday school and listened to rocky-faced old warriors sing with the kids:

> "Washing and wiping the dishes,
> Mending the baby's clothes,
> Working and praying for Jesus,
> Yes, there is room for us aw-ull."

Father Grant had a couple of little kids who showed up years later in San Francisco and became close friends of mine. One of them, the artist Richard Ayer, gave me his Missal, and my daughter Mary still carries it to church.

Father Grant died years ago in California. But a far more extraordinary man, one of the most remarkable people I've ever met in my life, was the missionary in the San Juan country. An aged man, he is still active, traveling over the deserts on horseback and saying Mass in the open air on altars of piled rocks. His vestments had been made for him by the Indians: leather chasubles ornamented like Navaho sand paintings, and albs of heavy cotton woven on Navaho looms and decorated with rainbows, clouds, terraces, and phallic symbols. Some Chicago musician had written for him a "Mass of Father Jogues." The Indians sat around and beat on drums and sang the Gloria and Credo and Sanctus to tunes that sounded a little like "Indianola" when they didn't sound like "Dardanella." It was most impressive.

At the end of the summer I was up in Jackson Hole and I headed east for the fall gathering on the Crow Indian reservation. By this time I was a fair horse wrangler and competent cook, so I got a pretty good job. In those days this was the last of the great, spectacular roundups. There were all sorts of cattle being driven in from what I guess was the largest single chunk of unfenced good range left in the country. This was real Wild West show cowboying. Part of the time I worked as a circle rider at night. Roping and even efficient driving were beyond me. I never really tried to learn. I just don't like cows. If forced to choose, I'd rather be a sheepherder. Most of the time I cooked: sourdough pancakes and steak for breakfast; steak and potatoes, canned tomatoes and canned peaches, sourdough bread at noon; steak, potatoes, canned tomatoes, canned peaches, sourdough bread for supper; boiled coffee, boiled tea, and always extra saleratus bread for those who didn't like sourdough. With few exceptions the steaks had to be thoroughly burned through and through, but I and one or two others ate rare meat and were kidded about it at every meal. It was the hardest work I have ever done but it was continuously exciting. The atmosphere was one of unrelieved melodrama, a little like living in the midst of a revolution. Away from the noise and the milling men, horses, and cattle, I suppose due to the scope of the job, it had tremendous exultation. Thoroughly worn out, dark as a Ute Indian, and trained down like a boxer, I headed back to Chicago, riding in the crummy behind a trainload of cows.

This job was a thorough nuisance. I got no pleasure out of running along the top of cattle cars, least of all in catching my meals on the fly. We never stopped long enough in towns to eat a proper meal, and then we'd lay over, waiting for a highball or passenger on some siding for hours in the midst of the prairie. Every time the train stopped I had to run alongside with a rod and pry loose horns and hoofs caught in the slats, and sometimes risk my life getting up a beast that had fallen down. Feeding and watering them, at least, was not my job.

Someplace in Nebraska we were held up for a long time outside a little town, on a siding just off a trestle over a creek. It was early evening, and there was a campfire under the cottonwoods on the bank of the creek. I went down to visit. It was a jungle, and the bums were cooking up slum gullion in a ten-gallon oilcan. They invited me to have some. There were carrots, turnips, potatoes, sweet corn, peas—a conventional mulligan except for the meat, which was pigs' tails.

"Where'd you get all the pigs' tails?" I asked. "Is there a slaughterhouse in town?"

Nobody said anything for a minute, and then the old man who was doing the cooking said, "You don't work for the railroad, do you, nursing them cows?"

"No," I said, "I'm just a workaway. I've already been paid off by the cattle outfit."

"Well," he said, "that being the case, I guess we can tell him. Before your cows were parked on that siding, there was a load of pigs there, most of the morning. I hope they didn't bleed to death before they got to Omaha."

CHAPTER 35

When I got back to Chicago I had a fair amount of money from the summer's work. I got a two-room apartment on Chicago Avenue and decided to fix it up as an exact setting for the kind of work and reading that I wanted to do that winter. Life had been happening more or less haphazardly ever since I left school. This was going to be a deliberately planned winter. I painted the walls a pale, soft blue, straight over all the woodwork, painted the ceiling white, covered the floor with a dull rust ragrug. A couch covered with blue denim, one old oak office chair with a blue denim-covered seat, two Windsor chairs, a classic walnut-topped table, blue chambray curtains, a small white plaster reproduction of Greek sculpture and a matching white plaster thing of cylinders and cubes by myself, two very geometric pictures, Vermeer's "Lady About to Throw a Pitcher Out the Window," a roll-top desk, and an easel—these were the room's contents. It was like a crystal, a perfect room for high thinking.

I started in right away, and I was lucky. I didn't have a clear idea of what I wanted, but some mysterious fate took care of me. I started systematically reading through Plato, and discovered A. E. Taylor and Burnet, and then Heath's great edition of Euclid and his *History of Greek Mathematics*. I got all the Hambidge *Dynamic Symmetry* books, and from them went on to a wonderful old-fashioned textbook of curve tracing, the like of which I've never seen again. I became interested in the mathematics of perspective, and found that there was something called projective geometry. This led to a momentous discovery. I brought home from the library Alfred North Whitehead's textbook on the subject. I must be one of the few people of my generation who came at Whitehead through this side door. I was entranced. Even the vocabulary thrilled me and harmonic pencils crept into my poetry for years afterward.

The same luck that had provided just the right new people in the past was with me again. Sam Putnam was in those days incomparably the most civilized and best-read man around literary Chicago. We became much closer friends than we had been in the past and spent long hours in fervid discussion of medieval poetry and Renaissance Platonism. He introduced me to a young man, little older than me, who was exactly the right comrade to share the special intellectual world which was beginning to effect me.

In those days Sam Lipschitz looked like a young Ronald Colman, with pink cheeks, active eyebrows, witty eyes, and carefully tended mustache. He had an extremely precise manner of speaking, and a repertory of ratiocinative gestures. He would chase an illusive idea rolling an invisible silver pellet in front of one eye, or twist his finger like a corkscrew into some knotty problem. If, in their young days, somebody had thought of casting Adolphe Menjou in the role of Paul Valéry, the result would have been Sam Lipschitz. He had read a great deal more of the sort of thing that was beginning to fascinate me, and introduced me to a whole library of books, a universe of discourse—that very term an invention of this universe of discourse. All I had read was Whitehead's *Axioms of Projective Geometry* and Bertrand Russell's early *Analysis of Geometry*. Together, Sam and I went through *Principia Mathematica* and the extraordinarily inventive and convincing cosmology of McTeggart, a world system as plausible and impossible as Judge Cooling's. We read all the criticism of McTeggart from the other side—Moore and Broad and the rest. The next step was that tar baby, *The Meaning of Meaning,* into which we tumbled headlong and were lost to sight for weeks. One evening Sam showed up in tremendous excitement. He had just discovered the book of books—of course—Wittgenstein's *Tractatus Logicus-philosophicus.* It was like being turned on to some incredibly efficient dope. We did everything but number our paragraphs with Roman numerals and our sentences with Greek letters. In all our conversation for weeks we pulled and twisted and gnawed every arrogant apothegm till we had exhausted it. One afternoon I went out to the beach, and walked up and down in a late-autumn storm, and came home and read a novel for relaxation; I still remember what it was—Conrad's *Victory.* In the back of my mind something began to build up, a vast conviction that had been growing in secret. That evening I opened the door to Sam, anticipating the possible end of our friendship. He came in and sat down at the desk and looked out the window. There on the desk was a stack of notes on the *Tractatus.* Sam looked sick. I said, "What's the matter, have you got a hangover?" "A hangover?" he said, and paused. "A fourth-dimensional vista." I knew. "It just hit me, too," I said. "I've been thinking about it all afternoon. That stuff is absolute bullshit. It's just a kind of bohemian *épaté*-ism." We went back over Wittgenstein to take him to pieces but midway we lost heart. "You've got to admit,"

Sam said, "it's a kind of poem." "Like Shelley," I said. "Like Shelley," Sam said. We returned to the lemmas of Pappus.

Sam had a friend, a young Greek scholar, who was Paul Shorey's brightest student, and the three of us embarked on a course of group translations of lyric poetry and philosophical prose. I returned to those states of exultation which I had discovered in my own translation of Sappho's "Apple Orchard," but this time with companions equally exalted. On my urging, we started reading medieval Latin, and every night this fellow, whose name I wish I could remember, showed up with a volume under his arm. We read the prose and poetry of Abelard. We started on Aquinas, and then Sam discovered a new book— Harris' *Duns Scotus*. Scotus was already a favorite of mine and since he was many times as complicated and mystifying and orderly as Wittgenstein, he kept us busy till Christmas. With him we read Charles Peirce, a startlingly similar avatar.

I have no memory whatsoever of any girls being around during these months. All my old girls were out of town. No new ones turned up, and I didn't seek any out. During all the intellectual excitement a kind of monasticism had crept up on me unawares.

I did have one outside activity. This was the winter of the last, and in many ways one of the best, bohemian restaurants. Harold Mann, Billy McKenzie, and I decided to start a clean, orderly place that served good food and which by its very atmosphere would eliminate the nuts and attract only the kind of people with whom we ourselves would enjoy spending an evening. At the very beginning I must have had a little money in it because I remember shopping for the furniture and equipment at Hartman's, the big time-payment furniture house where we discovered we could get unlimited credit with practically no down payment or security. The place was unpretentious and homelike, with peasant dishes and gingham tablecloths and a circle of easy chairs around the big fireplace. This sounds perfectly ordinary now, but it was far from being so in those days. One of the first people to wander in while we were fixing it up was a young advertising man who worked for J. Walter Thompson. We didn't have a name and he had an elaborate theory based on careful psychological analysis of such concepts as Lincoln's doctor's dog. He suggested that we should name it after a beast that he was sure would become the most popular of all advertising mascots. So we called it the Penguin Coffee Shop, the first place except for Frances Midner's bookshop in New York, which was its contemporary, ever to bear this name. There was no doubt but what this young man was marked for great success. His name was Arnold Gingrich; in the next year or so the founder, and to this day the editor, of *Esquire*.

After the place opened I had no business interest in it, but I took all my meals there. In the course of time Gingrich and a young photographer, Fritz Roder, bought out all the owners. I have a dim memory of a period in which a considerable portion of the better-dressed members of Chicago's bohemia were busy selling their interest in the place to one another, but it ended with Gingrich, and I am sure it's the only thing he ever lost money on.

For its brief life of one winter the Penguin was a wonderful place. The cook was a very black Negro called Panama, who could cook any dish of any nationality. He had been a sea cook and a chef in clubs in Shanghai and Buenos Aires. After dinner until midnight there was better conversation around the fire than could be found anywhere else in the country, and that includes the Brevoort and the Algonquin.

After Christmas the elaborately constructed intellectual tableaux I had made for myself must have worn out suddenly. I closed out my two-room personal Platonic Academy and went to New York.

I rented a basement apartment on Grove Street just off Sheridan Square. Upstairs lived two young poets—Allen Tate and, directly over me, Hart Crane. The week I moved in Crane was busy writing one of his best poems. At that period he was writing everything to what he considered jazz—in this case, Bert Williams' "The Moon Shines on the Moonshine." On his phonograph he had one of those old tin contrivances which picked up the needle and sent it back to the beginning of the record with a loud squeak. Hour after hour, day and night, I could hear coming through the ceiling "So still de night, in de ole distillery, de moon shine white on de ole machinery." It wasn't jazz, but it produced "Whitely, while benzine rinsings of the moon dissolve . . ." At the end of the street was St. Luke's, a pre-Revolutionary church run by Father Schlueter, one of the most remarkable men in the history of Anglo-Catholicism in America. I started going there regularly. At home, having Hart Crane for an overhead neighbor, my place became a continuous shambles of drunken hilarity. About the middle of February I was baptized, and that night my baptismal party was one of the historic Village brawls. The next day I left in a snowstorm for Holy Cross Monastery on the Hudson across from Poughkeepsie.

On the way up I discovered that I had lost my ticket, but the Irish conductor, when he found out that I was going to a monastery, told me to forget about it. Instead of taking the West Side Line and getting off in West Park, I went to Poughkeepsie and crossed the river to discover—afoot with a suitcase in a below-zero night with ten inches of fresh snow on the ground—that West Park was several miles on up the river. By the time I got there I felt very holy and penitent, like Henry the Fourth at Canossa. The monastery lay on a bench above the Hudson in a little meadow surrounded with woods, a big Georgian hotel-like building for living quarters, and a little rough, native-stone Romanesque chapel all shrouded in snow. Everything was dark and I pounded on all the doors without rousing anybody. Finally a long white face above a white habit appeared at one of the windows. The community was at evening prayers, and they had ceased to expect me. After supper of milk and bread and cheese, I was ushered to a typical rough-plastered monastic cell about eight by ten feet, with a cot, a commode and washbasin, a table and chair, a crucifix, a prie-dieu. At dawn I was awakened for morning prayers and Mass. I should explain that the regular prayers said by priests and members of religious orders are said eight times a day. In a semicontemplative order like Holy Cross they are sung in chapel, except when the members are traveling. They are called Matins, Lauds, Prime, Tierce, Sext, Nones, Vespers, and Compline. After Mass we all went in individually to the refectory and helped ourselves to breakfast from a large sideboard. At the other meals the community filed first into the chapel reciting a Psalm, and then back to the refectory, where we were served by novices. No one spoke at meals or, for that matter, at any other time except on feast days and Sundays, and during meals a lector read a brief life of the saint of that day and then a continued selection from some religious book. Although I was just a guest and not a postulant, I was given a white habit without cowl or scapular (a scapular is a long panel of cloth which hangs down to the hem of the skirt, front and back, and is worn only by those who have taken final vows). I took part in all the offices and other activities, served every morning at Mass, and otherwise comported myself like a member of the community.

The Order of the Holy Cross had been founded in America at the beginning of the century and was modeled, more or less, on a combination of the Augustinian and Dominican rules. The priests of the order spent half their time traveling as preachers, and the other half at the monastery, living a rather strict and cloistered life. Most of the founders were still alive, a small group of impressive, white-haired men.

The chapel had been built by Ralph Adams Cram and was a perfect example of his Romanesque work. He had planned to have it decorated with frescoes or mosaics. For this reason, and others, the order was anxious to obtain an artist member. Several postulants had appeared, and some had even served their novitiates, but they had all left after obtaining an expensive art education paid for by the order. At one end of the building, above the kitchen, there was a large studio with a big skylight, an extremely fancy easel, and every imaginable kind of artist's equipment. Into this I was ushered, and invited to make myself free. I had hardly expected anything like this. I had expected that the new men at the monastery—"fish," as they are called in prison and the Army—spent their time scrubbing the toilets, wearing hair shirts, and living on bread and water. When I came back to my cell after lunch, the table had been moved out and a desk and typewriter substituted. The monastery had the best small library I have ever seen. There was everything anyone would ever want in theology and related subjects, but there was also a vast amount of secular philosophy right up to date—all of Ogden's Library of Philosophy, Psychology, and Scientific Method, and all of Muirhead's Library of Philosophy, for instance, and all the leading journals. So, if I wished, I could continue the regimen I had set up for myself in Chicago. The food was simple—I suppose, monastic, but the cook was an excellent chef. So even though it was Lent we certainly ate well, if modestly. Immediately above the monastery the Catskills rose steeply over the river—one of the most beautiful settings in America.

Every day I painted, prayed, wrote, and walked through the snow-bound forest. Next door had been the home of the naturalist John Burroughs, recently dead. I made friends with his family and was permitted to use his little cabin off up in the woods. So began what is certainly the happiest period in my life.

I had arrived on the Sunday before Ash Wednesday, so I was able to experience the unfolding of the great two months' long liturgical drama of Lent, Holy Week, and Eastertide. I suppose I am just a natural-born monk. Everything about the life satisfied me completely. I felt no temptation for any of the worldly pleasures. Sex, for instance, never entered my mind. If I had been exalted riding night herd or climbing in the Cascades, or fishing in a mountain stream, I spent the days at Holy Cross transfigured. It was all one orderly rapture.

My interest in Catholicism had been more or less intellectual, and I had always fought shy of the common Anglo-Catholic passion for ritual and holy millinery. But life in a contemplative order like Holy Cross is just like in L'Oblat, only more so. In fact, an Anglo-Catholic order like Holy Cross, with its insistence on liturgical purity is far more solemn and beautiful than, at least in those days, anything it would have been possible to find in all but a very few Roman Catholic orders in Europe. Not Shakespeare nor any Greek tragedy could compare with the celebration of Lent and Holy Week. It was a kind of aesthetic possession which took over the personality completely and swept it away. At least in this season of the year, and in such places as Holy Cross, Christianity takes on all the character of an anthropological religion, as linked to the realities of life as the rites of the pre-Homeric Greeks or an African tribe—the stark, pre-Christian mourning of Ash Wednesday; the increasing sorrow and penitence of Lent, broken only by the Consolation of the Blessed Virgin and the Vespers of Mid-Lent Sunday; the distraught sorrow of Passion Week among the shrouded statues; the gathering darkness of Holy Week, with candles going out one by one; the bare white chapel in the cold spring night; brief rejoicing over the Blessed Sacrament on Holy Thursday, and the almost abstract tragedy of the chanting of the Passion at the Mass of the Presanctified. And then Easter, exploding with the completely pagan rites of the New Year on Holy Saturday and reaching a golden climax in the Easter Sequence—all this sung in the purest plainsong by a choir of twenty to thirty voices, trained not musically but by years of devotion.

Immersed in it, I found it totally convincing. At the end of Eastertide I went for a long walk by the river and through the mountains. All the trees were in bud and as varied in color, but far more subtle, than the forest of the New York autumn. Birds were singing everywhere. The underbrush was full of migrating warblers. That evening I had a long talk with the novice master. I explained to him that I found myself adapted to the monastic life. There was nothing whatever about it that I didn't like. I had felt no hardships but had enjoyed every minute of it, more than anything I had ever experienced. But I had no vocation whatsoever. Father Anderson was deeply moved and assured me that he understood me perfectly and respected my decision. "I think, Kenneth," he said, "this experience will turn out to be more valuable to you than you can know now. Let's hope it will always provide a memory which will be a focus and stable foundation for all your later life." And so it was. I went down to New York the next day.

As is apparent in this story, all my life I have been attracted by Catholicism. But what attracted me was not its Christianity, but its paganism. The Scholastic Philosophers entertained me not because they were apologists for Jesus but because they were refinements of Aristotle. The liturgical life of the Church moved me because it echoes the most ancient responses to the turning of the year and the changing seasons, and the rhythms of animal and human life. For me the Sacraments transfigured the rites of passage, the physical facts of the human condition—birth, adolescence, sexual intercourse, vocation, sickness and death, communion, penance. Catholicism still provides a structure of acts, individual and at the same time communal, physical responses to life. I have no objection to its mysteries; the easiest thing in the world to believe is a mystery. Utter impossibilities—that the infant Jesus came through the maidenhead of the Blessed Virgin like light through glass and that she in turn was assumed bodily into heaven, or that the fallen chief of the Seraphim and his fellows, metaphysically pure spirits without existence in time or space or contingency, are punished in a physical fire of endless duration—all this nonsense is as believable as the mysteries of Isis were by Plutarch or Proclus. What is absurd is precisely what St. Paul said—the theogony, the concept of the Deity and His action in history. It is inconceivable, standing in a painted and gilded room, the boudoir of a long-dead courtesan in the Vatican, that this is the historical manifestation of the redemptive power of the creativity of the universe. By this I do not wish to imply that I disapprove of the sexual life of the Renaissance Popes. Quite the contrary. The most offensive element in Catholicism, for me, is its sexual morality, and I believe that the hysterical frustration which it has engendered is the root of the incredible violence and dishonesty of the history of Western man since Constantine. I don't think puritanism is especially Protestant. The modern Church is unfairly criticized for its neopuritanism. The permissive morality of the Renaissance and eighteenth century which survived until recent times in the Latin countries was really an episode; the puritanism of the great medieval Scholastics and the Fathers of the Church is much more rigorous than that of Calvin, Luther, and John Knox. Mary Stuart would have had a far rougher time than she did had she fallen into the hands of St. Augustine.

Protestantism, at least in its orthodox forms, has always filled me with loathing. Its basic spiritual dilemma is simply incomprehensible to me. I have never found anything in my experience, internal or external, to justify a vision of the world suspended from two metaphysical poles, one utterly contingent and one absolute in every conceivable sense, and both lost in the night of nonbeing. For this reason not only is the whole Augustinian tradition meaningless to me—Kierkegaard has always seemed to me to be a miserable and silly man, badly in need of what the psychiatrists call "help"—but the existentialist dilemma which has haunted French philosophy since Descartes is likewise meaningless to me. Not only that, but what is after all only a subtle modification of it, the epistemological worry of the English, is at least as meaningless.

What I have gained from Christianity as such is a belief in ethical activism. This, I suppose, has come more from my own pietistic ancestors: I have never noticed it to be very much in evidence looking around me at High Mass, let alone in the faces of the congregation in the Marble Collegiate Church. It was not until many years later when I met a few people in the Quakers and the Fellowship of Reconciliation during the Second World War and when I first read Albert Schweitzer that I ever encountered it among professed Christians. That's not strictly true—it's there in Aquinas, or even Augustine, the belief in a continuously outgoing love and the binding force of a community of love, but nobody seems to pay much attention to it.

From the very beginning, when in my early adolescence I first started to think at all, I have always been continuously aware of what Marx calls human self-alienation in modern life—the lack of significant work, the lack of mechanisms in society to give meaning to the most important events and situations in life, the lack of organic community. Someday I suppose that if society does not destroy itself, it will have to evolve those things again. Meanwhile I still go to Mass if I can find a place where the sermons are not too degrading and the performance is conducted with dignity. As a matter of fact, the only Roman parish church in the world outside of monastic chapels that has ever completely satisfied me is Saint Séverin in the slums of Paris. So I go to the local Anglo-Catholic church in America and to monastic churches in Europe.

I am not sure that I can answer the question "Are you religious?" much less "Do you have a religion?" Lord Acton, perhaps the most sophisticated and intelligent sceptic of his day, said toward the end of his life that he had never suffered an intellectual doubt and that he had no sympathy with Modernist Catholics like Father Tyrrell and their struggles to adjust Catholicism to contemporary science and philosophy. Again, when the decrees of the first Vatican Council were finally promulgated, Acton said to friends who suggested that he become an Anglican that he saw no reason why he should change his religion just because the Pope had changed his. Behind these remarks lies something quite different from wit or paradox—the primacy of the religious experience. It is religious empiricism, true, but not in the fashionable sense of the word which confuses empiricism with instrumentalism or pragmatism in religious matters.

Beliefs are unstable things at best and an intelligent man holds millions of them in his life, almost all of them fugitive and contradictory. Furthermore, belief is easily come by. It is easier to believe in miracles than in the miracle of determinate order. Facts, happenings, experiences are different. We are not asked if we accept them; we discover ourselves living them.

From earliest childhood I have had not rarely but habitually the kind of experiences that are called visionary. They came long before the possibility of intellectual or even emotional qualification and they have never acquired such qualification in any definite or enduring sense. Not only has such experience been like that described by William James and other unbiased psychologists of mysticism; the first experience I remember clearly was like many such cases in precise detail. I was about four or five years old sitting on the carriage stone at the curb in front of our house on Marion Street in Elkhart, Indiana. It was early summer. A wagon loaded high with new-mown hay passed close to me on the street. An awareness, not a feeling, of timeless, space-less, total bliss occupied me or I occupied it completely. I do not want to use terms like "overwhelmed me" or "I was rapt away" or any other that would imply the possession of myself by anything external, much less abnormal. On the contrary, this seemed to be my normal and natu-ral life which was going on all the time and my sudden acute conscious-ness of it only a matter of attention. This is a sophisticated description in the vocabulary of an adult but as a five-year-old child I had no ves-tige of doubt but what this was me—not "the real me" as distinguished from some illusory ego but just me. I talked to my mother about it, and the curious thing is that although I remember that she was sympathetic I have no memory whatsoever of what she said.

Anyone who has ever read the slightest moiety of the literature on this subject will recognize the universality of the experience. Before I was ten years older I had encountered the same experiences in authors as different as Richard Jeffries, H. G. Wells, Huneker, Rousseau, and some improbable eighteenth-century rationalist, I believe Diderot—including the new-mown hay. As is well known, this latter factor occurs so often in autobiographical literature that people have searched for a hypnogenetic principle among the esters and glucosides to be found in ripe grass. I am inclined to think that ripe grass is only one of many factors that enter into the composition of the poet's rare day in June when everything can actually slip into perfect tune and the situation triggers total realization.

I have very little confidence in the primacy of hallucinogens whether self-induced in the blood stream by yogic manipulation of the auto-nomic nervous system, taken as drugs or manufactured in the body in morbid conditions of fever or come upon by accident in the environ-ment. All of these things have happened to me. Much later in this story I will describe my experiments with Yoga. I do not believe such trig-gers are either necessary or desirable. In fact, I believe that vision which is so conditioned is self-defeating because it must always be ex-ceptional.

I believe that an ever-increasing capacity for recollection and tran-scendence is developed by a kind of life rather than by manipulation. Buddhism is certainly pure religious empiricism. It has no beliefs, only the simply and purely defined religious experience which becomes for the experiencers an always accessible and ever-abiding present reality. The foundation for this is neither nervous-system gymnastics nor theo-logical notions. It is the Noble Eight Fold Path, whose culmination is the "unruffledness"—Nirvana—which underlies reality.

So likewise the vision of Christian contemplation. This is not something you see like an apparition, something that comes over you in a trance. It is a quality of habitude, the result of a kind of life, of innumerable acts done. Most of these acts have apparently nothing to do with mysticism as its practices are described in books. Almost all of them are simply the ordinary responses of the commonplace Christian life. There is only a kind of spectral rainbow or halo around the brilliant center of illumination which is the region of the practice of mysticism as such, but this depends upon the transcendent experience which is central to all while the transcendence itself is the end and culmination of the specially organized pattern of quite ordinary experience. For this reason the antinomian and sensationalist pursuit of vision which has become a fashion since the Second World War has had no appeal to me whatsoever. I think it is probably true that this is, as three thousand years of religious thinkers have said it was, the opposite of what it pretends to be. Certainly the evidence of contemporary fadism is that religious sensationalism results invariably in demoralization and disaster.

I am a Catholic—if I am one—not because I believe anything, whether I do or not, but because I do certain kinds of things and I do those things because by doing them I can hold to a habit of life which insures the accessibility of bliss of vision, of total knowledge of significance. Since this is an absolute qualification of life it is impossible to qualify it in detail or aspect. Does this mean that I believe that the world experienced by sense and reason in which I seem to live is only the surface of a world incomparably vaster and utterly different in kind in which life is really lived? Possibly so, but a statement like this is a belief, an interpretation which changes through the years while the experience is unchanging.

CHAPTER 36

Those were the days before the sea was organized, and it was easy to get workaway jobs. Over in Hoboken you could walk on a vessel, hand the skipper twenty dollars, and go all the way to Piraeus. I shipped out as a mess steward on a filthy rust bucket of one of the many Ellerman lines. It crossed to the Channel ports on both sides, came back around the Irish Sea and back across to Baltimore, and from there went down to Buenos Aires, which I think was its port of registry. I made the trip over and back, and this is all the seafaring work I've ever wanted. It was exactly like being locked up for a month in a cheap flophouse. We didn't, as a matter of fact, go to Liverpool and Belfast that trip, but came straight home from Plymouth. The longest layover was in Dunkirk. I bribed myself shore leave for the whole time and went up to Paris. The first couple of days I rushed about meeting the people who had been heroes of my imagination: Aragon, Soupault, Tzara, Cendrars, and the *Esprit Nouveau* and *Der Stijl* group, who were all in Paris. Many of these meetings took place at a party given by a disheveled and disreputable Polish countess in an even more disheveled studio back of Rodin's statue of Balzac. I think she still lives there and still gives parties to the latest things on Montparnasse.

I didn't like it. It seemed to me that the whole scene was corrupted by a faint but perceptible odor of fraud. I think now it was really the caste mannerisms of even the most revolutionary French intellectuals. American intellectual life, at least among the avant-garde of the Twenties, was a genuinely classless society. People came from family backgrounds of every description, probably a slight majority of them from the working class, and had an ethic or social morality derived from the Socialist and Anarchist movement. This was not political; it was a very strictly held code of personal relationships. Several years were to pass before the Trip to Kharkov, and the Frenchmen I met were not even nominally revolutionary—except the painters. I met Ferdinand Leger briefly one afternoon at a table in the Dôme. He was really the only one I liked. He certainly was proletarian enough; or, to be more accurate, he had completely the personality of a French skilled mechanic, and this he never lost until the day of his death. I sat for a week on *café terrasses* in Paris at its best—mid-June—debating whether to go back to the ship. That isn't quite true. Most of my time was spent walking hundreds of kilometers, systematically through every museum and all over the streets of Paris, until the small hours of the morning. All the time the necessity for what I knew would be a fundamental decision turned over and over in my mind. The one person whose advice was of value was Alexander Berkman, vastly changed from the man I had seen in my childhood. I didn't know it but he was already dying of cancer, and he killed himself a couple of years later. He said, "Go back. There is more for you in the Far West than there is here. You can probably become famous here but you'll just be another one." I went back to the ship, and in July was in Billings, Montana, with Bob, my first zebra dun.

I worked for a couple of weeks in Billings as a fry cook, and then went on up to Kalispell. Then I went over to the west side of Glacier National Park and got a job taking care of the horses for a large firecrew base. That year it seemed the entire west side of the northern Rockies was on fire. Fighting fire is without a doubt one of the hardest jobs known to man, and I managed to avoid it, but I certainly worked hard enough. Toward the end of August I quit, intending to go down to Missoula and meet the people who ran the literary magazine at the university.

I was camped one night on the edge of the forest by a beautiful Montana stream flowing over a bed of polychrome cobbles. While I was frying a grayling for supper an old man rode up. After we'd passed the time of day he asked if I was looking for work. I said that I was and he said, "I've got a crop of alfalfa to get in and some cows to bring down from the forest and the thrashing crew will be around in a couple of days. I've got a bad leg and could use some help." I thought maybe I could help him out for a couple of weeks. Then he said, "Before we close the deal I'd just like to know—do you carry a Red card?" I wasn't at all sure whether the answer was supposed to be yes or no. But I took my IWW card out of my wallet and showed it to him. He said, "I don't like to hire anybody who hasn't got enough sense to get himself organized." And that's all he ever said about the subject all the time I ever knew him.

When he got off the horse to help me break camp and saddle up, he was as bowlegged as though he'd spent his infancy with his legs tied round a log. His name was Billy Orville and he'd driven the last stage from Cody, Wyoming, to Billings, Montana. He'd been to Paris with Buffalo Bill and had fought in the last Indian wars as a scout. He had all the characteristics which fiction and the movies made standard equipment for a Western old-timer and in addition he was amazingly literate and well informed and one of the wisest men I've ever met. He'd been everywhere and done everything from the Rockies to the Sierras that there was to do except farm and now in his old age he'd retired to eighty acres of bottom land and a section of sparsely wooded range.

His wife was a gentle, sweet-natured old lady with pure-white hair and pure-blue eyes. She was, for an intermountain woman, quite a sophisticated cook. They had an ancient portable harmonium. The second night I was there she played and sang for a couple of hours, an impressive repertory of the popular songs of the Seventies and Eighties. It turned out that she had been one of those dance-hall girls made so famous by the movies, and he had married her in Deadwood forty years before.

When he was a young fellow starting out just like me as a horse wrangler and cookee, a horse had reared, tipped over backward on him, and broken his hip. Now that he was old, the hip gave him quite a bit of trouble. Besides the hip, I think he'd outgrown any passionate belief in hard work. The job was very easy. We'd get in a load of hay, let the horses rest, have a couple of drinks of black-fig wine, and then pitch the load up into the barn. Then it'd be time for a nice leisurely lunch and lots of conversation and reminiscences. After all, the entire opening of the West had taken place in his lifetime. There was little that had ever happened that he didn't know about and practically no place he hadn't been. He'd been a gambler, a U. S. marshal, a trick roper, as well as a plain cowboy and an ordinary prospector. Unlike most prospectors, he seemed to have been moderately successful. In fact, the capital to develop his homestead had come from some mining property in the mountains just above us and the cabins there served as a base for his summer range. After we got the wheat thrashed and the hay in we went up and camped there for a week and gathered about a hundred head of stock and brought them back to the valley for the winter. We spent most of our time fishing and brought in a couple of deer. We had a Nez Percé as a helper on our fall gathering and he and Billy sat around the campfire and swapped yarns every night until midnight while the autumn stars came up the sky.

When the job was over I hitchhiked south through the intermountain country, riding freight some of the time because there was very little auto traffic in those days, to El Paso.

At a party at Duncan Aikman's, the literary critic of an El Paso paper, I met a man who was planning to drive to Mexico City. He had a Ford, specially rebuilt and equipped with hard rubber tires and a Ruxton

axle. There were no through roads in those days from the American
border to Mexico City, and the worst connections among back-country
roads were those south of El Paso. We drove over most of northern
Mexico, and eventually had to abandon the car and go on by train.
The political revolution was dying down, but intellectually and artis-
tically Mexico was at the height of the wave. It was all very free and
open, even riotous. Nobody had become so famous as to be inaccessible.
The person I liked best was Siqueiros, in those days a still completely
genuine man, uncorrupted by politics. Orozco was the most impressive,
but he was inaccessible, not out of snobbery but because of his lonely
greatness. Rivera was simply dreadful, even then. The rest were better
than their French counterparts, but they suffered from the same caste
faults. There was a café rather like the Dôme where they all hung out
along with heavily armed politicians, bullfighters, criminals, prostitutes,
and burlesque girls. The most spectacular person of all was a photographer, artist, model, high-class courtesan, and Mata Hari for the
Comintern, Tina Modotti. She was the heroine of a lurid political assas-
sination and was what I guess is called an international beauty. I had
outgrown my fondness for the Kollontai type and she terrified me.
She was exterminated in the Great Purge. A wiry little tart, who later
became an actress, used to dance naked on the table, clad only in a
rhinestone glued to her navel, while people banged guitars and everybody shouted. I think at the time she was Siqueiros' girl; at least she
was always at his table, and years later when she was rich and famous,
killed herself because she was about to have an illegitimate baby.

One day a friend of Tina Modotti's came up to the table—a tall, well-
fleshed, natural pale blonde who looked rather like a Danish or Dutch
girl and was, as a matter of fact, an Austrian. She was one of the city's
most expensive prostitutes. She announced that she was about to go on
vacation to Oaxaca. I said that I would rather see Oaxaca than any
place in Mexico. "Why don't you come along with me?" she said. "I
haven't very much money," I said. "That's all right," she said. "I've got
plenty. Besides, the hotel won't cost much. It's run by a friend of mine,
a landsman."

To Oaxaca we went, and I lived for two weeks in a hotel on
the Paseo, an ancient palace with immense whitewashed rooms, and
massive black furniture, and, best of all, with excellent Austrian cooking
prepared specially for us. I loathe Mexican food, which has always
seemed to me only a slight improvement on Northern Ute cuisine. We
visited all the monuments and met all the people. Oaxaca was at the
height of its revolution and practically an independent country. We
danced most of the nights, and when we weren't dancing we were
singing and watching other people dance, and falling asleep in the

dawn, exhausted with lovemaking, our heads full of guitar music. When the two weeks were over I came straight back to the States. They say that Arthur Waley, the translator of *The Tale of Genji*, has never been to the Orient and has refused fabulous offers to teach in Japan. I have never had any desire to go back to Mexico.

It was early winter when I got back to Chicago, and the first day walking down Chicago Avenue I met my landlord of the year before. My attic room had just been vacated and most of my old furnishings had been stored with him. I moved back in, prepared to start where I had left off. Bard had opened a bookshop across the street and provided the only focus of any sort of intellectual bohemia on the Near North Side. The back room was full of people all afternoon and most of the evening. The rest of Chicago's bohemia had already gone into decline. Most of the old places, including the Dill Pickle, had been taken over by the Organization. The older generation was at last succumbing to a ten years' diet of bad moonshine. The people who hung around Bard were mostly quite young. The set of Jewish girls, fresh from the University, whom I had first met a couple of years before, now were maturing the fashionable intellectual causes of the next twenty years. The arguments were all about Trotskyism, Stalinism, Lovestoneism, Humanism, Gurdjieff, the Southern Agrarians, Thomism. There were even budding exponents of the folklorist school of the Southwest— young George Milburn, for instance. Bard gave variety in beard and yamilke with a passionate defense of Neo-Judaism, but it took the German gas ovens to start the movement which eventually overtook and surpassed him. In those days he was looked on as plain crazy.

One of the habitués of the place was a sickly, fat, pustuled young man who, to distinguish himself from the common gossip, called himself, not a Thomist, but a neo-Augustinian. He came at this via *À Rebours*, *Là-bas*, Gilles le Rais, and capers considerably more disgusting than those of the set around the Tea Leaf Shop in New York. He was married to a seventeen-year-old girl whom he used in sadistic, coprophilic rituals of his own devising. He eventually became a professor at a Catholic university and at the same time a notorious Stalinist, a borer from within the Catholic Church. He died some fifteen years later, I suppose in the odor of some kind of sanctity. His child wife had long since predeceased him in a madhouse. I had never met him. One day Bard left me to tend the bookshop and he came in. He had been browsing around for about ten minutes when I got a good look at him. I got up from the desk and walked over and said, "I don't know who you are but I can't stand you in this place another minute. Get out of here before I take you apart." He turned and fled.

With this single exception, and he never came back when I was in the place, the crowd around the bookshop was nothing if not wholesome. After all, out of it were to come many of the leaders of the Proletarian Thirties, self-sacrificing idealists if there ever were any. Curiously enough, these people, possibly because they almost all came from well-organized families of Jewish craftsmen, have survived the sacrifices of the Thirties. They sacrificed everything, from physical comfort to moral integrity. But those who did not die in Spain managed to rehabilitate themselves and are all fairly happy and successful people.

CHAPTER 37

I had come back to Chicago with a firm resolve to get married. Since I had organized my whole life and all its values in terms of fulfillment in what I suppose is a kind of platonic love, a total glorified comradeship, holy matrimony, it was about time I did something about it. I have a dim memory of having, in the course of the winter, proposed to three or four girls, all those I had ever cared for who were still about. I have a feeling that I was turned down because they sensed that I was making too rigorous demands, that I was too idealistic, as they say. Then, too, the prospect of such a life as I wanted to live was one of maximum insecurity. I was in exactly the situation which I had first learned about in the novels of Wells and Lawrence.

Just before Christmas I went over to call on Kenneth Thorpe one bright warm late afternoon. As I came up the steps of the red brick and sandstone Richardson house on Walton Place a girl opened the door ahead of me. She was dressed in a dull crimson coat with gray wolf fur at the collar and hem; she had deep chestnut hair, an oval face, a pale ivory skin with bright red cheeks, horn-rimmed glasses, and brown eyes with a gaze of incredibly angelic purity and seriousness. She smiled and said, "Aren't you Kenneth Rexroth, Kep's friend?" I said yes, scarcely able to speak. She said, "My name is Andrée Dutcher."

Harriet was alone in the Thorpe apartment. "Who is that girl, Andrée Dutcher, who lives downstairs?" I said. "She is a young commercial artist," she said, "and she's very anxious to meet you." "I just met her at the door," I said. "Did you like her?" Harriet said. "I intend to marry her," I said. "Well!" said Harriet, "I guess we had better get started. I'll ask her up to dinner."

She came to dinner and we sat about, talking about nothing in particular. Early in the evening we left together and she invited me into her room. From then on we were never apart, except to fulfill the routine tasks of life, for eight years. Shortly after Christmas we were married in the Church of the Ascension. Father Stoskopf and Father

Vaughan were so overwhelmed at the thought that they were losing a priest and even possibly a monk that they turned out a Solemn High Nuptial Mass, robed in the Easter vestments, and even pulled out an appreciable number of the choir to sing. It was the sort of performance granted only to crowned heads. Fasting and kneeling during the interminable postcommunion blessings of a Nuptial Mass which the celebrant chanted to plainsong I have never heard before or since—I have never attended a royal wedding—I fainted and had to be carried from the altar. My new father-in-law, a clothing designer and left-wing Socialist, was sure I had a vision.

Andrée was not merely what is vulgarly known as an idealist; her idealism was so absolute that it transcended what is vulgarly called reality altogether and created its own effective worldly practicality. Out of it she had made a technique of living which was far more successful than the successful techniques of anybody else. It was an inherent character and not the sort of thing to be influenced by books. However, in her adolescence she had read four books—Tolstoy's *War and Peace*, Wassermann's *The World's Illusion*, Dostoyevsky's *The Idiot*, and Wells's *The Research Magnificent*—and thought of herself as having modeled her life on them. I doubt if her philosophy of life would have been any different if she'd never read a book of any sort. Wells, of course, had been an influence on me, and I shared what might be called a general theory of human relations, the social ethic, of the others—although, I must say, I thought them excessively sentimental. There was an additional reason for the influence of Wassermann and Dostoyevsky on Andrée: she was an epileptic. At the time I met her she had just moved out of a slum in an alley on the Near North Side, which was certainly straight out of Wassermann. There were about twenty housekeeping rooms in the place, and one bath. All the people were, without exception, the spiritually halt, lame, and blind, the insulted and injured, the lovelost and outcast. In the years that she lived there they had all come to depend on her spiritually and, to a large degree, financially. It was a symbiotic community, a bound-in relationship like that between patients and staff in a state hospital.

Although she was the most highly skilled painter I have ever met, she made her living as a sweatshop decorator, painting lampshades and dinette furniture. She was so fast at this and had so little competition that she was able to make over a hundred dollars a week, far more money than most commercial artists made in those days. With this she had supported most of the roominghouse and completely cared for the alcoholic bohemian couple with whom she lived. Christmas the year before, hanging a bunch of mistletoe on a chandelier, she had tumbled off a ladder and gone into *grand mal*. Just before I met her she had decided that the life she was living was too much for her, and had moved out, got a decent apartment, quit her job, and started to become an artist. She worked only a few hours a week painting lampshades, just enough to live. I had received another windfall from an unknown relative, so we were quite well off.

Most of our time was spent in uninterrupted, enraptured conversation. We agreed about everything. We had read all the same books, and seen all the same pictures, and liked all the same music, and each of us was the first person the other had ever met like that. The only subjects she was relatively unfamiliar with were poetry and the classic theater. We spent whole days reading aloud to each other. I have never known anyone so vulnerable. Donne's love poems threw her into an excited coma of passion. One night, by the fire, I was reading Webster's *The Duchess of Malfi*. I looked up and she had fainted away. Prophetically I read her Henry King's "Exequy on His Dead Wife," and she was inconsolable all next day.

Visual experiences induced in her an extraordinary excitement. I showed her the little Cazin landscape of which I was so fond; also a painting of Corot's Roman period and a Pissarro of a hazy evening on the Boulevard de Sébastopol. Each time she turned away with her eyes full of tears and hurried out of the Art Institute. Chance arrangements of form and color in the park or on the streets would set her trembling. All this excruciating sensibility was accessible to an effortless technical mastery. It's true that she had never tried before to paint, noncommercially that is, and had to learn, but the learning process began far beyond where most people stop.

There was nothing sickly or high-strung about her. The social impression she gave was of ebullient calm—what advertisements call radiant good health, overlain by her unbreakable innocence. She was a tireless athlete, given to the same individual sports as I was. That winter we rode and skated in Lincoln Park. Many times we were the only people out and took along a string of horses for exercise. At first we got a discount for this, and finally, since we were so faithful, we weren't charged at all, so we could ride all morning. As soon as the water warmed up we were in the lake. Her favorite swim was a mile out to the breakwaters that lay off Chicago, where we would chase each other for a while over the tumbled limestone blocks, make love, and then swim back. At first I was terrified that she would have an attack while in the water, but in all the years to come of ocean swimming and mountaineering and skiing she never had an attack under such circumstances. This fact and others like it had led most doctors to believe that her epilepsy was psychogenetic. Her mother and aunt, and other people in the generation before them, had died of brain tumor, and she was convinced that her disease was organic and that in a few years it would overwhelm her. Just before she met me, after a completely happy day painting and swimming, she had attempted suicide.

I have no idea what her intelligence quotient was; it was certainly very high. I taught her how to play chess, and although I am a fair chess player, after a couple of weeks she could always win. Soon she was playing two or three simultaneous games and working out the most complicated chess problems for herself.

Right away we started painting together on the same picture without conflict, like one person. Except for watercolors, a medium I've always disliked, we continued to do this all our life together. Poetry I wrote myself, but as soon as a page or two of a first draft was done we'd go over it together. She had had a few piano lessons, so we got an old piano and she started to practice. This was one activity which was hers alone. I have never learned to do more than pick out the notes with one hand. If anyone asked me, "What single thing in your life do you most regret?" I would answer, "Never having learned the piano." However, we got all sorts of music out of the public library and had excited discussions over scores that we hardly comprehended.

From the first night our sex had the abandoned, idyllic quality that is supposed to be found in the South Seas, without conflict and without inhibition. That first night she was an easy and accomplished lover, but just before we were married she said, "I'm going to tell you something that I hope won't make you break off the marriage. I was a virgin when I met you." All this sounds like the perfect marriage, the relationship everybody seeks and almost nobody finds. That's right. That's the way it was. Ideologically, as they say, in politics or social relations she was an untroubled absolutist. Raised in a Socialist family, she had read all the old masters of the literature of revolt, but she needn't have; she was, so to speak, physiologically conditioned to their ideas and their moral simplicity. Kropotkin doubtless came to his opinions through struggle. She was unaware of the validity of any others. There was nothing whatever programmatic about it; she was simply what people mean by the term "free spirit." Hard as it may be to believe today, this was the least unusual thing about her. There were plenty of girls like that in those days, but the years proved that none of them was so perfectly resistant to corruption. I might be tempted by fancy ideological constructions and programmatic traps. She never saw anything but the bare, simple moral issue.

People who have superabundant love to give, and offer it carelessly and without demands, of course attract the lovelost. Although I had spent almost all of my few years of enforced adulthood with the insulted and injured, I had always kept my distance. In the course of that winter in Chicago we gathered about us a most extraordinary collection of maimed and terrified people, a bottom to the world of the dispossessed that even I, who prided myself on my complete social negotiability, never knew existed. Diseased and unemployable petty criminals, terminal alcoholics, illiterate cranks, and plain overexcited incompetents came and went. We fed them, listened to them, and commiserated with them. I don't think Andrée had any so-called principled position, but I am sure that she thought such people were the living embodiment of the true judgment of the human situation. I was not prepared to disagree with her. In fact, it was I who accepted it programmatically as a principled position. But I sometimes wondered.

Fate seemed to take a hand in that. We rented a handsome two-room apartment on the third floor of an old limestone mansion. It was not only comfortable but rather elegant, with a big old-fashioned bath with shiny brass fixtures, a carved marble fireplace in each room, and patterned parquet floors. We decorated it ourselves and furnished it in style. The second month we were there the landlady died, and the place was taken over by Ivan Sokolov, a Little Theater director who wrote Russian tragedies that sounded like parodies of Chekhov in the *Follies*. We stayed on, since we were the only people who paid the rent, but the rest of the house was turned into a "cooperative" for his cast, all of them crazier than he was. Soon there was no more money for coal, the heat went off, and we kept the place warm with the two fireplaces. He forced his beautiful but infatuated wife to steal our coal, so I built a little bin on our small back porch, and from then on she scrounged the streets for rubbish which they burned in their fireplaces. This didn't give off much heat, so they spent their time bundled in overcoats and covered up in bed, exactly like the characters in his tragedies of the Russian famine. Rehearsals of his plays always looked like staff meetings of an antarctic expedition. Show night, the furnace was fired up and the place was warm, but after a few heat shocks of this sort, the steam pipes burst, and shortly afterward, the plumbing. Our own lavatory was not affected, but finally the disorder penetrated to the bowels of the sewage system, and our toilet and bath bubbled up and overflowed the floor. Spring had come and we decided that it was time to set out for the West.

I realize that I have said almost nothing about the events, the people, or the intellectual development of this winter. They hardly exist in memory; it was not a time of intellectual development and people, but of constant deepening of the sensibilities, which was so intense and so completely shared with another that its all-enveloping, crystalline atmosphere has obliterated everything else.

I don't want to give the impression that our social life became a kind of hobohemian orgy; quite the contrary, almost all of our time was spent alone together. It's just that Andrée made herself accessible in a way that I had never permitted. Even that crazy winter in the tent in the Gray Cottage I kept the door to my room closed and spent most of my time by myself. In fact, it was there that I first started doing large pastels, a medium I have worked in to this day. I would paint for hours, by gaslight, turning out one picture after another, while all hell went on in the next room. Furthermore, although I have always been ready to listen and lavish with sympathy, I had been as careful as a priest in a confessional not to let such people get into me. To Andrée, this was immoral. I have often wondered what would have happened had we stayed in Chicago. But we didn't. As soon as spring came we made preparations to migrate to the West Coast.

After I had lived with her for a few weeks I discovered that Andrée had one annoying and embarrassing fault; one which she shared, incidentally, with many other epileptics. She was a kleptomaniac. I lived in constant dread that she would be caught purloining whole hams and roast chickens. We planned to hitchhike straight away as far as the Rockies, and then go at a leisurely pace to the Coast, camping out along the way, and then go on up into the Cascades and spend the winter camping, climbing, and fishing north of Lake Chelan. For this we needed a moderately light tarpaulin about eight feet wide and fourteen feet long. We searched all over Chicago for it but found nothing satisfactory. We were in the sporting goods department of Marshall Field's, where we had just bought two beautiful Bergen's rucksacks at thirty-five dollars apiece. We wandered back into a deserted area where they sold tents, canoes, saddles, and outboard motors. There were no clerks anywhere around. We stopped to admire a large umbrella tent with a fly stretched out in front of it like a porch. "Gee," I said, "that's beautiful stuff. And it weighs practically nothing. I think we should find out who makes it for them and have them make us up a tarpaulin." Andrée showed me a label sewn inside the door—the tent had been made in England. "Do you realize," she said, "that this fly is exactly fourteen by eight feet?" "Well," I said, "they wouldn't possibly sell us the fly separate from the tent." "Don't worry about that," she said. "You go out to the end of the aisle and give me jiggers." "I'll do nothing of the sort," I said. "You couldn't possibly get out of here with it." "You leave that to me," she said. "I'm going to take it whether you help me or not." While I stood trembling and watching the store go about its business half a block away, she folded the cloth into a long narrow strip about a foot wide, and then folded this fanwise in a pyramid. She had on a tight-fitting, tailored pony coat which she buttoned tightly over this cubic foot of piled cloth. "Come on," she said, "let's get the floorwalker." She staggered up and said, "Get me a cab, quick, to take me to Children's Hospital!" We were rolling down Michigan Boulevard in a matter of seconds, and from her shopping bag she produced a beautiful Swiss cook kit.

CHAPTER 38

The trip went exactly as planned: a succession of idle, wandering, late-spring days in northern Wisconsin and Minnesota. We took a side tour through the Badlands of North Dakota on rented horses. There it began to storm and never let up until at last we had to stop, mudbound, in Billings, Montana. In those days the only paved road in the state was a short stretch between Butte and Anaconda. After a week of rain it was impossible to move. We laid over in a tourist camp, waiting for the weather to clear.

There we made a fascinating friend, a hard-boiled, well-to-do man who seemed to know everything and believe nothing. He was especially well informed about revolutionary theories and movements, Marxist and other. For all of them he had nothing but contempt. For orthodox politics and politicians, his scorn was far beneath contempt. His knowledge of Montana life, politics, and society was intimate, bawdy, and exhaustive. I found it impossible even to guess what he did for a living, although I suspected he might be a lawyer. He was full of good advice and sound opinions, and the three of us sat up in the camp cookhouse around the fire every night till after midnight. One night I said to him, "Don't you believe in the integrity of any politician whatsoever? Don't you believe that a few rare people are motivated by a disinterested desire to serve society?" He didn't. "How about La Follette and Burton Wheeler?" I said. "You know everybody in Montana. I don't agree with them, but you certainly must admit that they are honest men and really believe what they say." "Did you ever go to a baseball game?" he said. "Of course," I said. "Uh hunh," he said. "What's behind the catcher?" "Why, there's nothing behind the catcher, except the umpire." "Oh yes there is," he said. "Think." "I can't think of anything. There's just the boxes in the grandstand." "What's between the box seats and the catcher?" "Nothing." "Oh yes there is; there's a wire net called the backstop. It catches the balls the catcher misses, and all the fouls that go off in that direction, so that nobody in the box seats gets hurt. That's the function of guys like La Follette and Wheeler, and believe me, they know it if you don't."

The next day the roads had dried off enough so that we started out in a caravan of about fifty cars, everybody equipped with shovels and chains and ropes and planks, digging each other out of the mud for five days between Billings and Great Falls. The first day out we were leading the caravan, riding in the car of our new friend. We bogged down, and it was impossible to dig our way out. We got a farmer and a team of mules that were plowing in the nearby field to give us a pull. The farmer seemed thoroughly intimidated. After freeing us from the mud he refused a ten-dollar tip. "No, thank you, Senator," he said. "It's been an honor I'll always remember." Our friend was Burton K. Wheeler. I guess this is what they mean by the school of hard knocks. Certainly a week with him was more illuminating than all the economics and political-science courses in all the universities in the country.

Once we found out who he was he seemed to feel duty-bound to act as our host in the state of Montana. In Great Falls he put us up at his hotel and introduced us to all the important people in town, among them the cowboy artist George Russell. It continued to rain. The river overflowed its banks. We were forced to lay over for another week. I will never forget those long evenings spent in the most mature and thoroughly masculine conversation I have encountered. It was rather like what the Reform Club is supposed to be—everybody was cut from the same cloth as Charles James Fox or Nye Bevan. They really knew all the answers.

The Montana Left of those days was a little different from the Populism of the prairie and plains states. In Nebraska or North Dakota the main enemy, or at least the big symbol, Wall Street, was far away. But these men spent every day at grips with the octopus and boa constrictor. They had no nerves, no illusions, and, like most Far Western professional men, they were curiously urban—but urbanites of a city which was gone—intellectual contemporaries of Junius and John Wilkes. They had the same appurtenances—a passion for gambling, an illimitable capacity for liquor (I never saw anybody even tipsy), and a taste for spectacular mistresses whom they escorted publicly.

When the roads dried up, the Senator persuaded us to accompany him up to Shelby, where one of the biggest oil discoveries to that date was only a year or so old. It was a slough of mud. There were a few houses from the days before the oil strike. The rest was a chaos of tar-paper shacks where hamburgers cost a dollar, whores cost twenty, and you could lose all the money you could carry in an hour. Surrounding the main stem were patched tents and hovels of scrap lumber, tin, and paper like the Hoovervilles of the depression, in which people had just come through the sub-zero winter.

Unfortunately I can't remember what it was all about, but the Senator paid me well to do some soapboxing for him. He himself went around shaking hands and listening to everybody's troubles and talking every night from the back of his car, two kerosene flares blazing beside him.

The roads remained impassable, but anyway there were no roads across the Rockies that far north, so we took a freight around the bottom of Glacier National Park. It was a string of empties, and it took forever. We sat in the open door of an empty boxcar, swinging our feet, and basking in the thin sunlight. The train was full of men headed west for the beginning of the season. Nobody bothered us, and the train crew treated us as honored guests. Whenever we pulled off on a siding, the shack would let us know how long we'd lay over, and we were even able to catch trout and grayling and cook them. Eventually we got around to the west side, and hitchhiked down to visit Billy Orville, where I introduced Andrée to my zebra dun which I had left there two years before. Billy was so hospitable that it was difficult to persuade him to let me do any work. After helping him with the spring plowing, we headed on west.

We hitchhiked from Wenatchee to Methow, and got one last ride up the Twisp River, and started hiking over the Cascades. A mile or so short of the summit we ran into a heavy pack of snow. On the west side the trail went down a cliff, which was covered with the steepest possible bank of snow several hundred feet high. We rolled our packs down ahead of us and slid off on our behinds, steering ourselves into protruding rocks and trees to break our momentum. When we got to the bottom we realized that it would be impossible to get back up until the snow had melted. Five miles down the trail a creek came down over a cliff. I had never seen more than a trickle of water in it; now there was an enormous waterfall pounding straight down like a huge fire hose and closing the trail to the west. We were locked in. We went back upstream a mile and up a little valley to a miner's cabin. There we spent two weeks with all the world shut out.

I had come to know the two prospectors well when I had worked in the country. They were elderly Swedes, hard-rockers who had worked all over the mountains from Arizona to Alaska. The cabin was beautifully built and immaculate. There was a large cache of flour, sugar, salt, beans, and prunes. We lived on this and on fish and porcupine.

My first experience in the mountains had made all the difference. Enraptured honeymoons out of the world like those with Nanda Devi and in Oaxaca and on the San Juan had functioned as crystals in the history of my own personality, out of which had grown its intrinsic structure. These two weeks were a geometric expansion of the same kind of crucial relationship. It's not just that I experienced everything anew and more intensely with Andrée in the ordinary sense with which that is said. The identification was so close and the increase in the power of the sensibility so extreme that knowledge took on transfinite forms which resembled nothing so much as the promises of those charlatans who advertise in newspapers—"One half of your brain is never used, awake your latent powers"—the psychological processes St. Thomas ascribed to angels. It is this kind of total identification with another in which two personalities multiply each other like squared numbers that is the quest of "spiritual alchemy" and other disciplines of so-called erotic mysticism. The evidence in, for instance, the writings of Thomas Vaughn is that the alchemist found it difficult to survive the experience. Possibly this is due to the fact that so often extraneous, even predatory, interests and demands were brought to it.

Nothing important happened. Just the daily round of the ecology of the forest in the mountains. One day coyotes came down the valley chasing a buck and making a manifold noise like an Oriental mob in pursuit of a politician. One night something started to scream off in the forest like the ghost of a child in a Japanese melodrama. It came nearer and at last went around the cabin bumping and clawing, screaming and weeping, and at last stumbled away. To judge from the sound it was something about three feet high. I had no idea what it was; in fact, I was committed to the scientific belief that such things couldn't exist. We sat by the fire, our arms around each other, not horrified but overwhelmed with complete disbelief. Still, we were sufficiently frightened that we didn't open the door. Years later when I saw one in action I realized that it had been a baby bear which had lost its mother. Deer, which had been tamed by the prospectors, came to the door and took leftover sourdough biscuits and salt from our hands, and grazed all day long in the pasture like cattle. One day they snorted and ran away. A few minutes later a cougar showed up, sat on his haunches, looked us over, and then went slowly on his way down the trail. There was a family of martens living in the down timber by the place where we got the water from the creek, and the newborn baby pups played in the sun like kittens. A fisher spent most of the days sleeping on a branch in full view of the cabin. As the days went by the meadow filled up with flowers, and as the snow melted from the peaks and passes it was replaced with a skirt of yellow avalanche lilies, as they call dog-tooth violets, Erythronium, in that country. At last one day we heard the bells on the pack train and the two prospectors showed up. After helping them get the cabin and the mine ready for the summer and stringing the fence around the meadow and listening to all the standard mythology of prospecting—lost mines and ghostly prospectors and caves of Spanish gold—we went off downstream.

At noon the next day we ran into a Basque sheepherder whom I had known two years before. He was on his way up into the high country with a pack string of provisions for several pairs of herders scattered around the mountain with their sheep. We had lunch with him and as we were about to go on he admitted that he had taken on a bigger job than he could handle alone. He had been supposed to pick up another packer at the head of the lake, but there was no one there, so he had come on up alone with eight mules and two extra saddle horses. He offered me the job. I suspect that he was quite capable of taking care of the stock, and was motivated more by a crush on Andrée than by any need for help. So we spent the next ten days or so working the stock along the ridges over makeshift trails or no trails at all, and camping every couple of nights with another band of sheep. Of all the men who worked in the Western mountains, certainly the most likable were the Basque sheepherders. They were men of a wider world by far than most cowboys, miners, or even Forest Service employees. In those days, at least, they had kept their own culture intact, and so were more deeply civilized men than even their Austrian, Breton, or Mexican fellows.

Crush or no, our boss treated Andrée with an adoring courtesy, and the herders we visited treated her like the Queen of Spain. Not least important, the Basques are the only people in the mountains who insist on eating well. Every night we had a banquet of venison, bear-cub steaks, Spanish rice with grouse, and *truite bleu*—sheepherders are excused from some of the game laws, and ignore the rest. After dinner, nights were spent singing and dancing around the fire. Our boss was a masterful guitarist and a most acrobatic dancer, and there was always at least one other guitarist in the camp. It was much better than the high holidays in Seville. Basque sheepherders seem to function on almost no sleep at all. After midnight we'd all roll up, spoked out with our feet to the fire, and the sheep would begin to come up from their night grazing. Before dawn, just beyond our heads, would be a wall of drowsy sheep, the lambs bleating softly and the ewes uttering an occasional guttural reassurance. At daybreak I got up, started the fire, went for the stock, and when I came back the men were already moving the sheep.

Sheepherders are looked down on by everybody else in the West. Possibly this is due more to envy than to the damage the sheep do to the range. Cattlemen have done a pretty good job of destroying the range wherever they got the chance. Then, too, sheepherding is a dusty job on foot, and cowboys have a knightly contempt for everybody who isn't on horseback. However, due to the dust, sheepherders bathe every night if they possibly can, and I have no recollection of ever having seen a cowboy out on the range allow water to touch anything but his face and hands. Not only are sheepherders more civilized than anybody else, but they have their own strong union and make more money. On the other hand, the favorite cowboy saying is "I'll work for the sons of bitches sixteen hours a day, three hundred and sixty-five days a year, for a dollar a day, but by God, the rest of my time's my own!"

Finally we came down to Stehekin at the head of the lake with a string of empty packs. There was no job open there so we took the boat down the long narrow lake between the mountains to Chelan. That night just as a sentimental parting with our boss was getting difficult to handle, Blackie showed up in the bar and created a welcome diversion. We loaded Ramón on a bus for Yakima, pretty drunk, but still perfectly, if effusively, courtly.

Blackie had bought a cabin in Chelan overlooking the lake. He had more jobs than he knew what to do with, and wanted me to go out with him to decorate a bar in Entiat next morning. I never let on. I said, "Well, I wouldn't want to go without my wife. She could help mix paints and wash the brushes and things like that." Next morning, before an audience that crowded the barroom, we started in—Blackie on a portrait of Glacier Peak on the center mirror, me on a string of ducks on one side, and Andrée on an assortment of trout on another. After she had been painting for about ten minutes, Blackie looked over and fell back with astonishment. She finished in less than half an hour and everybody cheered. From then on we were great successes. We painted buckeyes on every available space in the middle Columbia Valley, and when we weren't doing that we performed in store windows and blocked traffic. By late summer we had made quite a pile. It was time to move on. The three of us went down to Seattle for a week of parties with the last remnants of the Wobbly intelligentsia and the university Reds. There was no Seattle art movement in those days. Mark Tobey, fresh from New York, was painting very "figurative" portraits of society girls and bankers, which I believe he buys up and destroys today. We were offered jobs at the Cornish School and promised to come back in the fall.

Although we had been such a great success working with Blackie, and could probably still be doing it if we were all alive, parting with him was very different from the parting with Ramón. He just said "So long," got in his Ford roadster, and drove off. I have often thought he was what the other Blackie might have been in a better world.

In Seattle we learned that they had started to build a highway straight down the Oregon coast which would open up country which had hitherto been amongst the most isolated in the United States. We decided to see it before it was gone. We hitchhiked to Portland, out to Astoria, and started walking south.

In those days the coastal highway broke off somewhere around the center of the state, and even north of there it did not stay close to the ocean all the way. Except for short distances into a town to get food or something of that sort, we didn't hitchhike, and most of the time, even in the north, we were off the roads walking along the beach or high on the cliffs above the headlands. Eventually we came to the area where they were cutting through the new highway—Port Orford cedars and Douglas firs crashing, caterpillars and shovels wallowing among the ferns. Beyond that lay the special wilderness of the Pacific coast, the last left except for the Big Sur country in California. From there on we went by trail through the dense rain forest, then still the finest in America, along the beach and over the rocks.

There are few other coastlines in the world as beautiful. The west coasts of Ireland and Dalmatia are the only ones I know. There's only one thing wrong with it: like southwest Ireland, it has almost continuous rain. Engineers have told me that the Northwest rain forest is far more dense than anything in Africa or South America, where there is comparatively little ground cover or understory. I suppose there is no more beautiful forest in North America. Port Orford cedar and Douglas fir reach their prime in southern Oregon and are in some ways more beautiful than the California redwoods. The understory is thinner than the impenetrable jungle in the Puget Sound country, so that it's possible to see off between the trees. Where the forest did not come down to the sea the headlands were covered with thick native grass of the densest possible green, the kind of color that gives Ireland the name Emerald Isle. It is very different from the harsh yellow-green Spanish oat which has taken over the grassy coastal hills of California. Southern Oregon is covered with a cap of lava so that the cliffs and offshore rocks are a deep purple spotted with orange and gray lichen. For some reason that I do not understand, this usually produces beach sands of the purest white. Long stretches of the beach are of singing sands which squealed as we walked over them, a high-pitched, almost inaudible note like a dog whistle or the prolonged squeak of a bat.

The forest was so thick and dense that we camped wherever possible on the beach. Back of the high-tide line, piled against the cliffs, was an endless windrow—or wave row—of driftwood, great logs of the native forest, and strange shapes which looked like they had been carved by Brancusi of unknown hardwoods from across the Pacific.

Every night we worked our way down to the beach and camped where a stream of fresh water came out of the hills. Every night, after we had made camp, we searched through the driftwood and set up a circle of uncanny wooden sculptures around us, like Abraham camping among the massebahs of the Canaanites. Two or three times a day we swam in the sea. Neither of us had any experience with such a force, and why it didn't kill us I don't know. We soon learned to ride the surf, and would swim half a mile out, diving under the breakers, and come in riding the crest with arms outstretched and tumble over and over in the churning sandy water curled up like armadillos or hedgehogs.

By this time I had ceased to fear that Andrée would have an attack under such circumstances, and I suppose that she had long since decided that there would be no better way to die. As a matter of fact, all that summer she showed no signs of epilepsy, although she usually had several *petits mals* every day and a *grand mal* about once a week. We camped for several days by a wide river mouth, possibly Coos Bay, with a white village in the dark green forest across the water, a little constellation of lights shining through the mists at night. We filled several notebooks with drawings of each other, birds, sea- and landscapes, and many drawings of the mysterious driftwood. All the people we met were extraordinarily courteous and hospitable. Whenever we asked permission to camp we were invited to spend the night in the house, and had to use all our politeness to refuse. Then when we'd get the fire started on the beach, down would come the farmer's wife with a specially baked pie or potatoes and a chunk of roast.

At last we came to the California border and the first day into the state we took a detour away from the coast onto the highway. We got a ride from a traveling salesman and stopped for lunch at a roadside restaurant above a river mouth, possibly the Klamath. We weren't hungry so we each had a piece of apple pie and a cup of coffee. The salesman wanted to treat us but I insisted on paying for it. When I went up to the cash register the proprietor said, "Three dollars." I thought he was kidding. "Thirty cents?" I said. "You mean sixty cents, don't you? We had two pieces of pie and two cups of coffee." "No," he said, "I don't mean thirty cents. I mean three dollars. A dollar apiece for the pie and fifty cents for the coffee." "Go on," I said, "stop kidding. How much is it?" I stood there with my wallet in my hand, putting on my heavy pack and slightly off balance. "Listen, you son of a bitch," he said, "fork over the three dollars. We don't want bastards like you in this country." He came around the corner and hit me full in the mouth and knocked me down. As I went down I kicked him in the nuts and as he fell backward Andrée hit him over the head with a bottle of ketchup. The salesman grabbed us, threw us into the car, and tore off down the road. At the first gas station we asked where we could find a sheriff. "Down the road half a mile, the first house on the left." He was sitting on the porch, muddy logger's boots up on the railing, reading a newspaper and spitting tobacco, a star pinned to his greasy vest. We went up and made a complaint. He didn't even take down his feet, but drew a pistol and said to the salesman, "Get off down the highway and get those sons of bitches out of the country or I'll lock you all up." We had arrived in California.

Episodes like this were the common thing in the northern three counties of California in those days, and even now anybody conspicuously foreign finds it almost impossible to get service or accommodations. No colored person of any race is served at all. No Negro, Chinese, Japanese or Filipino is allowed to settle in the country. I don't know what happens to them nowadays if they try. Thirty years ago they never tried, or if they did they simply vanished. In Crescent City and Eureka we met the same kind of hostility, although not so extreme. However, we found it almost impossible to camp out. We would stop on the beach with no habitation in sight, build a fire, and in a few minutes up would come somebody on a horse and drive us off with a gun. For the next couple of days we lived largely on cold food out of grocery stores. I have been all over the Southern mountains, northern Maine, and French Canada, regions where outlanders are traditionally not welcome, but I have never met anyone like the malignant native sons of far northern California.

Pretty soon we came to the head of highway construction at the southern end, with the same bulldozers and dynamite, but this time in the redwood forest. Down the road a short way public camps began to appear, and we stayed for four days in the redwoods on the banks of the Eel River. This was the first experience for both of us of the redwood forest, like a Karnak of purple Ionic columns, and of the flora and fauna of the California coast range. It was all very beautiful and exciting, but the inhospitable humans made it difficult to appreciate. We swam and fished in the river. The water was low, still, and green, and full of orange-bellied, copulating newts. Andrée came running up to the campfire with a first bucket of water shouting, "The river is full of baby alligators, all fucking." That night when we cleared off the duff to lay out the sleeping bags, she discovered a far more startling baby alligator. It was a purple-spotted, newt-eating giant tiger salamander —quite a small monster. During the night we woke up and turned the flashlight on a pair of California ringtail cats—an animal like a very slender racoon—making off with our dried fruit. Striped skunks walked fearlessly through camp; deer snorted in the underbrush, and their eyes shone green in the firelight. In a shallow embayment we found trapped an emaciated steelhead trout, caught him in our hands, carried him over the rocks, and let him go. It was August and the leaves of the California buckeye were turning, and the grass was yellow. We wandered up and down the stream, painting watercolors of the new shapes and colors.

In Mendocino County we began to run out of money, so we caught a ride into San Francisco. Our last money went to pay the ferry, and we walked up Market Street to the post office where we had had a friend mail us five hundred dollars. It wasn't there. We walked out, and went up Mission Street, our packs on our backs, wondering what to do. A block from the post office we came on a wholesale furniture store with big display windows full of painted pseudo-French furniture. Andrée pulled me up.

"Look at that!" she said. "That stuff was done in Vogue studios."

We went up to the window.

"By God!" she said. "I painted every piece of furniture in that window."

In the doorway was standing a tubby little Jewish man with puffs of white hair over his ears. "Excuse me, lady," he said. "What was that you said?"

"I said I painted that furniture," Andrée said.

"Oh yeah?" he said. "Where did you paint it?"

"In Chicago," she said.

"What are you doing in San Francisco?" he asked.

"Just passing through," she said. "We don't like it very much."

"What's the matter with it?"

"The native sons," I said.

"Would you stay awhile if you had a good job?" he said.

"Well," I replied, "I'd stay awhile. We expected to find five hundred dollars in the post office. It isn't there, and we've spent all our money."

"Are you a decorator, too?" he inquired.

"I can paint a little," I said. "But I certainly can't paint like my wife."

"Could you spray furniture?" he asked.

"Of course," I said. "Who couldn't?"

"Okay," he said. "I'll give you thirty dollars a week, and if she can turn out them French pictures she can start at seventy-five. I'll lend you the money to get by till payday."

We went back to the workroom for a tryout and after a short consultation decided to take the jobs until our money showed up. We had planned to see the sights, eat a couple of Chinese meals, take the train back, and spend the winter in Seattle. That was thirty-seven years ago. Andrée has been dead for twenty-four years, and I am still here.

All sorts of contacts had been made for us in San Francisco. People had been written to. We had names and letters of introduction. San Francisco's bohemia was a tiny enclave in Italian North Beach in those days: a cooperative gallery that soon failed; a speak-easy; Isadore Gomez's (the old one down across from the firehouse); a restaurant, the Casa Beguine; the Montgomery block; a row of studios in the next block on Montgomery Street; and a few shacks scattered among the dirt roads and goats on Telegraph Hill.

We got a kitchenette apartment on the ground floor of an old mansion in the Western Addition and spent a week painting and decorating in the shop by day and painting and decorating at home at night. We made the rounds of the three public meeting places, and were immediately asked, as they say, everywhere. Everywhere in this instance meant at all social levels. Some North Shore family in Chicago had written their social equals in San Francisco that we were coming.

We became quite a fad. In those days what cultural life there was in San Francisco depended upon a small group of interrelated Jewish families. They passed us from dinner to dinner. They were very nice people and effusively hospitable, but we found ourselves a little out of our depth. San Francisco was still in the grip of the Jack London, Frank Norris, George Sterling tradition. Everybody we met considered George Sterling the greatest poet since Dante. We had never heard of him, so it took us a little time to catch up on our manners. The leading artists of the community were romantic, picturesque painters, devotees of a kind of simplified Hudson River School. In this environment we were outlandish curiosities. Still, everybody was friendly.

I don't want to give the impression that we were, young as we were, snobs about all this. One provincial culture is much like another, and San Francisco, in those days, was rather better than most. It's just that it took us a little time to learn the ropes. A few people understood what we were all about. There were a couple of young painters, a group of Socialist newspapermen, Gertrude Atherton—of all people—who turned out to be an extraordinarily wise woman with a wonderful knowledge and an all-suffering tolerance for people, and Ralph Stackpole.

Stackpole was the best friend we made. He knew everybody in town from top to bottom, and took us everywhere. Although his own sculpture, in those days, was somewhat conventional—rather like the work of the French sculptor Despiau, with whom I believe he had studied —he had been out in the world, knew what was going on, and in his appetite for people and ideas was extraordinarily alive and alert. Thirty years later when I met him again in France he was still just as vital and youthful, and his sculpture had become as original and profound as any being shown in Paris. In those days he had all the energy, the inexhaustible spiritual metabolism, of someone who would grow into a perennially youthful aged man. He came to see us right away, enthused over our pictures, went off with a manuscript of my poems, which years later I discovered he still knew by heart. He coached us on the social intricacies of the intellectual life of the city and briefed us on all the people he introduced us to. In addition, he took us to a succession of wonderful Chinese, Japanese, Italian, French, Spanish, and Basque restaurants. A few of them were so good, so modest, and so incorruptible that they have survived the long years of the San Francisco renaissance, or population explosion, to this day.

We tried to find people who corresponded to the radical bohemia of Seattle, Chicago, and New York. A few years before there had been a lot of them around, but as the Communists would say, the mass base had withered away in a series of disastrous strikes. The intellectual camp followers had become successful and part of the establishment. Otherwise the city gave us everything we could have found elsewhere —on a simpler level perhaps, but certainly on a more friendly one. San Francisco was far away from the art and literary markets of the world, so there was none of the savage crowding at the trough that makes New York or Paris difficult. I had begun to suspect that the world's capitals are poor places for artists to mature in.

San Francisco was not just a wide-open town. It is the only city in the United States which was not settled overland by the westward-spreading puritan tradition, or by the Walter Scott, fake-cavalier tradition of the South. It had been settled mostly, in spite of all the romances of the overland migration, by gamblers, prostitutes, rascals, and fortune seekers who came across the Isthmus and around the Horn. They had their faults, but they were not influenced by Cotton Mather. The large Italian population had come mostly from northern Italy. The largest town club in San Francisco is that of the Lucchesi. Poverty-stricken Sicilian and Neapolitan immigrants may have brought much to America, but it can hardly be disputed that Lucca would send over people with greater awareness of their cultural traditions. There was a full-time Italian stock company in the Verdi Theater, where my old friend Mimi Agulia, probably the best actress ever to live in America, was playing. There was a French theater which gave rather stiff and amateurish performances of Racine, Corneille, Beaumarchais, and Marivaux. Still, it was the French classic theater. There were three Chinese theaters that played every night in the week. Once Stackpole had introduced us to them, this alone would have been enough to keep us in San Francisco. It was a truly Mediterranean city, and yet it had none of the horrors of poverty that still make Marseille, let alone Genoa, Barcelona, or Naples, impossible for a sensitive person to work in very long. On the other hand, it had none of the cheapjack tourism which makes the Riviera unlivable. It was like an untouched Mediterranean village—like St. Tropez or the Cinque Terre in those days—and yet it was a great city, and in its own way not a provincial one but the capital of its own somewhat dated culture.

The ocean was at the end of the streetcar line. Down the peninsula and across the Golden Gate the Coast Range was still a wilderness, and the High Sierras were a short day's trip away. More important, nobody cared what you did as long as you didn't commit any gross public crimes. They let you alone and however much you might have puzzled them they respected you as an artist. At no time in all the years I have lived in San Francisco have I ever met with anything but respect verging on adulation from neighbors, corner grocers, and landladies. They were proud to be associated with an artist or poet. With Greenwich Village landladies or Left Bank concierges, this is simply not true, all the myths of the American inferiority complex to the contrary notwithstanding. There was an Anglo-Catholic church of the strictest persuasion around the corner from our apartment.

It was pretty apparent that we had found the ideal environment for ourselves, at least in America. After three weeks of tracing, the five hundred dollars showed up in the post office. We decided to stay and grow up with the town.

At that time, during the third week of our stay in San Francisco, Sacco and Vanzetti were executed. A great cleaver cut through all the intellectual life of America. The world in which Andrée and I had grown up came forever to an end. One book of my life was closed and it was time to begin another.

New Directions Paperbooks

Mangô Adigal, *Shilappadikaram*. NDP162.
Corrado Alvaro, *Revolt in Aspromonte*.
  NDP119.
Djuna Barnes, *Nightwood*. NDP98.
Charles Baudelaire, *Flowers of Evil*.† NDP71.
Eric Bentley, *Bernard Shaw*. NDP59.
Jorge Luis Borges, *Labyrinths*. NDP186.
Jean-François Bory, *Once Again*. NDP256.
Alain Bosquet, *Selected Poems*.† WPS4.
Paul Bowles, *The Sheltering Sky*. NDP158.
Kay Boyle, *Thirty Stories*. NDP62.
Breakthrough to Peace. (Anthology) NDP124.
W. Bronk, *The World, the Worldless*. NDP157.
Buddha, *The Dhammapada*. NDP188.
Louis-Ferdinand Céline, *Guignol's Band*.
  NDP278.
  Journey to the End of the Night. NDP84.
Blaise Cendrars, *Selected Writings*.† NDP203.
B-c. Chatterjee, *Krishnakanta's Will*. NDP120.
Jean Cocteau, *The Holy Terrors*. NDP212.
  The Infernal Machine. NDP235.
Contemporary German Poetry.†
  (Anthology) NDP148.
Gregory Corso, *Long Live Man*. NDP127.
  Happy Birthday of Death. NDP86.
Edward Dahlberg, *Reader*. NDP246.
  Because I Was Flesh. NDP227.
David Daiches, *Virginia Woolf*.
  (Revised) NDP96.
Osamu Dazai, *The Setting Sun*. NDP258.
Robert Duncan, *Roots and Branches*, NDP275.
  Bending the Bow. NDP255.
Richard Eberhart, *Selected Poems*. NDP198.
Russell Edson, *The Very Thing That Happens*.
  NDP137.
Wm. Empson, *7 Types of Ambiguity*. NDP204.
  Some Versions of Pastoral. NDP92.
Wm. Everson, *The Residual Years*. NDP263.
Lawrence Ferlinghetti, *Her*. NDP88.
  A Coney Island of the Mind. NDP74.
  Routines. NDP187.
  The Secret Meaning of Things. NDP268.
  Starting from San Francisco. NDP220.
  Unfair Arguments with Existence. NDP143.
Ronald Firbank, *Two Novels*. NDP128.
Dudley Fitts,
  Poems from the Greek Anthology. NDP60.
F. Scott Fitzgerald, *The Crack-up*. NDP54.
Gustave Flaubert,
  The Dictionary of Accepted Ideas. NDP230.
M. K. Gandhi, *Gandhi on Non-Violence*.
  (ed. Thomas Merton) NDP197.
André Gide, *Dostoevsky*. NDP100.
Goethe, *Faust*, Part I.
  (MacIntyre translation) NDP70.
Albert J. Guerard, *Thomas Hardy*. NDP185.
Guillevic, *Selected Poems*. NDP279.

James B. Hall, *Us He Devours*. NDP156.
Henry Hatfield, *Goethe*. NDP136.
  Thomas Mann. (Revised Edition) NDP101.
John Hawkes, *The Cannibal*. NDP123.
  The Lime Twig. NDP95.
  Second Skin. NDP146.
  The Beetle Leg. NDP239.
  The Innocent Party. NDP238.
  Lunar Landscapes. NDP274.
Hermann Hesse, *Siddhartha*. NDP65.
Edwin Honig, *García Lorca*. (Rev.) NDP102.
Christopher Isherwood, *The Berlin Stories*.
  NDP134.
Henry James, *Stories of Writers and Artists*.
  NDP57.
Alfred Jarry, *Ubu Roi*. NDP105.
James Joyce, *Stephen Hero*. NDP133.
Franz Kafka, *Amerika*. NDP117.
Bob Kaufman,
  Solitudes Crowded with Loneliness. NDP199.
Hugh Kenner, *Wyndham Lewis*. NDP167.
Lincoln Kirstein,
  Rhymes & More Rhymes of a Pfc. NDP202.
P. Lal, translator, *Great Sanskrit Plays*.
  NDP142.
Tommaso Landolfi,
  Gogol's Wife and Other Stories. NDP155.
Lautréamont, *Maldoror*. NDP207.
Denise Levertov, *O Taste and See*. NDP149.
  The Jacob's Ladder. NDP112.
  The Sorrow Dance. NDP222.
  With Eyes at the Back of Our Heads.
  NDP229.
Harry Levin, *James Joyce*. NDP87.
García Lorca, *Selected Poems*.† NDP114.
  Three Tragedies. NDP52.
  Five Plays. NDP232.
Carson McCullers, *The Member of the
  Wedding*. (Playscript) NDP153.
Thomas Merton, *Selected Poems*. NDP85.
  Cables to the Ace. NDP252.
  Clement of Alexandria. Gift Ed. NDP173.
  Emblems of a Season of Fury. NDP140.
  Gandhi on Non-Violence. NDP197.
  The Geography of Lograire. NDP283.
  Original Child Bomb. NDP228.
  Raids on the Unspeakable. NDP213.
  The Way of Chuang Tzu. NDP276.
  Zen and the Birds of Appetite. NDP261.
Henri Michaux, *Selected Writings*.† NDP264.
Henry Miller, *Big Sur & The Oranges of
  Hieronymus Bosch*. NDP161.
  The Colossus of Maroussi. NDP75.
  The Cosmological Eye. NDP109.
  Henry Miller on Writing. NDP151.
  The Henry Miller Reader. NDP269.
  Remember to Remember. NDP111.
  Smile at the Foot of the Ladder. NDP176.
  Stand Still Like the Hummingbird. NDP236.
  The Time of the Assassins. NDP115.
  The Wisdom of the Heart. NDP94.

**Complete descriptive catalog available free on request from
New Directions, 333 Sixth Avenue, New York 10014.**

† Bilingual.